Reality Police

Reality Police
The Experience of Insanity in America

by Anthony Brandt

William Morrow and Company, Inc.
New York   1975

1 2 3 4 5   79 78 77 76 75

Library of Congress Cataloging in Publication Data

Brandt, Anthony.
  Reality police.

  Includes bibliographical references.
  1. Psychiatric hospital care—United States.
2. Psychiatry—Philosophy.   I. Title.
RC443.B7   362.2'1'0973   75-4733
ISBN 0-688-02925-6

DESIGN BY HELEN WHEELS

TO MY MOTHER
AND THE MEMORY OF MY FATHER

Preface

The subject of this book is too large for any one person to comprehend, and it certainly cannot be adequately covered in a single volume. Space limitations have forced me to leave out a great deal, and limitations on my time have not allowed me to investigate every aspect of the subject. Thus the book says little or nothing about such controversies as those surrounding psychosurgery and behavior modification, which I leave to other writers, or about Professional Standard Review Organizations, which are just now being formed, or about the numerous theories of schizophrenia, which would have required a separate book. These things, and others I have not mentioned, are obviously important, but I have had to leave them out. I am sure I have also missed much through ignorance.

Whatever sins of omission or commission may be found herein, however, are in no way the fault of my teachers. I have gone to school to a great many well-informed and formidable intellects both inside and outside the mental health system, and I would like them to know how vital their help has been. I would like to thank first of all the many officials of state mental health systems who answered questions, gave me access to hospitals, mental health centers, and other facilities, and did their best to cooperate. At the facilities themselves many people devoted many hours to explaining their work to me. People at Bronx State Hospital, Boston State Hospital, the Menninger Foundation, Topeka State Hospital, Napa State Hospital, Harlem Valley State Hospital, the High Plains Mental Health Center—the list goes on and on. I also want to thank the personnel at Hudson River State Hospital in Poughkeepsie who, within the limitations imposed by that heavy bureaucracy, tried to be helpful, and in particular the Irish attendant who sang to Mr. R_____ and made us all smile. I never knew that man to be anything but kind.

Outside the system I have had an enormous amount of help from two organizations in particular: the Mental Patients Liberation Project in New York, of which I am a proud honorary member, and the Mental Patients Support Committee in Kansas. Members of both organizations made themselves available for interviews, and those I talked to were remarkably open about their often painful experiences. I would especially like to thank Dr. Louis L. Frydman of the University of Kansas, without whose active assistance, enthusiasm, and depth of understanding this book would be very much poorer.

Finally I want to mention those personal friends and relations who helped, not least by putting up with me when things weren't going well. Rudy Hopkins helped at a crucial time. Sally McLaughlin Bittner, a psychologist and an excellent friend, read most of the book and corrected many errors. Jody Sibert typed it and much more; the book is unimaginable without her. And Barbara and Kate and Evan lived with the excitement and the anguish and put up with the most from me, and nothing I might ever say to them could express my love and thankfulness.

Shrub Oak, New York
October 29, 1974

Contents

Introduction

"A man can never really know whether he isn't sitting in a madhouse."

Georg Christoph Lichtenberg

At odd, unexpected times the behavior of other people, even people we know well, will strike us as totally weird. I may be sitting at the supper table with my family and my daughter will do something she does all the time without my taking particular notice of it and it will suddenly occur to me: who is this *stranger* who eats her mashed potatoes cold? For an instant, for just the time it takes this question to sink back into the darkness, everything my intelligent, beautiful and wholly sane daughter does becomes alien and incomprehensible. Who *is* she? How *can* she like potatoes that way? It makes no sense to me. For the moment nothing she does makes sense to me. She dances alone in her room, reads wrapped in a blanket, throws the books she has read in the trash. All of this lies outside my experience, and while the moment lasts I sit there in amazement and consternation, as if someone I had never seen before had walked up to me and slapped me. For that brief moment a vast chasm separates us and one of us, I think, must be crazy.

An unpleasant experience; we don't like to dwell on such things. It's like those sharp twinges near the heart

1

that remind you you are mortal, that there is no security in life. It's like listening to the news and hearing that some idiot thought Bloomingdale's was controlling his mind and blew up the cosmetics department. The world can be an uncomfortable place. My wife and I exchange glances, smile, and shake our heads over this quaint custom of our daughter's waiting for the mashed potatoes to harden to a glutinous paste before eating them. My wife, at any rate, is on the same wavelength; she and I at least live in the same world. A sigh of relief: it's our daughter who's strange, not we. And then everything falls back into perspective. What's the matter with me? I ask myself. It's just one of her idiosyncracies. We all do crazy things; if we didn't we'd be as boring as clams. The momentary dismay, the sudden minor disorientation, passes. Once again we think we know what everyone is about. Wife and husband, friend and neighbor, even father and daughter, we speak to each other, exchange a thought or a feeling, and make it plain that we do indeed inhabit the same world and our experience of that world can be shared. She just happens to like her mashed potatoes cold.

At one time or another, however, most of us have known somebody whose behavior could not be put into perspective so easily, somebody for whom words like quirky or eccentric or idiosyncratic won't quite do. For some people Noah Levy is such a person. For some people it is no simple matter to put Noah into perspective. Noah is physically enormous, tall and heavy, a pyramid of rotundities, like a giant snowman. But unlike many people his size he is bouncy and alive, full of a rapid ebb and flow of excitement. He is subject to sudden flashes of insight which burst into his head like geysers and punctuate his discourse with "Aha! *Now* I see . . . ," or "Of course, *that's* the reason." His eyes and his voice are both vastly expressive of his enthusiasm. He affects you, in short, like some great dancing bear, an improbable synthesis of bulk and animation. If you like people who seem to be exceptionally alive, it would be hard not to like Noah—unless, that is, you found out he was crazy, *really* crazy, a genuine, certified "psychotic." Noah has been in and out of mental hospitals at least ten times.

Noah is full of fascinating and instructive stories about how he has affected other people, people who have not been able to accept the way he acts as merely, say, a little strange. The one I like best is the story about the time he decided to fly to Florida and visit his father.[1] Noah's father had retired on the earnings of the candy store he ran in Brooklyn for most of his life; but his second wife had just left him and he was lonely and he called Noah one night—could Noah visit him and Noah said sure. Noah and his girl friend, Emily, scraped some money together, gathered up the dog and took a cab to the airport. All this on impulse: Noah didn't bother to change his clothes. He was wearing a black buttoned sweater with no shirt underneath it, and he doesn't think he was wearing socks, either. His hair was long and he hadn't shaved in many days. Noah is big; with the black sweater stretched across the great belly, wide expanses of skin showing here and there, the beard, the forceful manner, he must have been a remarkable sight.

When they got to the airport they took the dog to the counter where you check in pets. Now Emily was always trying to get their dog mated, so when she saw another man there with his dog she went up to him and said, "Pardon me, sir, is your dog a male or a female?" The man, somewhat startled, no doubt, didn't answer her. Noah was feeling very protective of Emily and he started to get angry when the man didn't answer. Emily tried again.

"Pardon me, is it a male or a female?"

This time the man answered. "Male," he said. Noah didn't like the gruff way he said it, but for the moment, at least, he let it pass.

When they boarded the plane the door to the cockpit was open. Noah had never seen the inside of a cockpit before, so he stood there for a minute looking it while Emily went back to find seats. When he joined her she was talking to the gruff man with the dog, who, it turned out, lived in the East Village and was really a friendly sort of person; Noah, who is really a friendly person himself, responded in kind. Then Emily asked Noah to get her a cup of coffee, so he went back to the front of the plane to get a cup of coffee from the stewardess—or rather, a cup of half milk, half coffee. The stewardess, naturally, was harassed and had lots to do before the plane took off, so she gave Noah a cup of coffee with the standard amount of milk. Noah pointed out her error and she, no doubt annoyed and wanting to get rid of him, told him she didn't have any milk. What? exclaimed Noah loudly, a big airplane company like this doesn't have any milk? He got the milk; but of course by this time he had made himself thoroughly conspicuous, blocking the aisle, inspecting the cabin, demanding service. To people with a strong sense of order and propriety, just the sight of him must have been a definite affront.

But now it came time to sit down. Noah returned with Emily's coffee, took a seat on the aisle, turned to their newfound friend, and asked him for his company on the trip to Florida.

"Listen," Noah said, "my girl friend is probably going to fall asleep on the plane, I just know she will, and I won't have anyone to talk to. Do you think you could possibly talk to me during the flight? I'd appreciate it very much; I'm desperately in need of someone to talk to."

It was a human request, to which our East Villager made a human reply. "Look," he said, "I've had a hard day, I'm really not up to it." In effect, no. But having said this he continued to stand there next to Noah in the aisle, not making a move to find a seat.

"All right," Noah said, "if that's the case, go sit down." Let us assume that he said it, shall we say, emphatically. Noah was hurt, of course, and starting to get angry at the man all over again. But the man continued to stand next to him in the aisle. So Noah raised his voice and told him once more to go sit down. And that did it.

Who could have known there would be FBI agents on the plane? They were there, apparently, to deal with hijackers. Noah was no hijacker, but he seemed to be some kind of hippie or bum, and he was visibly angry and making loud, vaguely threatening noises in the narrow confines of the airplane. It was enough to trigger the agents' early warning system, and they came charging up the aisle toward Noah, credentials in hand. Now Noah got really angry and let go. He grabbed the credentials from the agents and tossed them back over their heads, calling them every nasty name he could think of. One of his curses struck a nerve. "Motherfucker," he shouted at an agent: a word the agent would not abide. He pulled his .38 and shoved it against Noah's head. Noah by now was on his express train and didn't even hesitate. "Shoot, motherfucker! Shoot, motherfucker!" he yelled, and Emily started screaming, "Don't shoot him, I'm his nurse! Don't shoot, don't shoot!" and there was uproar.

We can easily imagine the reactions of the other passengers on that airplane. They could not help but have noticed this strange couple and wondered about them, and now they were making this god-awful racket. People are half rising out of their seats to see the action, and they are shaking their heads and getting frightened and suddenly they notice the gun and they want to get off that plane fast. Panic lurks just beneath the surface of the crowd on an airplane anyway, even when there's no obvious cause for alarm. And now here's this fat man, screaming curses, asking to be shot. The whole thing is crazy and scary. The fat man must be crazy. People like him should be kept off airplanes. Off buses and subways. Off the streets.

A man can never really know whether he isn't sitting in a madhouse.

The FBI agent hung onto his cool and didn't shoot Noah. Instead he and his fellow agents told Noah and Emily to leave the airplane: come quietly and you won't get hurt; it will go easier for you, and so on. But Noah didn't want to leave. He wanted to go to Florida. His father was lonely and needed him and he had paid for his ticket and he wanted to go. So the FBI cleared out all the other passengers and left Noah and Emily there in their seats and in came a bunch of New York City's finest, five or six big, burly ethnic types in blue. It was all up, of course, and Noah was willing now to go off the plane, but the first cop who came down the aisle, the chief cop, the leader of the band, happened to remind him of his father, so Noah reached up out of his seat and kissed him on the cheek. That didn't sit at all well with this police panjandrum. So instead of being gently persuasive in the manner they are famous for, they started to poke Noah with their sticks to prod him out of there. Which only made him stubborn. They finally had to carry him off the plane, cuffs on his hands and ankles, not an easy thing to do, given his size and weight. Once off the plane they took Noah to Queens General Hospital, and Queens transferred him to Metropolitan Hospital in Manhattan. To the psycho ward, of course. It was never a question of Noah having broken a law. No: he had to be crazy.

Crazy is the word we use when we cannot understand someone's behavior and it is behavior that disturbs us or that we don't approve of. It's a limit word. Up to a certain point you're eccentric or peculiar but basically all right; you can like your mashed potatoes cold, you can even give your husband mashed potato sandwiches for lunch as Blondie does to Dagwood and still be counted as a member in good standing of our common culture, a coinhabitant of our world. But beyond a certain point you no longer belong. At some point which no one can define precisely, you have gone too far, violated the taboos, broken the rules of society; you are beyond the pale, a nut. Note that it was not some *law* that Noah broke but a social rule, something not written down in any code of justice anywhere in the United States. Thou shalt not raise thy voice in a Boeing 707. That is all Noah really did. He didn't strike the fellow from the East Village, or even threaten him. He didn't pull a gun and try to hijack the airplane, he didn't lift somebody's wallet. In short he didn't commit a crime. He committed a social impropriety. He dressed inappropriately and he shouted at someone, and that was enough to call down the FBI and get him in trouble. Thereafter he cursed and shouted some more, he defied authority, he told somebody with a gun to go ahead and shoot him, and he kissed a cop on the cheek—a series of "inappropriate reactions." Who in his right mind would ever have done such things? No question about it—he'd flipped his lid.

No question about it? Apparently no one on the airplane had any question about it, although other interpretations were available. Noah could have been stupid and not have understood that that's not the way to behave. Or he could have been malicious and created an uproar just for fun. But no, everyone gave him the benefit of the doubt. He was crazy; he was a mental case and belonged in a mental hospital. Yet who are these people who are making this judgment? There were no psychiatrists on the airplane. Nobody gave Noah a Rorschach or a Thematic Apperception Test before they hauled him off to the banana farm. Not professionals, in other words, but everyday "normal" people, police and passengers, decided he was crazy.[2] Which is a way of saying that we—you and I, the public—made that diagnosis. Nor did we consult the *Diagnostic and Statistical Manual* of the American Psychiatric Association before doing so. On the basis of nothing more than the fact that what Noah did made no sense to us, on the incomprehensibility (to us) of his actions, we sent him to the psycho ward.

And that is the way it is. "Crazy" is the name we give to behavior we don't understand and can't or won't deal with. Whether it is a stranger on an airplane, the weird loner in the apartment next door, or a member of our family, our own son or daughter, if we don't know what's eating them and can't figure out why they do the things they do and can't control them and bring them into line, then they're "crazy," they've "gone bananas," they've "freaked out." We needn't be any more sophisticated than that. Let the psychiatrist decide whether it's schizophrenia or involutional melancholia or some other arcana they suffer from. *That's* the psychiatrist's job. He confirms and refines what is fundamentally our diagnosis. He works for *us*. Hey, Doc! We can't live with this crazy freak. Treat him, "cure" him, do what you want with him, but get him off our hands, OK? The doc is only too happy to oblige.

Noah Levy, however, not too surprisingly, does not consider himself a crazy freak. Noah believes himself to be a member in good standing of the same world you and I live in. He loves his family and his dog as much as any man. He eats the same kind of food you and I eat; he drives on the right side of the road; he brushes his teeth. He was elected once to the presidency of a union organization. If we exclude the episodes in mental hospitals his record would indicate nothing but that he is an upright, respectable citizen. Noah knows perfectly well, of course, that the way he behaved that day was not what we might call prudent. But that in his opinion doesn't make him crazy.

He had a reason, indeed, for everything he did that night. He even had a reason for wanting the FBI agent to shoot him.

> In my head, it goes like this: I wanted him to shoot me so that I could be a martyr for the Mental Patients Liberation Project in New York and throughout the world. I wanted to be the saint of all the so-called crazy people in the world. The way my head was thinking, to achieve my martyrdom he had to kill me.

He kissed the cop because he reminded him of his father. He shouted at the man from the East Village because he was hurt and angry. He had reasons for what he was doing. They may not sound like sufficient reasons to us, but then how can we explain why it disturbs us when our children prefer their mashed potatoes cold or our teenage sons sew flowers on their jeans?

But it is not a question just of defending Noah Levy. The things he did were definitely imprudent under the circumstances. According to the unwritten rules of society people are supposed to control their impulses, not act them out. The question is whether neglecting to control yourself, letting go, automatically indicates that you are crazy or psychotic or insane. We might after all use words like free or spontaneous or inspired instead. There are many ways to interpret behavior. Even behavior which conforms to some norm is subject to interpretation. Everyone has met people whose behavior matches some version of normality but who nevertheless prove to be, once you get to know them, frightening lunatics; or people who behave in the most bizarre ways and yet make eminent sense in their discourse and their lives. Who shall tell us which one is crazy, which sane?

I do not believe any behavior is inherently "normal."

"Normal" behavior is a construct, a performance, an architectural facade thrown up to hide the most diverse, complex uncertainties of instinct and ego. That facade is only as stable as we can make it, and even for the most "normal" of us that may not be very stable at all. My own experience has taught me that. In order to find out for myself what it was like to live through the process of being labeled "mentally ill," being committed to a mental hospital, being "treated" there and so on, I voluntarily entered Hudson River State Hospital in Poughkeepsie, New York. When I went in I was, I believed, a sane and stable man, the most stable man, some of my friends had said, they knew. Now I know better. I acted crazy when I went in, told them I was hearing voices, I was scared, I needed help; but behind this act I was in good control of myself, taking rapid mental notes the whole time. I was, in fact, elated: I had pulled it off.

Eleven days later I was in a state of panic and had to get out. One more day, I was certain of it, and something inside me would have broken. It sounds melodramatic, but it's true. I don't know whether I would have screamed, slumped into a catatonic state, begun to speak in tongues, or whatever. The point is that I am not that stable. I have a limit. I know that now, and if the pressure gets heavy enough long enough to push me past that limit something will break and I will go crazy.

I am convinced that that possibility exists in us all.

Come to think of it, maybe that's why we are so quick to consign people like Noah Levy to a mental hospital. On that airplane Noah was a living reminder to the others that they, too, could step over that limit, fall into that abyss where they didn't really know what they might do next, where an impulse would float into their minds and they would really act on it, without thinking, without holding back. Most of us have laughed hysterically at one time or another. But suppose we couldn't *stop* laughing. We have all thought occasionally that our friends were making fun of us behind our backs. Suppose that thought just took us over.

The possibility of insanity exists in us all.

The fact is that we know very little about what goes on in other people's minds. We hear them speak, we see them behave, but this is merely evidence, it has to be interpreted; and if we choose to interpret it as being crazy, that is *only* an interpretation and as such it says as much about *our* frame of mind, testifies as much to our fears and apprehensions, as it says about the people whose behavior we are interpreting. I can't even fathom why my daughter likes her mashed potatoes cold. If someone does something we don't do or wouldn't do or haven't done, it makes no sense to us. We may explain someone's strange behavior as a manifestation of an unresolved Oedipus complex or a manic-depressive psychosis, as neurotic symptomatology, obsessive-compulsive behavior, as a character disorder—these are only the psychiatric explanations, and only a few of them. We may explain it sociologically as an aspect of deviant role-playing, in Marxist terms as a product of alienation, in genetic terms as an inherited deficiency, biochemically as an excess of serotonin or some other neurotransmitter in the brain, in behaviorist terms as an instance of maladaptive learning. There are so many ways to explain it. But none of these explanations is definitive; all of them can be and have been applied to the same pieces of action. They are hypotheses, theories, opinions. We really don't *know* what moves people to do what they do. And if we don't *know*, any action we may take with respect to it, any attitude we may come to hold toward it, can be based on nothing better than a guess. However thoroughly analytic, however insightful we may try to be, when it comes to explaining someone else's behavior we are guessing.

We put people in mental hospitals, then, on the basis of a guess. There is a fundamental issue at stake here between those who are called crazy and those who call them so. Crazy people are people who break social rules most of us take for granted. Calling people crazy is a way of judging them for having broken the rules, for having behaved, that is, in ways we can neither understand nor accept. The punishment is institutionalization in the broad sense of the word; we subject them, if not always to a mental hospital, then to a mental health system which is designed to do the same thing a mental hospital does, namely isolate them, find out why they behave as they do, and "resocialize" them to the mores and norms the rest of us live by. Under the guise that we are helping them, "curing" them, in fact, from putative disease, we put them in a place, a physical place like a hospital, or a psychological place like a treatment system, where their behavior can be systematically watched over and controlled—without their necessarily ever having broken a law.

The issue is that we are operating in an ill-defined gray area of unwritten social codes, of tacit assumptions about what is "normal" and what isn't. We have the power to institutionalize a Noah Levy and attempt to restructure the way he behaves on an airplane, in a movie theater, anywhere. I have the power, given the help of a friendly psychiatrist or two, to institutionalize my daughter and re-direct her liking for cold mashed potatoes. Ridiculous? No—*I do have that power*. And there are people who, having that power, abuse it.

Noah may not want to have the way he behaves re-built. Or it may be impossible to change him. Or it may be that the way he behaves actually makes more sense in the situation, is healthier, *saner*, in some basic way, than the way the rest of us behave. Isn't it better, after all, to vent your anger than to bottle it up and give yourself ulcers? As long as you don't hurt anybody, as long as you don't break the law, why not indulge your impulses? All Noah really did was raise his voice. He got angry and showed it. Is that a crazy thing to do? It may, on the contrary, be very sane. It is a well-known fact that middle-class

Americans cannot easily express anger; anger for us is something we bottle up. In consequence we go into therapy to learn how to deal with the profound rage which, having no outlet, eats at our insides like a cancer.

Noah thinks he should have gone to jail, not to the hospital, for the incident on the airplane. But, he says,

> They gave me no choice in the matter. It isn't as if they said, do you want to go to jail, or do you want to see a judge or whatever; they didn't. I don't think I could have gotten more than thirty days for disorderly conduct with this plane incident.

Noah is one of a growing number of mental patients and ex-mental patients who would rather be tried than treated, who would prefer to be thought of as criminals rather than mental patients. Their position is well worth our attention. It is not just the fact that any of us could go crazy and find ourselves in their place. It is the fact that nobody *knows* who's crazy and who isn't. Being crazy is a highly relative thing; so much of it is in the eye of the beholder. And the beholder has the power. Your husband or wife might become alarmed at your new habit of doing crossword puzzles in bed until two in the morning. Your daughter-in-law could get fed up with you, old man, sitting around in your undershirt and not shaving even when her neighbors come over to play bridge. Your secretary might be shocked at the way you cut your toenails while you're giving her dictation.[3] Weird, doctor. It's very embarrassing; people just don't *do* that. I mean, I'm really worried about him. I think he needs treatment, don't you? If the doctor agrees, *they have the power to put you away.*

This book is about the exercise of that power, about what happens to people we call crazy, or more often "mentally ill." About what the psychiatrists who work for us do to them and for them in the name of mental health. I should make it plain that I am not writing from an in-built antipsychiatric bias. I don't dislike psychiatrists.

What I have deep reservations about is the power we give them to institutionalize and try to restructure people whose behavior distresses us for one reason or another—people we all too readily call crazy.

This is not to say that there is no such thing as *being* crazy. I have met people who are very radical in their views—furious is a better word—about the treatment they received as mental patients but who know, and freely admit, that at one time in their lives they had lost control over their thoughts and actions. Noah Levy is one such person. Noah believed a few years ago that he was going to be the next mayor of New York City, that it was ordained to be, that indeed everything, every little event in his life and the life of those around him was working toward that end. To put it in a positive way, Noah has (or once had) the capacity to lose control over not just what he does but what he thinks as well. Psychiatrists call such a belief system a delusion. That particular delusion I can only call crazy.

But if people do go crazy it need not follow that they become "mentally ill." That is a term which jumps to a conclusion, assumes a knowledge we do not possess. The "mental illness" germ has yet to be isolated, schizophrenia is manifestly not something like pneumonia. Indeed, the psychiatric belief system which posits "mental illness" and divides it into various "disease" entities may well be as delusional as Noah's belief that he was going to be the next mayor. The term "mental illness" is simply another interpretation, a metaphor, as men like Thomas Szasz and many others have abundantly shown. In this book I surround it with quotation marks. It is a dangerous term. To call people "mentally ill" is a way of giving other people power over them on the basis of a science which is much more apparent than real. It seems better to use a word like "crazy," which carries no legal weight and might easily be applied at one time or another to any of us.

I
Reality Police

Institutions (churches, governments, universities, industries, languages) do not exist merely to satisfy pragmatic needs and desires. Much more fundamentally, they function to construct and secure a sense of reality.

Michael Novak, *The Experience of Nothingness*

I

Most mental institutions use a kind of crude test to determine who among all those knocking at their gates ought to be admitted and who ought not. Psychiatrists call it the Psychiatric Examination or the Mental Status Examination, but those are only its formal names. What it is is a reality test.

The way psychiatric handbooks and textbooks describe it, the examination is supposed to take about an hour and cover not only the prospective inmate's personal psychiatric history and that of his family, but important parameters of his mental functioning as well: recent and remote memory, his ability to add and subtract, his attention span, and so on.[1] In most mental institutions, however, the test is much more perfunctory and covers just two factors: the person's complaint, his story, what brought him to the hospital in the first place; and his orientation to the world. For what definitively separates the crazy from

15

the sane, them from us, is just this second factor. Does he
live in the "real world," this poor lost soul, or in a "fantasy
world" of his own making? Is he in touch with "reality"
or out of touch? At the heart of all definitions of insanity
lies this distinction between our reality (society's reality)
and theirs.

As I say, the test is crude. It consists for the most
part of a few simple questions. Can you tell me the date,
please? Can you tell me what year it is? Your name? Who
is the President of the United States? Do you know who
I am? Do you know where you are? Do you know why you
are here?

(Do you live in the same world we live in?)

A simple test: he may pass or fail, our hapless knocker
at the gates, but it doesn't matter, the institution will
probably take him in anyway.[2] The function of the test is
clearly not to exclude sane people from the institution.
Nor can it be convincingly passed off as a diagnostic procedure, since the giving of it is usually so perfunctory, the
whole thing taking on the average perhaps eight or nine
minutes. It is rather a ritual, a little affirmation of faith
psychiatry performs, faith in our mutually-agreed-upon
understanding of ourselves, the world, and our relationship to the world. Faith in reality. Yes indeed, I am a psychiatrist. The President is real, a real person, and not some
automaton the Disney people have made to look real and
fool us. No, this is not a space ship, this is a room and
those are the walls of the room and its floor and its
furniture. That thing in the corner there is not a toilet,
it's a plain wooden chair. A ritual of affirmation, and of
denial, too. What *we* are experiencing is real, whereas
what the insane are experiencing is *not real*.

But what is this reality which psychiatry (and the rest
of us, too) is so intent on affirming? Let us suppose that
you are the prospective inmate of this fortress of reality
and you are something of an amateur scientist, and the

psychiatrist asks you about the chair in the corner and you, proud of being scientifically with it, say that you see a collection of electrons, protons, and neutrons with enormous spaces between them held together in the illusory solidity and rigidity of wood by powerful atomic forces capable, if released, of destroying the entire hospital and everything else for miles around. Delusional thought content? Ideas of reference? Whatever its category, an alarming answer; the psychiatrist didn't really want to know about your hidden scientific expertise. But of course you are right; the chair *is* a collection of protons and other particles. You have merely substituted one reality for another, the scientific variety for the commonsense or everyday. *For there is more than one reality.* Nevertheless, your answer, which would seem to be inappropriate under the circumstances, would certainly throw some doubt on your mental condition.

Now suppose you said something else; suppose you said that you saw a toilet in the corner and there was a face in the toilet staring up at you and you were terrified. And you insisted on it, yes, that's a toilet and that horrible face is in it, get it away from me! and you covered your own face with your hands and clearly meant what you said. The chair symbolizes something awful to you, in other words, and the symbolic meaning has become more real to you than the actual chair everybody else sees there. So what do we do now? Is there a symbolic reality as well as scientific and everyday realities? If so, is it somehow less real than the others?

The chair is that collection of particles, isn't it? We can't *see* that, however, just as we can't *see* it as a toilet. Why then do we accept the scientific reality and reject the symbolic? Why indeed? Any science in which the scientists cannot be sure, when they discuss the fundamental elements of being (subatomic particles), whether they are talking about matter or energy must either cast the reality of reality in doubt, or the reality of science. But we don't want to hear about that; let the physicists worry about quantum theory and the uncertainty principle. However crazy scientific reality may seem we can put up with it because it doesn't get into the football scores, it keeps out of the way, and when it does come to our attention it comes bearing gifts, nice things like electronic computers and television sets and Saran Wrap. It doesn't charge into the kitchen, in other words, and say that's not a chair you're sitting on, you fool, that's a hydrocarbon.

But as to the chair being a *toilet*—well, if you see toilets where there are chairs you may see monsters where there are pussycats or elephants where there is nothing; anything is possible in such a world, and that can't be. We can't allow that. You might decide that the people in your car pool were spies and try to report them to the police. Or you might shoot your husband because you thought he was a werewolf. If we all operated as if symbols and metaphors were real, the world wouldn't run at all.

Granted. Yet that doesn't answer the question about the "truth" of symbolic realities. A clockwork world may not run well in a surreal universe, but we still cannot say with absolute certainty that symbolic realities have no validity. A kind of uncertainty principle is at work here, too, just as it is in atomic physics. The fact is that *all* realities, even our common garden variety, are in some sense symbolic. Take that lowly chair in the corner. Nothing, it would seem, could be more concrete, more factual, more *real* than that chair. Everyone knows a chair is a chair. That was something we learned when we were babies. It was in our first-grade readers; there was a picture of a little wooden chair, just like the ones around the work table where we made our plaster ashtrays for Daddy, and the word *c h a i r* spelled out under the picture and the blank space in our workbooks where we had to write it in. That's what it *is:* a chair.

But we had to learn that.[3] At one point we did not know what those strange objects "were." In the beginning we did not know what any objects were; we did not discriminate, in fact, between ourselves and objects at all. Freud calls this primary narcissism, Piaget calls it radical egocentrism; in the beginning, they both claim, babies feel themselves to be at the center of the universe, *their* universe, and they are omnipotent within its sphere. It is only later that the baby begins to understand that all is not within his power, that objects such as Mommy *are* *objects,* not part of him and not perfectly obedient to his needs. But he must be taught this "fact." As D. W. Winnicott explains it, the mother, by initially meeting the newborn infant's needs when those needs present themselves,

> gives the infant the *illusion* that there is an external reality that corresponds to the infant's own capacity to create. In other words, there is an overlap between what the mother supplies and what the child might conceive of. To the observer, the child perceives what the mother actually presents, but this is not the whole truth. The infant perceives the breast only in so far as a breast could be created just there and then. There is no interchange between the mother and the infant. Psychologically the infant takes from the breast that is part of the infant, and the mother gives milk to an infant that is part of herself.[4]

But later, according to Winnicott, through a psychological as well as physical weaning process, a process that is not dependent, in other words, on the mother having breast-fed the infant, the mother gradually *disillusions* the infant as to its omnipotent ability to create what it needs, and in this disillusionment the infant begins to conceive of a reality external to himself. Winnicott emphasizes, however, that this is not an automatic process. *"If all goes well,"* he repeats over and over again, the baby will learn to distinguish between that which is under his absolute control and that which is not—will learn, that is, what is magic, fantastic, illusory, and what is "real."

What this suggests is that "reality" is not given to primary raw perception as something which is self-evident.[5] The baby does not *naturally* divide the world into me and not-me, he is not born with this ability but must rather acquire it through a process of progressive frustration and disillusionment. As every parent knows, he acquires it very slowly. Even at late stages in development inner fantasy remains in certain circumstances as "real" to the child as external reality. Raw perception *by itself,* to repeat, does not present the world to us as an organized reality. Reality is an *inference* from further data, in Winnicott's scheme from the data of increasingly frequent disillusionment which the mother manages for the infant as she weans him. Reality is an inference: a mental construct. The mind organizes the data of perception via the experience of frustration into a system we call reality.[6]

A system which includes the mental construct "chair." We organize the raw perception of brown, hard, L-shape with legs, and the experience of sitting on these perceptions into the idea (and the word) "chair." Rather, we are taught to organize it so. And this idea we call "chair" is necessarily symbolic. It is an abstraction, that is, from raw perceptual experience; it organizes the inchoate experience of the object into something orderly, fixed, and permanent, something which will exist whether we are experiencing it or not, something deserving of a name: "chair." The name is symbolic because it refers to the existence of other similar objects of perception, objects of which we may have no direct immediate experience but whose existence the name invokes. The name makes possible the division of objects into classes and it invokes their presence. Building upon this and many other such names, such classes of objects and events, we are taught to construct a world of such classes, a language naming and describing them, in short a "reality," what Berger and Luckmann call a "symbolic universe." It is symbolic necessarily because even when the object or event is before our eyes we cannot *know* it directly. Even when we see it we must still invoke its existence through the magic of symbolization, through the system of words and mental images and references to other objects by which we describe it. By which, to take it one step further, we *create* it. As Marshall Edelson puts it,

> . . . the assumption underlying the notion that so-called reality confrontation is an antidote to phantasy is: there is one true reality; it is possible to know it directly, independently of any imaginative apprehension or valuation of it. But it would seem instead that all knowledge of reality is symbolically mediated. Reality is always a symbolic creation.[7]

Let me say it again: this symbolic system we call reality must be taught. Reality is not something "out there" but a kind of knowledge which the individual infant must acquire in progressive stages as he grows up.[8] The process by which the individual comes to acquire it—comes, that is, to believe in this symbolic system—is called socialization. As Berger and Luckmann convincingly demonstrate, the symbolic universe we call reality is constructed *collectively,* it is a social product, and knowledge of it is organized into and acquired by way of institutions. The primary socializing institution, of course, is the family. The mother teaches the child to objectify his perceptions of her: she is not part of him but exists in her own right. As his first contact with reality she must *teach* him that she is real. On the foundation stone of this primary organization of his experience, his experience of her, she can then begin to build a world for him, teach him what else is real, what else must be symbolized into a system. This system includes, of course, not only what things "are" but what they are for, not only the names of things but their purposes. He must learn not only that a chair *is* a chair but also that it is *not* a chair unless it is specifically made to be a chair, a thing designed to be sat on. The system further includes knowledge of "things" besides objects. Patterns of behavior are an essential part of the reality system. If Mommy and Daddy and Sister all use a knife and fork, Johnny will learn first what a knife and fork are (their names), then what they are for, and finally that he too must use them. Eventually he will learn to use them so well that the use of them will become automatic, a piece of his social reality, a pattern of behavior he takes as much for granted as any of the objects he may sit on. Reality is a symbolic ordering of experience, a world-system, and if that order requires you to eat with a knife and fork, believe me that requirement is real.[9]

To summarize, then: reality is an idea of order imposed on the chaos of perceptual experience. Our ideas of reality mediate experience and bring it under control. Table manners, for example, are a highly elaborated order of behavior designed to bring the experience of hunger under control; they make it possible for people to share food instead of fighting over it. Our idea of a chair is an ordering idea enabling everyone who shares the idea to react to it in the same way, so that we don't have to worry about someone reacting to it as if it were something else: a collection of atomic particles, a toilet, firewood, or whatever. The teaching of these ideas of order has been institutionalized. It is primarily the institution of the family which teaches us about table manners and chairs and other fundamental aspects of the world. The schools reinforce these teachings and teach us still others, the churches still others, and so on. Collectively these and the rest of society's institutions present us with a ready-made symbolic system, a symbolic universe, and at the same time constitute a social order which embodies that sym-

bolic universe and confirms its reality. To repeat, however, none of this is given. We have to be taught this
order, we have to be made to see the world the way we
see it. Our world is not self-evident.

The drift of what I am saying ought to be obvious
by now. Put at its simplest, if reality is a social construct
then it is relative to the society which constructs it and the
period of its construction. Reality is both culturally and
historically a relative phenomenon. Even such rock-bottom
categories of reality as space and time have different mean-
ings to different peoples. An outstanding example may be
found in the work of Benjamin Lee Whorf on the Hopi
language. According to Whorf, the Hopi Indians of the
American Southwest have no past, present and future
tense and no separate word corresponding to the English
word "time." Our concept of time as an abstract con-
tinuum, a separable and measurable element of reality, is
foreign to the Hopi. His language handles the experience
of duration in a wholly different manner; he does not
separate duration itself from the duration of an event or
an object through space. His concepts of motion, distance,
and duration blend, once again, in a different order of
reality from ours. This order is no less "real" than our
own. The Hopi world view works. In certain ways, in fact,
it is more scientifically "accurate" than the world view
embodied in an Indo-European tongue such as English.[10]

What would happen to a Hopi who took a psychiatric
reality test? If he failed, would that mean he was crazy?

It is easy to answer no. Obviously a Hopi can only
be crazy in the context of his own culture and its symbolic
universe. But whether we understand that collectively,
as a society, is another question. Would we, for example,
accept a Hopi living next door to us? He probably
wouldn't mow the lawn. He might do fertility rites in
the garden and his squaw might breast-feed the babies
right there on the front steps. The long hair, the funny

clothes: after a while we neighbors might get together and ask him to go back to the reservation. Property values and all that. And if he wouldn't go back other things might start to happen—anonymous complaints to the police, a little friendly harassment, just the kids having some fun. The county health department would probably be called in at some point to see about the garbage in the back yard. Then somebody would be bound to complain about some "crazy" behavior. Look at how the guy stares at us—why *doesn't* he go back to the reservation in the face of all this? The psychiatrist would probably decide he was crazy *not* to. The psychiatric commitment papers would be filled out. It has all been known to happen. A reality system which challenges our own can be terribly disturbing.

Socialization goes on all the time, every day, for everybody, and it is a coercive process. In the suburbs people are socialized to keep their lawns neatly trimmed, and heaven help those who don't. People from alien cultures are socialized in more formal ways. The Federal Government maintains an elaborate system of schools on Indian reservations and makes every effort to teach Indian children the language, the history, the reality of white Western culture. We should all know by now to what end. Primary socialization takes place in the family in the first few years of life. By the time the Indian gets to his reservation school he is already socialized—to Indian tribal reality. This is a reality which in the Sioux (and many other tribes) includes an ideal of noncompetitiveness totally at odds with Western standards. Sioux children do not volunteer to answer questions in school because doing so would embarrass those classmates who do not know the answer. Competition to them means that one person succeeds and the rest are humiliated. So Sioux children sit impassively at their desks and will not compete.[11] Western schools are founded on competition, inherent in the concept of grades. Sioux children do not do well in school. Similarly their parents do not do well in Western society. They retreat into silence, apathy, alcoholism; into suicide. Erikson observed sadly that the Indian has no real identity in white middle-class America. The Indian cannot feel like a real person in the context of a society which will not accept the reality of his world view.

People who do not feel "real," who have lost contact with "reality," frequently go crazy. So it is with the Indian. Trapped between two "realities," all too often he finds himself in a white middle-class American mental institution—along with many other people with whom the socialization process has not worked.[12] All of them are crazy by the standards of (white middle-class American) society. They have all failed the (white middle-class American) reality test. They must therefore all be resocialized. We have many institutions whose function it is to socialize people, family, schools, churches, and so on. And then we have this one powerful institution to *re*socialize them if the process fails.

Michael Novak is right on target. Institutions, he says, "function to construct and to secure a sense of reality." To no institution does this statement apply more than to the mental health system. Reality so-named is its very special province. You only enter this system through the ritual of the reality test. You only leave it when you have convinced the system of your submission to that reality.

But we must have a very shaky sense of reality to go to such lengths to enforce it. We have given the reality police immense power to arrest and "institutionalize" us, for years if necessary, just to persuade us that a chair is a chair. To be sure, every culture enforces its sense of reality by some means or other. When a Navaho goes crazy the tribe employs elaborate ceremonies to bring him back to Navaho reality. But even the most complicated of these ceremonies takes no more than nine days. At the end of the

nine days, if the deviant Navaho is not cured, well—so
be it.[13] The Navahos have no mental hospitals, nor do
they institute five or six years of psychoanalysis for those
who can afford it. The Navahos live with their crazy person. Why don't we?

Sometimes we do live with our crazies. Sociologists
have shown that a great deal of crazy behavior goes un-
detected; where it is detected it is often ignored.[14] But
generally we refer behavior that violates our sense of reality to this enormous institution, the mental health system,
whose specific task it is to enforce our sense of reality, the
complex reality of white, middle-class America. No wonder the Indian rejects it. Used to squatting or sitting on
the ground, he must first learn that a chair is a chair and
what a chair is for. Then he must learn that this other
object that looks like a chair but has a velvet rope draped
across its arms is not a chair at all but a work of art, a
Louis XVI chair, and it is definitely not to be used the
way an ordinary chair is used. If anything, it is to be wor-
shiped. This other object, however, which looks just like
the Louis XVI chair but which Nelson Rockefeller happens to be sitting on—well, that's another story entirely.
A chair is a chair is a work of art is an investment. It might
indeed be better to squat.

We will have more to say about these matters as we
go along. The mental health system, I have indicated, enforces a white middle-class American sense of reality; we
will see how this came about historically in the rest of this
chapter. Subsequent chapters will show how this system
works today and how people experience it. Right now
there is just one more obvious but essential point to make.
The United States contains within its geographic boundaries Navaho, Hopi, and Sioux, Mennonite, black ghetto
and Hasidic ghetto, upper-class rich and no-class hippie
freak, Middle Western and Californian, Puerto Rican,
Irish, Italian, Polish, Oriental, and innumerable other re-

alities. Some of these are distinct and seldom mingle with the rest; others are less distinct and mingle freely. But all of them are relative culturally and historically to each other. No evidence of an absolute external reality exists. Even the physicists talk about probable realities, of "things" tending toward reality, of reality as a potential, not an actual. All realities are relative to the time and the culture which produced them. Within this broad, fragmented social structure where the most diverse things are "real," the mental health system enforces only one symbolic universe, one sense of reality, based on one cultural tradition and one set of values. That fact seems crazy in its own right.

II

We forget sometimes that institutions such as mental health systems are not "natural," are not inevitable the way hair growing on men's faces is inevitable. The mental health system is a social invention. Once upon a time it did not exist. People called it into being, created it, named it, and made it a part of their reality, all at a certain point in history, for certain reasons, stated and implied.

Like any invention, however much it has been developed, the system embodies important characteristics dating from its origins, just as governments embody characteristics dating from their constitution. An understanding of its origins is therefore essential. "It is impossible to understand an institution adequately," say Berger and Luckmann, "without an understanding of the historical process in which it was produced." [15] Especially is this true of the mental health system. To a degree unusual among institutions this system retains the fundamental practices with which it began.

The mental health system was invented in the United States in the 1820's and 1830's. Before that time it cannot

be said that the country had anything we could dignify
with the word "system." Before the 1820's and 1830's
America dealt with the insane in informal, nonsystematic
ways. Those insane who were not violent were allowed to
roam at large, or their families cared for them, or if they
had no families their communities found someone who
was willing to care for them for a fee and boarded them
out, the money coming from the public pocket. If they
were a nuisance sometimes they were put in jail, more
often in the poorhouse. In this nonsystem, it is very important to note, the insane were not differentiated from
idiots, poor people, or other dependents; all these categories belonged to one class then, what we might call the
welfare class. There was no meaningful segregation of the
insane within that class.[16]

This nonsystem was by no means perfect. In fact it
was subject to large-scale abuse. Local communities were
entirely responsible for their own dependent class and
within broad limits they were free to exercise that responsibility as they saw fit. That usually meant as cheaply
as possible. Jails were therefore generally small, dark,
damp, and cold and the insane and the feebleminded and
the poor rotted in their cells. In those communities with
poorhouses the insane were usually allocated to basement
rooms with the rats. Some communities used an auction
system; dependent individuals were auctioned off to the
lowest bidder, to the person who would offer to house
and feed them, that is, at the lowest cost to the community.
To make up for his possible losses the successful bidder
would then frequently work his poor madman unmerci-
fully while housing him in an unheated shed out by the
barn and feeding him gruel. These practices were not
particularly humane, nor were they meant to be. They
were merely economical. But nobody raised a great hue
and cry. Nobody really gave the problem much thought.
America was thinly populated, the insane were not much

in evidence, and ad hoc measures were sufficient to deal with them.

It must have been in the cities, as the cities began to grow, that the insane first became problematic. In cities behavior of any kind, deviant or conforming, becomes more visible simply because there are more people to observe it. As the demographic concentration rises, the pressures on behavior become more intense. We have already seen that people will not tolerate loud, angry talk in the crowded confines of an airplane, talk they would just walk away from on the streets. Something similar holds in cities. Cities concentrate people in a relatively limited space. We have no historical microsociology of American city life; [17] we cannot say with authority that this is the way it happened. But something like it must have been the case. In Boston, in New York, in Philadelphia, on the crowded wharves, in the busy downtown streets of these early American cities, crazy behavior must at some point have become intolerable. We can refer to no case histories, but there must have come a moment in the public mind when old Elizabeth patrolling the markets carrying her doll or crazy Jedidiah standing on the corner of Wall and Broad Streets calling out to God for revenge on these sinners must have threatened something basic, some burgeoning sense of propriety, of the way things in a well-ordered society ought to operate. Thus was born, we assume, a public readiness to perceive crazy behavior by itself, apart from the problem of dependency in general, as something that had to be dealt with.

At the same time certain American leaders, spokesmen for the emerging moral and economic order which constitutes white middle-class American reality, were becoming aware of novel developments in Europe having to do with the insane. The Europeans had just invented the insane asylum. For centuries crowded little Europe had *confined* the insane, but confined them as in America with the poor, imbeciles, libertines, criminals, and other "use-less" human beings. Now, however, in Paris at Bicêtre and La Salpetrière and in England at the Quaker Retreat in York, the Europeans were *segregating* the insane from other dependent groups in their own separate insane asylums. Furthermore, they were treating the insane at these asylums and they were achieving "cures."

This treatment was called "moral treatment" and it is well-known in the history of psychiatry as a prototype of the "therapeutic community" which is now fashionable in mental institutions. But this only obscures its character. In fact moral treatment was the prototype for *all* sub-sequent practice up to and including the present in the therapy of insanity.

What was the nature of this moral treatment? How did it work?

First, it isolated the insane from other people. This was a new thing to do. The insane were suddenly a separate case, defined exclusively by their insanity, by their broken relationship to reality, and no longer by the dependency or poverty they might share with others. And so serious was the nature of their break with the real now thought to be that they had to be separated from others in order not to contaminate them. As Foucault makes clear in his book *Madness and Civilization,* this separation was not effected for the benefit of the insane. It was to protect the other dependent groups from the insane.[18]

Second, in these new institutions an overtly moral regime was established. Under this regime standards of behavior were imposed, and the degree of an inmate's mental improvement was measured on a simple scale of adherence to those standards. Was an inmate diligent in performing the work assigned to him? Was he polite in his dealings with others? Did he refrain from offending people with bad table manners or embarrassing them with insane talk? If he did what he was supposed to do, what a good grocery clerk would do in the company of his betters, he was improving, he was being "cured."

But of course he was not a grocery clerk, he was an inmate in an insane asylum. And this fact emptied the inmate's behavior of its content. At the Quaker Retreat in York, for example, work was a requirement with which all the inmates had to comply. Everyone had work to do, repetitious mechanical work such as pulling weeds which was supposed to calm the mind and to instill in the inmate at the same time an idea of the sovereign virtue of work. In a God-fearing middle-class society people work. It was very simple, a self-evident good—except that the work the inmate had to do was meaningless. He was not paid for it, it contributed nothing to his own good or society's. It was assigned to him only to make sure that he did it. It was purely formal, a rote performance, an absolute compliance to the work standard.

An even better example is the behavior exacted of the inmates at York at the Director's periodic teas. Foucault quotes the following description of such an event; the inmates

> dress in their best clothes, and vie with each other in politeness and propriety. The best fare is provided, and the visitors are treated with all the attention of strangers. The evening generally passes with the greatest harmony and enjoyment. It rarely happens that any unpleasant circumstance occurs; the patients control, to a wonderful degree, their different propensities; and the scene is at once curious and affectingly gratifying.[19]

But of course these teas were not "real." No genuine social interaction took place between the Director and his guests, not at the level of spontaneity, of actual communication. Everyone talked politely about the weather and the crops, everyone decorously sipped his tea and nibbled on his biscuits, no one tried to change the water into wine. But it was all a performance. And the Director was also the

Audience and the Critic. He judged behavior, he measured
the lapses from propriety, he kept his eagle eye on the
violent maniacs, and under the intense pressure of his
relentless observation the inmates conformed. Once again,
however, it was a compliance without content. The proprieties were observed, but not for the usual reasons.
We normally observe the proprieties in order to facilitate
communication with each other. The inmates at the Retreat observed the proprieties because to do so was regarded as *in itself* an absolute good.

An unstated psychological process was at work here.
At first the inmate conformed for fear of punishment.
Moral treatment did not do away with physical restraint,
as is commonly supposed. The cold water showers, the
fetters and chains, the tranquilizing restraining chairs were
still in use. Only where they had once been used as crude
forms of treatment, they were now used explicitly as
punishment: punishment for violating a standard of behavior. After a while, however, as an inmate learned to
conform, the threat of punishment was no longer needed.
Isolated from genuine communication with others, always
within range of the Director's eternally watchful eye and
of his moral authority, the inmate inevitably began to
watch himself, to become self-conscious and to see himself as an object among objects, a person among persons.
And the person he saw was the person the Director saw: a
madman. And he was ashamed. He knew himself as a
shameful object *he himself could not relate to*. At that
moment "cure" began.

This is, we might note, the process of alienation *par
excellence*. Modern psychiatry has applauded moral treatment as a humane and highly effective therapy, a great
improvement over confinement, the auction practice, the
jailhouse cells and the poorhouse cellars, the indifference
of the eighteenth century to the insane. But we ought to
know what we are dealing with. When a person in-

ternalizes his isolation, becomes isolated from himself, sees himself from a distance as an object—a shameful object at that—then he is alienated, not cured.

If it was an alienating process, it was also a resocializing process.[20] It worked in the same way primary socialization works; patterns of behavior were forced on the subject until he could not do without them. And it worked by essentially the same means. The asylum was a kind of family, says Foucault, with the Director as the father. He filled the father's moral role as arbiter of behavior. His self-conscious integrity and righteousness served as a conspicuous example to his family, making them only too conscious of their own faults. Under his guidance they came to internalize the standards of society and to feel guilty for not having done so in the first place. Just as parents punish children for breaking rules and continue punishing them until it is no longer necessary, until the children start obeying the rules on their own, even when nobody is watching, so the Director punished his charges until they did the same. And it was all very uplifting. The Director was not just any father but the Director, a Victorian father, a great moral authority. A proto-psychiatrist.

America's moral and spiritual leaders bought this idea wholesale. Here was a method that promised to "cure" the insane; further, it was humane; and finally it substituted internal for external restraints, it made the insane feel guilty for being insane. There is no more efficient method of social control than guilt. In Boston, New York and Philadelphia leading citizens led movements to establish philanthropic institutions modeled on the York Retreat. In 1832 the State of Massachusetts established the first such public institution, the asylum at Worcester, putting one Samuel Woodward in charge. Woodward was a physician, but more than that he was a moral authority: a Director. Under his direction the Worcester institution was also modeled on the moral treatment ideal.[21] It in turn became the model for similar public institutions all over the United States.

One of the most surprising aspects of this young system was that it had nothing to do with medicine. The men who founded the early institutions were social reformers, not doctors. The system was in effect before doctors became involved. The doctors who did become involved in it were not psychiatrists. Psychiatry as a profession did not exist in the early 1800's. The system created the profession. Gerald Grob, who seems to know more about the history of mental institutions than anybody else, is explicit on this important point:

> . . . psychiatric thought and practice had not played a dominant part in shaping the structure and functions of these institutions. Instead the reverse was true. Psychiatry was, to a large extent, molded and shaped by the institutional setting within which it was born and grew to maturity. Many dominant characteristics of psychiatric ideology were but rationalizations of existing conditions within mental hospitals as well as popular attitudes. The mental hospital in its formative years was an institution created by society to cope with abnormal behavior and to provide care and treatment for a variety of dependent groups; the result was that psychiatry—despite its claims about its scientific and medical character—reflected the role assigned to it by society.[22]

The early psychiatrist was then simply a Director glowing with the patina of medicine. As Grob says, in the beginning of this system medical ideologies played no part in asylum practice other than to rationalize it. To a large degree that remains true to this day.

So does much else that I have noted about these early institutions. Another surprising aspect of the system is how little it has changed. The system no longer uses moral treatment *per se,* but it retains most of its main features. At the heart of modern mental hospital practice lie the

very same ideas, the very same principles of operation
which animated moral treatment in the early 1800's. The
primary difference is that those ideas have been bureaucratized. We will know all we need to know about the
system's history when we see how bureaucratization occurred and what it meant for life inside the mental institution.

The bureaucratization of the system appears to have
been unavoidable. Moral treatment was founded on an
imitation of the family. For the imitation to work the
asylum had to be kept small. The State Lunatic Asylum
at Worcester was designed to hold a maximum of 120
inmates. The Director, it was felt, could call everyone
by his first name with only that many people to direct;
his fatherly moral authority could operate intimately.
But of course there were more than 120 crazy people in
Massachusetts, many more. Fifty of the Boston House of
Industry's five hundred inmates were adjudged to be insane, and its director was only too anxious to get rid of
them.[23] Other poorhouses across the state probably held
a similar proportion. The jails were full of insane people,
too, and there were many in private homes or just living
in their various communities who had never been in an
institution. Now there was a place to send them. Once
the idea caught on, once families and poorhouses and
judges began to realize that they could get rid of their
lunatics, get them off their hands, it was only a matter of
time before the numbers knocking at the gates became
unmanageable.

There is no need to go into the details. Pretty soon
the Worcester asylum was holding many hundreds of inmates, far too many for the Director to know personally.
More asylums became necessary. Eventually Massachusetts
boasted eleven state mental institutions. The original reformers, the moral and social leaders, were thinking about
treatment and actual "cures," but the public was inter-

ested only in getting rid of the insane because they could
not tolerate their behavior. They did not care what went
on inside the asylum. They only wanted the insane off
the streets. The society was becoming middle class, and
behavior on middle-class streets is nothing if not respectable.

As the asylums grew crowded their arteries hardened:
bureaucratization set in. Bureaucratization permanently
altered the character—but not the idea—of moral treatment. The practices once meant to serve as genuinely
therapeutic instruments now served an entirely different
end. Asylum practice abandoned its therapeutic goals and
concentrated on preserving order and discipline within
the institution.

Clara Lathrop testifies eloquently to this change.
Clara was a young woman from Rochester, New York,
who believed that a boarder in her house was poisoning
her. Today the psychiatrists would probably label her a
schizophrenic, paranoid type, assuming, of course, that the
boarder was not in fact poisoning her. But whether or
not she had any basis for her paranoia, her family soon
provided her with one by committing her to the Lunatic
Asylum in Utica against her will. This was in October of
1880. She finally managed to get out on a writ of habeas
corpus in December of 1882—with her family still trying
to keep her in the asylum. At the time of her release Clara
apparently still believed that she had been poisoned, and
quite possibly she believed it to the end of her life. In
the meantime, however, she found her way to New York,
trained herself as a stenographer, wrote a book about her
experiences, and lived free.[24]

Clara Lathrop had a great deal to say about the
bureaucratized life she was forced to live at Utica. Let us
begin with her comments about the Director. Her Director was John P. Gray, a physician, editor of the *American
Journal of Insanity,* a power in the field that was not

yet called psychiatry. And of course a moral authority: a Director. Except that Dr. Gray did not exercise his moral authority directly. In the two years Clara Lathrop spent at Utica she saw Dr. Gray on the wards only once. He made no attempt to interact with inmates; on the contrary, he avoided them. The staff interacted with inmates. Dr. Gray considered it his job to administer this large complicated institution, and that left no time for the inmates. Nevertheless he continued to make the crucial decisions about who was "well" enough to leave and who was not. Usually he decided that nobody was "well" enough to leave. In effect, then, he retained his authority —Lathrop calls it "One Man Power"—but delegated his morality, scattered his father role out among the staff. By this peculiar delegation of his putative moral insight the staff now became the arbiters of proper behavior within the institution.

Who were the staff? Dr. Gray had a few assistant physicians on his staff. These men had not been trained in "psychiatry" but were receiving their training on the job. They were not even allowed to join the association of mental institution superintendents, which eventually became the American Psychiatric Association. They were responsible for the inmates but they had no authority over their care. Young Dr. Blumer, for example, was supposed to make a round trip through the female wards —six miles of walking—twice a day and to supervise the feeding of the inmates besides.[25] All he had time to do, of course, was to report on problem cases. And Dr. Gray himself made the decisions about medications, assignment to other wards, and so on, in disposition of these cases. The assistant physicians were in effect trainees.

That leaves the attendants. The attendants were in constant contact with the inmates and it was to them that the father role had in fact been delegated. And who were the attendants? They were hired for the most part

from the servant classes. For the most part—it depended
on the circumstances. At the New York Lunatic Asylum
on Blackwell's Island criminals from the prison were used
as attendants.[26] At Utica the attendants were servant types,
immigrants, usually; Dr. Gray liked to use Welsh immigrants because, according to Lathrop, they were very
loyal. Lathrop used to argue with them, insisting on her
sanity, and she would get a reply such as "You must be
insane, or you would not be here." [27] Being there *proved*
you were insane: a neat little nineteenth-century Catch 22.

Of course it was a farce. The attendants had no training in moral treatment or any other kind of treatment.
Their job was to feed the inmates, see that the linen was
changed on schedule, get people into and out of bed on
schedule, get the ward floors scrubbed on schedule, in
short run the ward efficiently and control the behavior
of the inmates to that end. In their eyes bad behavior was
behavior which disrupted the efficient operation of the
ward. Good behavior was behavior which enhanced effi-
ciency, behavior which made their job easier. Lathrop
sums it up nicely:

> I saw that the principle studied was to reduce the whole
> ward to the same level,—the sane as well as the insane,
> the refined and cultured, the vulgar and ignorant,—no
> word of kindness, sympathy or encouragement was
> spoken to any one, and the peculiarities that many
> patients exhibited incident to their insanity were a
> matter of laughter and ridicule to the attendants, the
> object being to make themselves as little trouble and
> fatigue as possible, which could be more readily achieved
> by reducing the entire ward to the condition of a herd
> of cattle, which must be goaded, not coaxed into
> submission.[28]

"As little trouble and fatigue as possible"—that was the
crux of it. To that end, not to a therapeutic end, the
attendants enforced standards of behavior, the institution's

standards of behavior. The institution was still after submission, but not to an internalized sense of guilt, a therapeutic self-consciousness leading to self-control. The attendants were ignorant of such delicate psychological niceties. They wanted submission to the institution as an institution. In other words, to them. These laughing, cruel, ignorant people had become the institution's moral authorities.

The institution also exacted submission to a work standard. Under moral treatment, however, inmates worked because work was a moral good, it pacified and disciplined the mind. Now inmates worked because the institution had work to be done. Lathrop observed that "all the labor of the institution was performed by the patients." [29] The laundry, the ironing room, the sewing room, the kitchens all used inmates as unpaid help. The work was now useful, in contrast to the practice of moral treatment, but the workers had become slaves.

The ultimate object of moral treatment had been to establish in the inmate a self-control based on remorse, on an awareness of the folly of your former lunatic behavior, on submission to yourself: internal controls. The institution still insisted on internal controls, but now it administered them by mouth. The doctors called it medicine. Historians have neglected the use of drugs in mental institutions, but Lathrop and others indicate that they were used heavily.[30] Today the standard psychiatric drug is Thorazine; in the 1880's it was Chloral, a powerful sedative. Earlier, opium and morphine had been used as sedatives, too; later bromides became popular. The primary purpose all of these drugs served was to keep patients under (internal) control. Lathrop gives some idea of how they were administered.

> She [an inmate noted for her physical strength] was allowed the privilege of carrying the medicine trays, which were heavily loaded with cups usually filled with

drugs, through the wards for the attendants. This did not
end her duties, however, for when patients refused to take
these powerful mixtures, having perhaps learned their
injurious effect, the poor victim would be forced to the
floor by several attendants aided by this powerful woman,
who would sit upon the victim's chest and hold her down,
while the medicine was poured down her unwilling
throat.[31]

It sounds melodramatic, but it still goes on. Try to refuse medicine in a state hospital today and four burly
attendants will grab you, one for each limb, and spread
you out on the floor while a nurse gives you a double- or
triple-dose injection in your butt.

Lathrop's story goes on and on. She describes at
length her fruitless attempts to convince the doctors, the
attendants, anyone who would listen that she was sane,
her fruitless attempts to send letters outside (all mail was
censored) to people and organizations who might help her.
She describes physical abuse, refers obliquely to her suspi-
cion that a doctor drugged and raped her, mentions the
boredom which is the most pervasive feature of asylum
life, details in horror a visit to the back wards where old
women lay chained to the floor, talks about the "Utica
crib," a wooden cage which Dr. Gray invented, and more.
All that she said remains true to this day. To be sure,
the Utica crib is gone—who needs it when Thorazine is
so effective? Many states no longer allow the censorship
of mail. Chains have been replaced by restraining sheets.
But the rest has not changed. The asylum is an institution
outside time, says Foucault, "always oriented to anachro-
nistic structures and symbols." [32] In a sense it has no
history.

I remember reading a book by a man named Julius
Chambers shortly after I left Hudson River State Hospital.
Chambers was a reporter and in 1876 he got himself
committed to an asylum in New York with a high-farce
imitation of a lunatic fit. When he got out twelve days

later, like Lathrop on a writ of habeas corpus, he wrote
a series of newspaper articles exposing conditions in this
particular institution. The articles became the book.[33] I
remember reading it in awe and disbelief. Everything,
everything was the same. In one hundred years nothing
has changed. You cannot believe *any* of psychiatry's claims
about a revolution in mental hospital care. Isolated as it
were by definition, fatally protected from the social evolu-
tion which affects other American institutions, American
mental hospitals retain intact the practices they adopted at
the beginning.

And the public has ignored the situation. It is not
from lack of evidence. From the 1850's on down, exposé
after exposé, written by former madmen, pseudo-madmen,
would-be madmen, by reformers like Dorothea Dix, sometimes even by the doctors themselves, has made its momentary sensation. Clifford Beers' *A Mind That Found
Itself* went into multiple printings over the years and
effected the founding of what is now the National Association for Mental Health. Books by "Inmate Ward #8,"
"Jane Doe" and others have told the Lathrop story or
the Chambers story over and over again.[34] As recently as
1948 Albert Deutsch's sensational *The Shame of the States*
exposed unbelievable abuses in the system. As recently
as 1969 Anne Barry faked a psychosis and spent seven
days in Bellevue and wrote a book about it.[35] What has
it all led to? Not much. We consume sensations like so
much shortcake. From the 1870's to the 1970's none of
these exposés has changed the basic structure and function
of the mental institution. We find them too *useful* to
change. As one Director ironically put it in 1872,

> Hospitals . . . are supposed to be kept up more for the
> safety of the community and the convenience of friends
> who wish to be relieved of the trouble of taking care of
> them at home than for the welfare and benefit of the
> patients themselves.[36]

That's the way it was. That's the way it is.

It is a strange idea to have an institution specifically designed to enforce a version of reality. We can begin to see now what that version of reality is. It is real to work at work which serves neither you nor society but merely an institution. It is real to be docile and take your medicine. It is real to obey all authority, but especially that authority which derives from the Director, whoever he may be, whatever it may be that he directs. It is real to observe a stringent regularity in your getting up and your lying down, in your coming and going, your eating, in all your activities. It is real to be isolated, alone, walled off from the world. It is real to have your life totally controlled by others. It is real, in short, not to be free.

Since the 1870's and 1880's the mental health system has elaborated itself enormously. From the Freudian beginnings in the 1890's psychological therapies have multiplied like rabbits. Institutional sub-forms of all types have sprung up: child guidance clinics, halfway houses, day hospitals, crisis centers, suicide centers, community mental health centers, outpatient clinics. The birth of the concept of neurosis has enabled the birth of private office practice in psychiatry. Clinical psychology and psychiatric social work have appeared. We now have more than twenty-five thousand psychiatrists in the United States and untold other therapists, licensed and unlicensed. We no longer have just mental institutions; now we have a huge self-perpetuating system of which the state mental institution is only the most visible element. I will try to cover as much of this giant system as I can in the chapters which follow. But we must not let the complexity of the system overwhelm us. This is a system which in its origins and in its practices is simply and clearly a system of social control. A reality enforcer. If we remember that, we have hold of the thread which will guide us through the maze.

II
Getting into the System

> A pluralistic society must learn to live with a great degree
> of mental and behavioral deviation.
>
> Nicholas N. Kittrie, *The Right To Be Different*

I

I have said very little so far about the phenomena
which stand at the center of this book, the phenomena of
insanity itself. I have talked about a variety of different
realities but I have not said much about the overwhelming reality of the experience of going crazy. I have talked
about the mental health system as a reality police force
but I have given no hint, except perhaps in Noah Levy's
story, that there might in fact be a need for such a force,
no hint that insanity is a brute personal and social fact
capable of arousing great revulsion and panic both in the
person who experiences it and in other people, and that
it therefore *must* be subject to some type of social control.

Without getting into a definitive discussion on this
issue now, on whether we do need reality police, let me
nevertheless acknowledge the reality of what we are dealing with, let me recognize with all due ceremony the
power of insanity, its triumphant sovereignty within its
own realm. There is only one way to do this. We must
refer to accounts by the insane themselves.

43

I will begin with Barbara O'Brien's book about her
six-month descent into the extraordinary world of Hook
Operators, a world as persuasively vivid as Tolkien's
Middle-earth or Swift's Brobdingnag. She woke up one day
to find three "hallucinations" in her room:

> When I awoke they were standing at the foot of my bed
> looking like soft fuzzy ghosts. I tried feeling the
> bedclothes. The sensation of feeling was sharp. I was
> awake and this was real.[1]

This was real. You go to bed one night feeling, let us say,
very depressed, very unhappy, uncertain about your life,
but not crazy, and when you wake up the next morning
three fuzzy hallucinations are standing by your bed. Their
names are Burt, Hinton and Nicky and they talk to you.
They are your Operators. They control everything you
do. They *own* you; they even have a deed. Which makes
you, of course, not a person but a Thing. Operators are
everywhere controlling everybody, it turns out, but nobody knows about them. Yours are conducting an experiment, however, letting you in on their presence just to
see what happens, to see what difference it makes. Unfortunately, the world of Operators is complicated and
other Operators object strenuously to this experiment and
these other Operators will destroy you if they get their
Hooks in you. Quite literally destroy you. So you are in
great danger. But of course there is nothing you—whoever you think *you* are by now—can do about it; you are
entirely under your Operators' control and can only pray
that they know what they are doing.

That is how it began for Barbara O'Brien. She spent
the next six months of her life wandering around the
United States living out this experiment. Her story possesses a logic and coherence which we might almost call
literary; really, her "delusion" was a work of genius. But
most insanity probably doesn't happen that neatly. Bert

Kaplan, in his book *The Inner World of Mental Illness,* prints an account by a young man written *in medias res,* while he was passing through a particularly crazy phase, and it seems to be closer than Barbara O'Brien's story to what it is probably like for most people. Here is a sample:

> I can't do what I feel I am esposeto to
> Music works on my sex emotion and I am learning how to let it out by different means than I have been tought
>   Without Jesus we can do nothing
>   When you wish upon a star. red—stop amber—cauiton purple—be on look out Green go ahead with what you are doing God help us to take advice from other people and show them we can take being talked about and not get mad or lose you temper How music grew bauer and Peyser At last Dr. Hughes I've come to my desion. I am ready to let people know by living more in reality and quite runing from myself. Because I a not a balby and more. but a man with God giving emotion's [2]

Kaplan says that "we are closer to the illness" here than in any restrospective account like Barbara O'Brien's which recollects in tranquility what the experience was like.[3] It certainly looks that way. It looks as if this young man has put his thought processes down on paper directly, as they were happening, without ordering them the way the rest of us do when we present ourselves. Here is thought liberated from all conventional restraints of logic, coherence, even of spelling: a presentation of raw free consciousness. And it is crazy.

An account like this, however, raises questions about our ability to relate to "raw free consciousness," if that is what insanity is. Is it a genuine communication, something which tries and somehow manages to find an echo in our own experience? Or is it impenetrable, totally private? Barbara O'Brien, as I said, makes sense; her experience possesses an imaginative wholeness and power, a coherence, which a novelist might envy. Her delusion made up a story which she then lived. And the story gives her insanity a meaning. The story of her insanity constitutes, in effect, a radical "lived" criticism of the social reality which triggered it. She was involved in a viciously competitive office situation where everybody was struggling for power and trying to manipulate and control everybody else. Her Hook Operators were an obvious metaphor for that situation. She simply turned the metaphor into a reality: Burt, Nicky and Hinton. In Gregory Bateson's phrase, hers was a "metaphor which is *meant.*" [4] And we can relate to it as a metaphor even if we cannot relate to the reality she experienced. We relate to her reality, that is, metaphorically; and her story thereby communicates to us.

But here, in this selection from Kaplan's book, we have something else; if there are metaphors here, they do not carry their meaning with them. There is no coherence, no structure, nothing here but a compound of free association in which we cannot recognize anything, perhaps, except plaint: a cry. But even animals cry out. Only the apparent use of language distinguishes this utterance as a human communication.

Of course, we cannot and should not isolate what is written from the context in which it was written, the circumstances of the man's insanity, the story of his life. Without his story we would have trouble interpreting his words in any case, no matter how logical and coherent. But Kaplan gives us little of this; he presents this simply as a text, as what I call "raw free consciousness" liberated onto paper. If we are to relate to it, to treat it as a communication, we have no choice, I think, but to treat it *as a freedom,* to find its meaning, that is, in the fact that it simply is consciousness freed from the restraints of spelling, logic, and syntax, from the restraints that make experience communicable.

Suddenly we find ourselves at the heart of the matter.

For isn't this the most dangerous aspect of insanity, its liberation from restraints? Isn't it precisely this freedom which the mental health system seeks to control? We live by social conventions which are institutionalized in language, in systems of what Goffman calls interaction rituals, and in more formal institutions such as the family and the schools. All of this we discussed in the last chapter. From the point of view of society, then—let us say from the public's point of view, for the public is the controlling agent—insanity can only manifest itself as consciousness (or behavior, or both) liberated from these institutions and thereby defiant of them, as all liberty is a defiance of one restraint or another.

But can there be any liberty which is not conscious of itself as liberty? Let me turn to still another account, this one by a woman named E. Thelmar who first published her book in London in 1909: *The Maniac*. Thelmar's book is one long unbroken nightmare of strange voices shouting wildly in her ears, seduction by fiends, out-of-the-body experiences, terrifying visions, repeated sensations of dying, sensations of being buried alive, tortures of all kinds, both physical and mental, loss of identity, and more. The following section illustrates as well as any what it must have been like for her to live through this madness, which lasted for about six weeks, and what she made of it all as well:

> About two hours or more, later, I returned quite suddenly and most fully to consciousness, to find myself sitting up in bed, gasping, with a most frightful sensation of suffocation.
> At the left side of my bed stood my brother Oliver, and at the right Mrs. W. I recognized both instantly.
> I thought, "I am being strangled!"
> Immediately a voice said to me, "No, you are not being strangled, but some fiends are strangling Ray Hall [her imaginary lover] in his rooms, and that strangles

you—because you are not two, but one. For the same
reason, if you can manage, by strength of Will, to keep
alive, you will keep him alive and defeat the fiends that
are trying to kill him. Exert your Will, and fight for
your life and his."

I gasped frantically for breath, combating the
overwhelming sensation of suffocation I was experiencing.
I beat the air wildly with my arms, and began
exclaiming, as loudly as my strangling breath would
permit—

"I am alive! I am alive and well! We are alive
and well!"

My brother and Mrs. W. seized my arms on either
side and tried to hold me, but I beat the air more
frantically than ever.

"Say it!—Say it with me!" I cried to them both. "I
am alive and well—We are alive and well! Say it! Say it!"

"Yes, yes!" they said, and repeated it, endeavouring
in vain to hold me still.

"I am alive and well! (Water! Water!" I cried in an
agonised aside to my brother.) I felt at the last stage
of suffocation.

"Yes! Yes! my dear girl!" he exclaimed. I can see
his face of frightened horror now.

He retained hold of my arm with one hand, while
with the other he stretched out to the washstand near,
and dipped the tumbler in the jug and handed me some
water.

"I am alive and well!—I can swallow!—I cannot be
suffocating!—I am drinking water!" I gasped between
my lips, as, with superhuman effort, I drank the water.
"I am alive and well!—I can drink!—Hold on, Ray Hall,
I am alive! I will keep alive! I will save you. I will save
us both, they shall not kill us! Hold on! Hold on till
I save you!"

For perhaps a quarter of an hour or so I battled
for our two lives thus, in full, agonised consciousness;
then, in the same sudden way in which I had come to
consciousness, I again quitted it, utterly and completely.

They tell me I continued this shouting and
screaming for hours. None of it, except precisely what I
have described, ever penetrated to my consciousness.[5]

Something about this account, about her book as a
whole, strikes a false note for me. Perhaps it is too dramatic. Is she putting us on, as she seemed to be putting
on her brother and Mrs. W? All that she says is probably
true, yet it cries out for interpretation: what is *really*
going on in this woman's mind? If we can believe her
(she claims, interestingly, to have total recall of everything that happened to her, yet here we see her unaware
of large portions, and making a point of her lack of awareness—which may for her be a metaphor for denial of responsibility), here is a consciousness alternately conscious
and unconscious of itself, awake and aware of her behavior
for a period of time, then awake but not aware. Is such
a thing possible? We come directly upon the quagmire of
Freudian mechanisms of repression. Yes, such a thing is
possible. That her insanity was a liberation from a lifetime of repression there can be no question. Thelmar
was a maiden lady of excellent reputation, she makes that
plain; her "normal" behavior was perfectly proper. Her
insanity is, or seems to be, a letting go of an enormous
boiling mass of sexuality and rage repressed beneath her
all-too-proper exterior: a lifetime of frustration.

But she nowhere acknowledges this fact. She let herself be seduced by fiends, swore and cursed like a sailor,
took a phantom lover, and in general acted out in living
fantasy all that she had not let herself act out in reality.
And this is a liberation, a defiance of custom and convention, of all the standards of normal behavior. But her
account, while it makes this clear, denies any collusion
on her part in this behavior. Throughout her book she
stresses not her consciousness but her unconsciousness,
how little she knew of what she was doing. So we get no
sense of release from her; she does not present her be-

havior as if *she* could relate to it, as if her mind really had held secret desires under tormented control and now they had spoken out at last. She finds no meaning in her insanity, and thus no liberty, whereas it is liberty which is its meaning. It is as if she would deny this meaning, as if, in the interests of propriety, she would sever all ties with her experience and declare it null and void—an absurdity.

This is a pity. We can impute a meaning to her experience but she cannot. And it is the search for meaning that is crucial; for this search is what, in some sense, insanity is about. The insane *are* communicating with us. They communicate through their insanity. That is, their insanity is a message, or perhaps more accurately, a message about a message—a metamessage—and the metamessage takes the form of a challenge: see if you can figure out what this message is. I defy you to figure me out. I am "out there," outside the conventions and restraints you call reality, at large and at liberty. What I do and say are beyond your experience and understanding. Find a "reason" for it, if you can; categorize it; contain it. Insanity is indirect discourse.[6]

My point is that insanity is a social phenomenon, it exists in a matrix of institutionalized social conventions, in a symbolic universe, to return to Berger and Luckmann's phrase, and that it finds its meaning in relation to this symbolic universe, in opposition to it, in defiance of it. It is *not* a private phenomenon with no public or general significance. It exists in a dialectic relation to society; society and insanity are connected terms.[7] If Thelmar can find no meaning in her insanity, it is because, representing what she imagines to be the interests of society, she denies the truth of this relationship.

Reading her book, however, we can sympathize with her denial. These liberties her insanity took with her were fearful things. So it must be with many of the insane, and we can, if we listen carefully, hear in their meta-messages of defiance a muted plea. *Please* find a reason for what I do or say. How can they help but be afraid of themselves? The popular conception of schizophrenia is of the "split personality," the Dr. Jekyll and Mr. Hyde, the wild, lascivious person contained within the proper prim one. While this does not gibe with psychiatric definitions of schizophrenia, it expresses a truth about insanity in general, apart from its specific modes. The insane *do* embody two opposed "persons," one socialized as we have all been socialized, willing to follow conventions, to eat with a fork and wear decent clothes and speak in English sentences, the other liberated, set free like an animal from its cage. This division and opposition within the person mirrors the division and opposition within society at large: on the one hand, the system of conventional, proper, expected behavior, the behavior which facilitates human communication and interaction; on the other, insanity as a social phenomenon, in its dialectic of opposition to these conventions. The person becomes a metaphor of the social division.

This makes of insanity one subset of that larger system of outlaw phenomena, of existence "out there," outside the symbolic universe, which sociologists designate by the term "deviance." Insanity is the brother of crime, perversion, and unlawful phenomena of all types.[8] All such phenomena become subject to opposing systems of social control. And we control them individually in ourselves; we each have private systems of denial and avoidance just as efficient as E. Thelmar's. For it is clear that we are each of us capable of insanity: "Madness represents the emergence of deep-seated tendencies present in all human beings. . . ."[9] There is no meaning in insanity unless we recognize this fact, recognize in a formal way the sovereign power it may exercise over any one of us: ". . . the being of man not only cannot be understood without madness," says Jacques Lacan, "but it would not be the being of man if it did not carry madness within it as the limit of its liberty." [10]

Lacan says it well. We need the phenomenon of insanity, even if only as a dramatic expression of what, at the outside, we are capable of, should our restraints fail us. And in our need we must acknowledge its peculiar attractive power, its ability to fascinate and frighten us at the same time. It is like a black hole in the depths of outer space. Black holes are hypothetical collapsed stars in which all the distances between atoms and atomic particles have vanished. The resulting mass is so dense that a piece of it the size of a Ping-Pong ball weighs as much as the earth. These "holes" have an incredible gravitational pull; it is so powerful that neither light nor any other form of energy can escape it. Everything that falls into these holes is transformed. And everything, eventually, will fall into them; they gradually draw surrounding free matter into them, growing and growing until one day, the astronomers speculate, they will swallow the universe. Insanity is the black hole of human experience: it is that frightful, and that fascinating. No wonder we want to build walls around it.

That is what we are doing right now, at any rate. At other times in history the experience of insanity has been less terrifying to men. Now, however,

> The mass neurosis of our age is agoraphobia; men are terrified of disintegration and of too little direction: they ask, like Hobbes's masterless men in a state of nature, for walls to keep out the raging ocean, for order, security, organization, clear and recognizable authority, and are alarmed by the prospect of too much freedom, which leaves them lost in a friendless vacuum, a desert without paths or landmarks or goals.[11]

We ask for walls. The mental health system is such a

wall. It keeps insanity not out but in, confined; it is like some vast zoo into which we drive the wild beasts running free "out there" in the jungles of civilization. Inside the zoo psychiatry reduces their liberty to a determinism. It cages them with explanations. That is the way it works. The question of whether such a zoo is necessary, the question I raised at the beginning of this section, is, perhaps, once we have looked hard at the phenomenon of insanity, unreal. The system of control is there and the people, terrified and fascinated, attracted and repelled, feel it to be essential. Every social system, as Berger and Luckmann point out, contains similar "therapeutic" subsystems whose function is specifically that, to tame what is wild in men, to resocialize them to conformity with accepted reality.[12] But in our age, as Isaiah Berlin notes above, the fear seems to be greater, the terror growing; and the mental health system is growing in response.

Or perhaps it is the other way around. Perhaps the mental health system is growing not in response to anything, but on its own; perhaps the system of control is itself out of control. Which brings us in a roundabout way to the subject of this chapter. There must be an interface, a point of contact, between insanity and the system that controls it. The insane must somehow get into the system if they are to be controlled. The means by which this happens, however, are not well defined; it is not clear who the insane *are* or where they live. While the mental health system may be found in institutions and the offices of psychiatrists and other more or less obvious places, the insane have no such location, they are everywhere, they are *among us*. As a first step, and *the most important step in the whole process of controlling insanity*, the mental health system must therefore appeal to us to recognize the insane among us and round them up. In the interface between insanity and the mental health system, then, there is a third term: we the public. Both sides address their messages and their metamessages to us. Which makes *us* the reality police.

II

The mental health system is growing, and someday it may be capable of rounding up and branding everybody with any trace of wild beast visible in his behavior. Kenneth Keniston imagines such a time in an essay entitled "How Community Mental Health Stamped Out the Riots (1968–1978)," in which a tyrannical government, under the umbrella of a community mental health ideology (whereby all social problems have been transformed into psychological problems), sends to its 247 "Remote Therapy Centers" (concentration camps updated) not just crazy people but anybody—and especially alienated inner-city dwellers who think their problems arise from social conditions—who challenges the smooth, efficient functioning of the status quo. Keniston makes it clear that this future would be merely a carrying through into practice of ideas "already in existence in 1968." [13]

As if to flesh out Keniston's sketch, Nicholas Kittrie has written a whole book on the growth of what he calls the "therapeutic state" (which is a state of mind as much as a political institution).[14] Kittrie demonstrates thoroughly the extent to which behavior which was formerly regarded as criminal—or simply ignored altogether—has become subject to "therapy." Alcoholics, drug users, juvenile delinquents and sex offenders are all coming more and more to be dealt with not as breakers of the law but as "sick" people, people with "mental illnesses" known as alcoholism, drug addiction, homosexuality, or some other form of supposed psycho- or sociopathology. Mental patients, of course—and Kittrie devotes a section to them, too—have been in that position for a long time. The American Psychiatric Association has recently declassified homosexuality, bowing to the pressure of gay liberation groups, but only, perhaps, to make room among its seventy diagnostic categories for some new disease. [15] Maybe "politicopathology"—an excessive or fanatical interest in politics. We all know people with this "disease," after all, and they certainly make a lot of trouble. But it is no joke. The Soviet Union notoriously sends political dissidents to mental institutions.[16] A few American psychiatrists have suggested that our own politicians ought to be subject to psychiatric screening. At any rate, as Keniston says, the ideas are "already in existence." Kittrie's therapeutic state is definitely growing.

We may take comfort in the fact, however, that it has not yet reached absolutist proportions. As it functions at present the mental health system is not smooth and efficient but haphazard and inefficient, a sort of Rube Goldberg contraption, and a great many people who appear to be crazy escape the butterfly net. Barbara O'Brien, for example, wandered the United States for half a year, moving about at her Operators' whim, and only once in all that time did she come in contact with the mental health system. Shortly after her Operators introduced themselves to her she passed out in a bus depot. When she came to she was babbling and the police took her to a psycho ward. She talked her way out of the hospital, however, the day after they admitted her. Six months later, just four days before her Operators finally disappeared, she went to see a psychiatrist—at Hinton's direction. But by that time it was almost over. So for six months Barbara O'Brien managed to conceal her insanity from everyone she encountered, including the psychiatrist who pronounced her sane and let her out of the hospital. Not until her insanity was at an end did she actually get into the system.

In a true therapeutic state that would never have happened. There would have been some mechanism, some psychiatric screening process, designed to discover people like Barbara O'Brien and get them into the system. It would not be difficult to imagine such a mechanism, although putting it into practice would be something else. Most psychological tests—the Wechsler Adult Intelligence Scale, the Minnesota Multiphasic Personality Inventory, and of course the Rorschach—have built-in signals which warn the tester of unusual, and perhaps crazy, patterns of thought. The government could simply administer these tests at points of contact between the public and governmental institutions, say when people apply for a driver's license or a Social Security card. The schools might administer them; employers might give them to their employees.[17] Through some such relatively simple administrative device a "mentally healthy" personality might be made a prerequisite to participation in the life of the society, with compulsory therapy provided for those who were "sick." A setup like this would have caught up with Barabara O'Brien eventually.

But we don't have that kind of system yet. The closest we have ever come to a national psychiatric screening device was in World War II, when the armed services administered psychiatric examinations to all draftees and volunteers. The resulting rejection rate, running well over 20 percent in some places at some times, and reaching 18.1 percent on the national average for the entire period of the war, rose far beyond what might have been expected from rates of mental hospitalization per unit of population or other indicators of the prevalence of psychiatric problems in the country as a whole.[18] It was very disturbing. If we do someday come to resemble Kenneth Keniston's image of our future, historians may trace its origins to the sense of alarm created by this World War II experience.

That alarm was very probably a contributing factor in the efforts which were made in the late 1940's and on into the 1950's to measure precisely, with all the variables accounted for, how many people in the general population were suffering from psychiatric disorders. The best known of these efforts is probably the Midtown Manhattan Study conducted in the mid-1950's by an interdisciplinary team of psychiatrists and sociologists. Selecting 1,660 New York residents as a representative sample of the midtown population, the team interviewed each one of them for an average of two hours, basing the interview on a questionnaire that had taken a year to prepare. It was a mammoth undertaking, as the cliché runs. Two psychiatrists then rated the subjects, on the basis of the interview, on a six-item scale which started at the top with "Well" and ran through "Mild Symptom Formation," "Marked Symptom Formation," and other categories to "Incapacitated" at the bottom. The three bottom categories were placed in a metacategory called "Impaired," which meant that the people in them were "characterized by symptom formations that tend to reflect halting, laming, or crippling effects on the performance of one's daily life roles." [19]

The Midtown Manhattan results made headlines. According to the Study, a mere 18.5 percent, less than a fifth, of their interviewees (and by extension, all of that area's residents) could be considered "Well," which meant free of psychiatric "symptoms." Far more, 23.4 percent, fell into the metacategory of being "Impaired." But the authors thought even this high rate underestimated: ". . . we estimate with 95 percent confidence that in the Midtown population universe the mental morbidity rate stands in a range somewhere between 21.9 and 25.9 percent. . . . it seems likely that the true rate stands closer to the high point in this range." [20] A full quarter of the people in Midtown Manhattan were, then, crazy enough to be severely hampered, even "crippled," by their "symptoms." And these "Impaired" people outnumbered the "Well" people by a considerable amount. This was staggering information.

Even more staggering, however, was the fact that the mental health system had never seen the great majority of all these crazy and half-crazy people. Only a quarter (26.7 percent) of the people the authors labeled psychiatrically "Impaired" had had any contact at any time in their lives with the mental health system. The authors considered it self-evident that these people needed "help," yet only 5.4 percent were getting it currently. Even at the bottom, in the "Incapacitated" category, about two thirds (64.5 percent) had never been to a psychiatrist, a psychiatric clinic, a mental hospital, anywhere where they might have received "help." [21] There was not now and never had been any contact between these very crazy people and the mental health system.

Midtown Manhattan created something of a furor in the press and no doubt confirmed the opinion of many people both in and out of New York that it is a crazy city. But the Study is open to criticism on many grounds. It is not clear, for example, that the Study made sufficient allowance for the diversity of cultural attitudes to be found in New York. As we said in the last chapter, what is a "symptom" to an Italo-American may be perfectly "normal" to a Hungarian refugee. Any attempt to fit the behavior of diverse groups to a single mental health scale must inevitably lead to questionable results. Then there is the question of the interviewers. They were psychiatric social workers, clinical psychologists, and social caseworkers, people with status as mental health professionals and semiprofessionals, and subject, most of them, to a certain kind of bias: namely, a tendency to see something "wrong" with almost everybody. They were "casefinders," in other words, and they everywhere found "cases." [22]

But the crucial objection is not interviewer bias. We can allow for that. What is fundamentally at issue is whether mental health is a measurable entity at all. For just what is it that constitutes being "Well?" As soon as we try to define what this term means we fall into a hopeless morass of ambiguities and imprecisions. Being "Well," say the authors of Midtown Manhattan, means not having any "symptoms" of "mental illness"; the absence of illness constitutes health.[23] But this definition only raises the question of what a "symptom" is, and a host of other questions besides. Here the Study falls apart. Midtown Manhattan simply takes "symptoms" for granted. If a person worries a lot, that becomes a "symptom" of underlying anxiety. Underlying anxiety, it is assumed, is pathological. Something is "wrong" with that person; he isn't "Well." We never really learn whether or not he has something to worry about. Suppose his children had been kidnapped but, like Alfred E. Neuman, he wasn't worried at all. No underlying anxiety there; he is free of "symptoms" on the Midtown Manhattan scale. Does that make him "Well?" Let me refer to myself. I worry a lot; I worry about this book, I worry about my children growing up with too many problems, I worry about my friends who don't have any money, I worry because my wife doesn't drive too carefully. Does that mean I have a lot of underlying anxiety? Are all my worries "symptoms"; that is, are they unreal? How do we distinguish between real worries and unreal worries? I know very few people indeed who aren't worriers, or who don't get depressed sometimes or withdraw from other people sometimes. I always thought such things were part of being human—which is admittedly another imprecise term. But no, according to the Study, these are "symptoms." We are almost all sick, it appears; very few of us are "Well."

Obviously the question of what constitutes being "Well" threatens at any moment to collapse under its own weight. Psychiatry has never reached agreement on the subject. Freudian doctrine takes the position that indeed there is no such thing as being "Well." Mental health is an ideal we can never expect to attain; we are all sick, it is only a matter of degree as to how sick we are.[24] For Freud, "symptoms" or complexes of "symptoms" can be traced to unconscious conflicts from which none of us is free, as it were by definition. Given the universality of these conflicts, especially those he associates with the Oedipus complex, all behavior becomes symptomatic—or at least not "Well." Other psychiatrists, however, have different ideas about being "Well." Some say that a person is mentally healthy when he has mastered his environment: Hitler, perhaps, in 1939. Others say that he is healthy when he approves of himself or likes himself or is content with the way he is, still others that it is a function of "self-actualization," the development of his full potential. Marie Jahoda, in her book *Current Concepts of Positive Mental Health,* identifies *six* major groups of concepts associated with the term mental health.[25] These six groups do not include the Freudian concept discussed above.

It is hard to imagine how anyone could claim that a study based on such fuzzy, value-laden, and controversial ideas as this was science. And in fact not too many people have taken Midtown Manhattan seriously. Nor have other prevalence studies fared much better. David Mechanic, reviewing the literature, found ranges of measured "mental illness" in studies of various population groups of from less than 1 percent to over 60 percent.[26] Joseph Giordano, in a paper on ethnic factors in mental health, suggests that prevalence studies are falling into disuse.[27] As a phenomenon at large in the world, insanity, it would seem, cannot be quantified. Trying to count the insane is probably harder than counting birds in the woods. At least we know a bird when we see one. But the insane look, and sometimes act, the way you and I look and act. How then can we tell who they are?

It ought to be apparent that such crude studies as

Midtown Manhattan cannot tell us who they are. All that Midtown Manhattan gives us is a very rough probability: there are probably a lot more crazy people out there than the mental health system knows about. I mean people with delusions about being the next mayor of New York, other people hallucinating angels among us, still others smacking their heads with their hands every ten seconds, and Barbara O'Brien, listening to Hinton tell her what to do: they are walking around out there, just as we are. But this is something we knew already, perhaps; most of us have had enough experience in the world to know this to be the case. Midtown Manhattan, if it accomplishes anything at all, merely confirms our experience, lends it a "scientific" halo. In their terms, there is a large discrepancy between the numbers of people who need "help" and the "help" available. The mental health system is not big enough, not by a long shot, to accommodate all the people who "need" its services.

From the system's point of view, of course, this is evidence that there ought to be more services. The public ought to feed more money into mental health so that the system might grow. The authors make this explicit: "It [the Study] indicates that the need for [mental] health services is far greater than has been previously realized." [28] But from our point of view the Study may simply indicate that a lot of people with "symptoms" of insanity are coping quite well—or at least adequately—with their lives and *don't need "help"* at all.

It is admittedly difficult to find scientific evidence, or any kind of evidence, to support this point of view. What evidence we have points in the other direction; it indicates a demand for services greater than the services available. Most psychiatric clinics have long waiting lists. Most psychiatrists have full schedules and must turn people away. As new facilities are built and the system expands, demand seems to expand even more. But demand is not the same thing as need. People who don't need services often demand them. Most psychiatrists treat, and prefer to treat, people who are not very crazy at all, people who manage their lives fairly well but worry a lot or withdraw from other people a lot or get depressed, people psychiatrists sometimes call "normal neurotics." Conventional psychiatric wisdom distinguishes the neurotic from the psychotic on the basis of the former's being in contact with reality, while the latter is not. What this generally means in practice is that the neurotic is somebody who can function well enough to get to the psychiatrist's office on time. It is not at all clear that these are the people who need "help." In Midtown Manhattan, for example, *more* people at the top level of the "Impaired" metacategory ("Marked Symptom Formation") were currently under psychiatric care than were people in the middle range ("Severe Symptom Formation").[29] The people who are getting help may be getting it because they want it and will pay for it, not because they "need" it. They have been sold on psychiatry as a solution to their problems, perhaps, and so they show up in the mental health system as patients demanding treatment. But do they "need" it?

I am more interested in the people out there who "need" help but don't demand it. Midtown Manhattan made an effort to distinguish within the "Impaired" metacategory among people who were or had been in treatment, people who were not in treatment but might consider the mental health system as a source of help, and people who were not in treatment and perceived "no professional person or agency as haven of possible relief for the disability and distress they suffer in their daily lives." The largest group by far was the last: 44.2 percent by their count.[30]

In other words the largest group of apparently crazy people out there are those who want nothing to do with the mental health system. The demand for services is more than matched by indifference or possible outright hostility to the system. Evidently many people think they can get along without the services of the system, and they evidently succeed at it, too. Their "need" for services is not therefore a *felt* need but a need imputed to them by the authors of the Study. But if they don't *feel* a need for help, how real can their "sickness" be?

It is a complex matter, this question of recognizing your "illness." From the medical point of view, people are sick when they contract a disease. Classically the disease results from attack by a microorganism of some sort, a bacillus, a virus, a fungus, or else from the malfunction of an organ within the body, as in diabetes. The patient is passive in relation to the disease; it is something that has happened to him: a misfortune. From a sociological point of view, however, the situation is much more complicated. Sociology recognizes the possibility of motivation on the patient's part toward disease. That is, the patient may be malingering, or he may be hypochondriacal, or he may be looking for the "secondary gains" which come with being accorded the "sick role": being taken care of, receiving attention, being released from work and other responsibilities. The patient may, in other words, be willing himself, consciously or unconsciously, to be sick. Other people also recognize this possibility and they make judgments about the patient's condition and may well deny him the "sick role" and the rewards and obligations that go with it.[31] Or he may deny himself this role. We all know people who, though their fever may be running well over 100°, keep right on with their routines, never admitting to anyone else that they might be sick. From the sociological point of view, then, becoming sick is by no means an automatic process, and the presence (or absence) of microorganisms or malfunctioning organs is only one variable.

The situation is even more complicated in the case of "mental illness." No one has isolated any microorganisms associated with it or found conclusive evidence of brain malfunction in those deemed "mentally ill." The presence (or absence) of "mental illness" is almost entirely a matter of judgment. Who makes that judgment? Not, initially, psychiatrists. As we saw in relation to Noah Levy's case, other people, lay people, you and me, make the judgment. If we didn't decide that we ourselves, or our wives or husbands, our sons or our employees or whoever were in some sense crazy, we would never take them or ourselves to a psychiatrist in the first place. Before someone can get into the mental health system, in other words, people out there in the world must decide that what is wrong with him is specifically a "mental illness" and not something else: an eccentricity, malingering, stupidity, malevolence, or what have you. It is this which makes us the reality police. Psychiatry has as yet little power to come and apprehend us where we live. The system depends on us to bring ourselves and our loved ones in. This decision, therefore—that someone is "mentally ill"—is the most important step, as I said earlier in this chapter, in the whole process of controlling insanity. Without someone taking that step, the system would be helpless.

In relation to the Midtown Manhattan findings, what this means is that a great many people out there with "symptoms" are not making the requisite judgment about themselves. Or their families and friends are not making that judgment. On the contrary, these people are denying the evidence of illness, or ignoring it, or they are getting along with it, living with it, or they are calling it by another name: yes, he's a strange man, but after all, he's my husband; well, Tom's had problems ever since the war; Lavinia isn't crazy, you know, she just likes to talk to herself. For one reason or another they resist the "mental illness" label and tolerate the "symptomatic" behavior. Or they may even acknowledge that someone is more or less crazy and still tolerate him. When the authors of Midtown Manhattan talk about "the extent of potential demand for professional intervention," then they are really chasing a red herring. Demand for psychiatric services would increase within this population only if its level of tolerance were to decrease.

It follows that one way the system may grow is to work to *reduce* the level of tolerance for "mental illness" in the community. And in fact the system does work in this direction. The system expends much money and energy on what it calls "education." The National Association for Mental Health devotes itself to this cause, and with great sincerity, distributing pamphlets by the millions, arranging speeches and lecture tours, forming local chapters, all to spread the word: "mental illness" is a disease which proper psychiatric care can cure, if only it is perceived in time. Psychiatrists make frequent pronouncements on the emotional ills of society. The Group for the Advancement of Psychiatry publishes documents on psychiatric aspects of national problems. Leading figures in the system write columns for the newspapers, while Ann Landers advises her crazier correspondents to get professional help. Even television educates us to this end. A few days ago I saw a show called "Lisa, Bright and Dark." [32] Lisa was a pretty teen-age girl who began acting strangely, breaking off with her boyfriend for no apparent reason, banging her head against the bed, cutting her name on her wrist, burning her clothes. She was doing a lot of wild things. Not all the time, to be sure; she had periods of complete lucidity, during which she begged her parents to send her to a psychiatrist. But Mommy and Daddy, who were very rich, resisted seeing Lisa's acts as requiring psychiatric care. For various selfish reasons they wanted to believe that she was just under stress, or unbalanced from breaking up with her boyfriend, *anything* but crazy. Not until Lisa threw herself through a glass door did they see the light.

It was pure corn, but then so are most advertisements. To make sure we got the message, after the show Roy Menninger of the Menninger Foundation, America's most prestigious psychiatric organization, came on the air and told us what it was all about. "Mental illness" afflicts millions of young people like Lisa, but if you discover it in time (just like cancer and heart disease and tuberculosis), treatment is successful in the great majority of cases. So swallow your false pride, mothers and fathers, and get thy children to a psychiatrist. As if the psychiatrists didn't have enough business already.

I hope this doesn't seem too cynical. These messages are generally very well intended; Roy Menninger obviously meant what he said. But they do not always have the comforting effect they intend. Bastide, among others, notes that "some surveys have . . . shown that the efforts made to spread modern ideas about 'madness' tend to go against the intentions of their promoters: they make people even more anxious, and this anxiety has a harmful effect on mental health." [33] As the public's level of anxiety rises, people become more rigid and their level of tolerance falls. As tolerance levels fall and people become less and less willing to put up with craziness among them, more and more behavior gets the crazy label pinned on it. The net result is a greater public demand for mental health services.

As demand increases, the system grows. In 1971, according to the National Institute of Mental Health, there were 4.2 million "patient care episodes" in psychiatric facilities across the United States. The corresponding number for 1955 was 1.7 million. Population has increased, to be sure, but NIMH allowed for that; according to their report, "the patient care episode rate per 100,000 population just about doubled between 1955 and 1971." [34] What can these astonishing figures mean? Are there twice as many crazy people now as there were in 1955? Or is more and more behavior being defined in psychiatric terms, as Nicholas Kittrie claims? Whatever the answer, there can be no question that the "therapeutic state" is no mirage hanging over the desert horizon but a real destination we seem to be moving towards at accelerating speed. In 1955 the NIMH budget stood at a mere $14.1 million. By 1971 it had reached $389 million. Recent Nixon Administration attempts to hold back Federal spending on mental health failed in the courts. The Congress seems firmly committed to a growing mental health system. In 1955 we had 10,623 psychiatrists in the United States, or 6.4 per 100,000 population. By 1966 the figure had grown to 19,532, or 10 per 100,000 population.[35] Now we have some 25,000 psychiatrists. It is not just a matter of figures. I know people in the system who think *everybody* should be in therapy. Why? Presumably because none of us is "Well." It is a short step indeed from thinking everybody is "sick" to Kenneth Keniston's hypothetical 1978, where "therapy" has become an oppressive totalitarian absolute.

III

Let me say it for the third time: the most important step in the whole process of getting into the system, the step the mental health educational apparatus aims at, the step Lisa's parents would not take, is the decision that someone's behavior is crazy and therefore that this person requires professional help. But for all its importance, this is the step in the process we know the least about. Some attempts have been made to study it, but for practical reasons most of these studies have concentrated on people who are already in the mental health system: clinic applicants, hospital patients, and so on. That builds a bias into the study; since the subjects are already in the system, the decision process which brought them there has to be viewed retrospectively. The story is complete, in other words, and you are looking at it after the fact. And of

course completed stories always seem inevitable. But we
already know that the decision that somebody is crazy is
not inevitable, that it never gets made about perhaps the
majority of "crazy" people. There is no practical way to
study a decision that does not get made.

The few sociologists who have looked into the matter
have, nevertheless, discovered some interesting things. In
a study on the wives of mental patients conducted in the
mid-1950's, Yarrow, Schwartz and others found that the
wives had frequently gone to great lengths to *avoid* interpreting their husbands' behavior as a manifestation of
"mental illness." During the prehospitalization period,
many wives either denied that there was anything wrong,
or they widened their interpretation of what constituted
normal behavior, or they found ways to explain away abnormal behavior as a temporary aberration. In short, they
adapted to their husbands' behavior, and their adaptation
was frequently successful.[36]

This is not the place to get into it, but a great deal
of relatively recent psychiatric theory centers around this
family adaptation to "mental illness." Yarrow and her
colleagues see the husband's "mental illness" as a self-
evident fact; family theorists, however, following the lead
of D. D. Jackson, R. D. Laing, Gregory Bateson, Jay
Haley, and others believe that the "illness" resides not in
the "sick" member of the family so much as in the structure of the relationships within the family, a structure
which pins the "sick" member in an impossible situation,
Bateson's famous "double bind," from which insanity is the
only escape. Laing was the first to popularize this point of
view; his book *Sanity, Madness and the Family,* written in
collaboration with Aaron Esterson, showed in a number of
detailed case studies how the "illness" of the "sick" family
member was in every case a *rational* response to the situation of that person's life and history.[37] As with every
psychiatric theory, the "double bind" theory is contro-

versial, and nearly everything Laing says is in dispute. But the theory may help to explain what happens in families which fail to bring "mentally ill" members to the attention of the mental health system. Some families, says Laing, stabilize around the "sickness" of one of their members; he or she expresses, as it were, the pathology of the whole family system. Where this stabilization occurs, the family would have a vested interest in preventing the kind of change which might result from successful treatment of the "sick" member. Treatment might destroy the family structure, even though that structure has been achieved at a very high cost to one member. Such families would not be likely to bring "sick" members for treatment.

On the other hand, they often do just that. It is dangerous to make easy generalizations about the insane. Families bring their "sick" members in so that psychiatry can confirm the family processes which have made one member "sick." They expect psychiatry to validate their pathological structure. And of course psychiatry frequently obliges, salting the "sick" member away in a mental hospital.

Other studies tend to confirm the findings of Yarrow, Schwartz *et al.* Sampson, Messinger and Towne report on some of these and conclude that

> First, both before and after hospitalization some type of accommodative pattern ordinarily evolves between a disturbed person and his family which permits or forces him to remain in the community in spite of severe difficulties. Second, it is the disruption of this pattern which eventually brings a disturbed person to psychiatric attention.[38]

These authors trace two patterns of response on the part of spouses to disturbed behavior in their marriage partners; in one pattern the spouse copes with the behavior by withdrawing from it, isolating the behavior from herself or himself, while in the other the spouse becomes over-involved. It is in the latter case that the family is more likely to seek the help of the mental health system; in the former case husband and wife are in effect strangers, they keep to themselves, and when one of them does go crazy the other tends to withdraw even further. Especially if the abnormal behavior is temporary or intermittent, the family may go on forever, never coming within the purview of psychiatry.

David Mechanic has tried to sum up some of this case research and generalize the factors which lead to the initial decision that behavioral problems are psychiatric in nature.[39] He identifies the "visibility" of symptoms as a prime factor in leading other people to define someone's behavior as crazy, and he postulates the seriousness of the consequences of this behavior to the person's family or group as another factor. He also notes that

> When the vulnerability of the group increases, its
> toleration for deviancy decreases. During stress situations
> and crises, vulnerability increases, group solidarity
> becomes more essential, and deviation is treated more
> harshly, especially where the deviation exacerbates the
> crisis and further increases group vulnerability.[40]

Anything which increases stress on the person's family or group, then, decreases tolerance for the person. The level of tolerance for crazy behavior, once again, is clearly as important as the behavior itself in determining under what circumstances people decide that someone is, indeed, insane.

Still other factors appear to influence the decision whether someone is crazy. Social class is very important; numerous studies have shown that lower-class Americans are much less ready than upper- or middle-class Americans to perceive abnormal behavior as a psychiatric problem. The classic on this subject is Hollingshead and Redlich's

Social Class and Mental Illness, an exhaustive survey of
the mental health system and its clients in New Haven,
Connecticut. Their work led them to this conclusion,
among others:

> Perception of the psychological nature of personal
> problems is a rare trait in any person and in any class,
> but it is found more frequently in the refined
> atmosphere of classes I and II [the upper class, more or
> less] than in the raw setting of class V [lower class]. As
> a consequence, we believe that far more abnormal
> behavior is tolerated by the two lower classes, particularly
> class V, without any awareness that the motivations
> behind the behavior are pathological, even though the
> behavior may be disapproved by the class norms.[41]

Their data makes clear that middle- and upper-class people
are both more knowledgeable about psychiatry and psychological influences on behavior, and less tolerant of
behavior that violates the norm, than the lower class. That
makes perfect sense.

It also makes sense that lower-class people would want
to protect their members from the mental health system.
They tend to have poor experiences with institutional systems generally; the schools, the police, the welfare system
all ignore or exclude them at best, abuse them at worst.
They seem to have a special distrust for psychiatry. Say
the authors:

> The worst thing that can happen to a class V person is
> to be labeled "bugs," "crazy," or "nuts." Such judgment
> is often equal to being sentenced for life to the
> "bughouse." Unfortunately, this sentiment is realistic.[42]

Not until one of their members becomes violent or uncontrollable in other ways, usually, will the lower classes
seek help. Even then it is often the police who decide
that the problem is psychiatric and force the person into
the mental health system.

Naturally these attitudes have had an effect on the delivery of psychiatric services to the poor in American ghettoes. At the Martin Luther King, Jr., Health Center in the South Bronx, a model for delivery of health services to black and Puerto Rican populations, efforts to train the paraprofessionals recruited from the community as mental health workers have failed. These workers exhibited the same antipsychiatric attitudes as the population they came from, and they refused to be put into the position of having to tell their friends and neighbors that their child-rearing practices were destroying their children's mental health or some such matter. It is difficult in any case to distinguish "psychiatric" problems from the multitude of other problems which afflict these people: the rats that keep them awake all night, the violence and crime they must live with, the drug and alcohol abuse, the inability to get jobs that pay living wages, and so on. Mrs. Diana Paul, the forceful woman who runs the mental health operation at the Center, insists that the mental health problems of her clients are basically socioeconomic in nature, not psychiatric. The psychiatrists who work with her have generally been of little or no help. They are from another world, she says, and cannot relate what they know to the life of the poor.[43]

Ethnic factors as well as class factors affect the decision that someone is crazy. Many studies have demonstrated, for example, that Jews generally have a high opinion of psychiatry and are much more willing than other groups both to see behavioral problems as psychiatric and to turn to psychiatry for help. Jewish patients, on the other hand, are generally also more critical of individual physicians and tend to shop around for medical (and presumably psychiatric) care.[44] Other white ethnic groups avoid the mental health system as best they can. The Irish, for example, do not voluntarily submit themselves to psychiatric treatment nearly as often as Jews and do not benefit from it as much when they do. Many lower-class Italians still believe in the "evil eye," and their preferred remedy for medical problems or "symptoms" of any sort is ritualistic: white magic against black. Melvin Glasser sums up the evidence on white ethnic groups and concludes:

> They [blue collar workers] do not understand the aims of psychotherapy and hence they fear and ridicule it. Their emotional stress is expressed in essentially physiological and symptomological complaints. They resist the slim possibility of outpatient psychiatric help as it is now offered them, with denial of problems, withdrawal or acting out manifestations. Their expectations of psychiatric treatment on those occasions when it is available to them are specific and direct. They want pills, drugs, machines which are concrete and will "cure" quickly. They are confused and unhappy with psychiatry's methods and dubious of its results.[45]

Clearly, given this kind of attitude, most white ethnic populations will try and often manage to handle friends and relatives with behavioral problems outside the mental health system.

The sociological data on ethnic, socio-economic and other factors which influence the way behavioral problems are perceived and handled are more complicated than I have space to explain here. Sometimes people we would by all the standard measures consider lower-class prove surprisingly accepting of psychiatric interpretations of behavior; some Jewish people are not accepting; and so on. Keeping the fact that there are exceptions in mind, however, we can still talk about the gross social tendency in certain groups and classes much of the time, and in all groups and classes sometimes, to deny, explain away or ignore evidence of insanity in their members. It ought to be clear by now that their friends and relatives may go crazy right in front of their eyes, may stay crazy for years, in fact, and many people, perhaps most, will never do anything about it.

The mental health system draws only one conclusion from this fact: let us educate the people to the presence of insanity among them. Then they will bring the insane to us to "cure." The system, in other words, sees this fact as a problem: its problem. But that is only one way to look at it.

Another way is to look at it as evidence of a deep and perhaps essential ambiguity in our feelings about insanity. Earlier I talked about its power to attract and repel us at the same time, to evoke simultaneous horror and fascination. I suggested, furthermore, that it is a meaningful social phenomenon whose meaning resides paradoxically in its very challenge to meaning. Without such challenges, perhaps meaning could not exist; if we were all uniformly orderly, the idea of order might collapse. It may, therefore, constitute a kind of social wisdom to allow this phenomenon to run loose in the world. Gregory Bateson talks about the necessity, if a species is to survive, to maintain a high degree of genetic diversity within its population: "Such a population expectably functions as a storehouse of genotypic possibilities." [46] A species must maintain a certain genetic flexibility, that is, in order to meet changing conditions within its environment; the greater the storehouse of possible mutant types, the greater flexibility the species has to adapt to environmental changes. He goes on to apply this principle to human societies. If we do not provide for the widest possible diversity in our own populations, if we permit our social structures, our institutions, both formal and informal, to become too rigid, we shall not survive. To survive, says Bateson, we must *exercise* our flexibility.[47] Insanity, I submit, as a social phenomenon, exercises the flexibility of the social structure. It tests the limits of its tolerance for meaninglessness: that is, for a meaning which challenges received social reality, a meaning which stands outside conventional restraints upon meaning.

This suggests that for maximum social flexibility society must forego too great an emphasis on order and control. A certain balance is necessary between order and disorder. The culture seems to reflect this need; people react to psychiatry and the mental health system with as much ambiguity as they react to the insane. For if we all carry the possibility of insanity within us, then the power we grant psychiatry over the insane becomes by implication power over us all. The insane disturb us and threaten us, they are difficult to live with, they embarrass us, they make no sense, they may be violent. It is convenient indeed to have a system which will take them off our hands. But suppose we go crazy? What will happen to us? The liberty of one must be the liberty of everyone; and vice versa.

The mental health system threatens our liberties on a deeper level, too. Most psychiatrists believe that we are all, sane and insane alike, merely acting out, blindly and unknowingly, dramas we learned—and then forgot—in childhood. Our lives are an old movie we run over and over again. Our personalities and the freedom we take for granted to change them—*who we think we are,* in short— are mere epiphenomena of deeper unconscious structures which, the closer we get to them, the more deeply we repress. Most psychiatrists would reduce all human freedom to a determinism. Instinctively we recognize this as another kind of challenge to the possibility of meaning in our lives, and we resist it.

Attitudes oscillate, however, over time. At the present moment we seem more willing to accept psychiatric control than to live with the insane. As we have seen, the mental health system is growing. As we are about to see, there are many roads through this system; they branch out like a tree. But they all begin with the definition of some-

one's behavior as crazy rather than criminal or eccentric or
what have you. We make a choice as to what someone's behavior reveals, and this choice becomes the port of entry
into the mental health system. We are choosing insanity as
an explanation for behavior more and more often. As a society we seem to be losing our collective tolerance for the
insane, and this may be a very serious error.

III
Paths to the Mental Hospital

It is hard for a mortal who acquires power not to misuse it.

Sigmund Freud

I

So someone has decided that there is something wrong with you. Or someone decided a long time ago that there was something wrong with you, but now he won't put up with it any more. You're just too crazy, too weird to endure. You embarrassed her in front of her mother, sitting there moodily stirring your food, only to break abruptly into gales of laughter. Or he can't explain your absence at official functions that all the other wives faithfully attend. Or you jumped up and shouted in church and the whole congregation looked around at you and stared, so your minister decided to intervene. Or maybe you're confused, you think you see funny things out of the corners of your eyes, you sense something behind you all the time; something is definitely the matter, and you want help. Or the police have just picked you up for throwing garbage at passing cars. Whatever the case, the basic, door-opening decision has been made: you're crazy, and somebody has to do something about it.

What happens then? A large variety of things can

happen. The police may take you straight to Bellevue. Your local psychiatric clinic may refer you to another clinic, and that one to another one and so on until, lost in what the profession calls the "referral jungle," you give up. You may take yourself to the emergency room of a general hospital.[1] You may make an appointment with a psychiatrist in private practice, a psychologist in private practice, a psychiatric social worker in private practice, a Christian Science healer, your priest or minister, or your astrologer. You may walk into a community mental health center if you have one nearby. You may walk into a mental hospital. Or somebody may do all these things with you, for you. Whatever the specific situation, however, what is happening in general is that you are entering the mental health system. And entering the mental health system means, with few exceptions, becoming subject to psychiatric power.

People who have not had a bad experience with the system may doubt the reality of this power. Most mental health professionals, naturally, maintain a benign view of the system and of their own good intentions working within it. In their view the system helps people who want and need help desperately, and even if it sometimes does have to coerce people a little, it's only for the good of those who don't know what's good for them. People who have been in therapy and have been helped by it generally think well of their therapists; if their therapists do exercise power over them, to them it is only the power of persuasion. And with its vast "educational" system psychiatry has tried to develop a positive image in the public mind, an image from which psychiatric power is, of course, absent. It remains, therefore, to demonstrate first that this power exists, and second that it is often used arbitrarily, nontherapeutically, and needlessly.

Stan Hamilton can do this better than I can.[2] Stan's life has been totally changed by psychiatric power. He is one of the ex-mental patients I have interviewed, and I think his story exemplifies nicely what psychiatric power can mean in a given situation. But first let me tell you who Stan is. A tall, handsome, articulate man in his middle thirties, Stan has lived most of his life in conventional middle-class ways. For fifteen years he worked for a large company in upstate New York, servicing electronic equipment. He was very successful there; he made over $16,000 a year, he had a couple of patent disclosures to his credit, and he was holding down a job which called for a master's degree in electrical engineering, all on the basis of a high school education. At the same time he was running a land-development corporation of his own in a nearby county and he was involved in a local drug-abuse program also, helping teen-age kids.

He took a lot upon himself, in other words, and he had trouble sometimes standing up under the pressure. For a number of years he had been under the occasional care of a psychiatrist, and he had twice voluntarily entered a private hospital for a short series of what the profession calls electroconvulsion therapy (ECT), what everyone else calls shock treatments. His managers did not take this fact too seriously, however. As Stan explains,

> Well, that's kind of part of my nature. I have tremendous bursts of creativity, it's kind of the way I've always been. I have vast amounts of energy and accomplish substantial successes, followed by a period where I tend to crash and level off and have a down. But that's a very basic part of my nature when I become very enthusiastic about what I'm doing and get very, very involved. It's worked pretty effectively I think in terms of career-type success. In fact at [the company] the fact that I had several hospitalizations didn't seem to interfere with my career at all.[3]

So the company took Stan's depressions in stride. But apparently his psychiatrist did not.

One day Stan went to see him on a routine appointment and the psychiatrist persuaded him to check into a private general hospital for a short rest.

> I had gone in there voluntarily for a couple of days rest, having seen the psychiatrist that I was going to on a routine appointment, and with the agreement that all I needed was some rest and I could leave any time I wanted to. And he came in the following day and talked to me, I had been there overnight, and he said, "I'm going to keep you here."
>
> And I said, "Well, you can't do that, you know; I'm free to leave any time I want to," and we got into quite a discussion over that. "Well, you're my doctor," I said; and he had told me I could leave whenever I so desired. His position was that he was going to keep me there, and I told him that the only way he could keep me in the hospital was to do a commitment on me and I said, "I don't think you're going to do that," and we got into a very long discussion and exchanged some words and he was much angrier even than I was and he said, "Well, if you don't stay, I'm going to have the Health Officer come up."
>
> So the County Health Officer was called and in the course of this commitment proceeding, which lasted five minutes or so, I asked the Health Officer what the grounds for commitment in the state of New York were and he told me the business about [lost word] and he showed me the papers. There were two cops present and my aunt.

"I'm going to keep you here." It was a unilateral decision on the psychiatrist's part; he did not ask Stan's permission, he did not suggest it as an option for Stan to consider, he did not try to persuade him. He told him he was going to keep him in the hospital. In New York, it requires the signature of two physicians to commit someone to a mental hospital against his will. The County Health Officer was quite willing to second the psychiatrist; as Stan tells it, he was a rubber stamp, County Health officers are rarely psychiatrists; not being psychiatrists, they are not likely to question the judgment of one. We all know about the proprieties among doctors. So Stan wound up in a state mental hospital, confined against his will. He had broken no law.

That is psychiatric power.

As Stan explains it, his psychiatrist was doing this out of anger more than anything else. Stan was defying him—he wanted to leave the hospital—and this made the psychiatrist angry. In the end he became cruel.

> My aunt came in near the end; this guy was talking, "How would you like to go home with your aunt?"
>
> I said, "I certainly would."
>
> And he said, "Well, I'm going to commit you anyway."
>
> These two cops that took me up to the State Hospital, they were talking to me on the way up, and they had sat through this whole thing and one cop said to me, he said, "Stan, I've been in on some shit details before, but boy, I've never seen anything like this." They really thought I got railroaded.

Even the police were offended by this arbitrary exercise of power.

Stan's life has been changed, changed utterly by what happened to him that day. He no longer works at the company, his land-development venture lies dormant. He does not believe anymore in the goals he once pursued. His experience has radicalized him. In full possession of his reason, he found himself subject to the whim, the unreason, of another man. Free, law-abiding, successful, and sane, he suddenly discovered that none of this mattered, that in America you do not have to be a failure with no resources or manifestly crazy or a proven criminal to be locked up against your will. The constitutional rights which apply to the rest of us do not necessarily apply to mental patients. Psychiatrists enjoy a power which no other medical specialty enjoys. They can put you away, institutionalize you, deprive you of your liberties, lock you up without recourse, in many states, to a court of law. Once they have locked you up they can practice barbarities they call "treatment" upon you, wipe out your memory with ECT, drug you into two- or three-day comas, strip you naked and strap you into a restraining sheet,[4] throw you for days or weeks or months into a seclusion room,[5] all without your consent, against your will. Perhaps I am being naive, but I cannot help but regard this as an outrage.

Perhaps I take a certain risk, too, in claiming sanity for Stan. He was clearly sane talking to me, but he may well have been crazy to some degree at the time of his commitment. On the surface, his cycles of ups and downs look like what psychiatry calls a manic-depressive psychosis. In my judgment, however, Stan is an eminently sane man whose own description of these cycles as simply "a very basic part of my nature" has to be taken at face value. In any case it is not a question of my or Stan's judgment versus the psychiatrist's. Stan's sanity or insanity is *not* the issue. The issue is psychiatric power. If we take our constitutional liberties seriously, then nobody ought to have the power to deprive anybody else of his liberty, much less practice "treatment" upon his mind and body, unless and until that person has broken a law. That is a basic protection. Until we make a law against going crazy, we have no right to exclude the insane from this protection.

We will look at psychiatric commitment laws in the next chapter. Right now I want to examine the kinds of personal and social relationships which the commitment laws enshrine. I want to talk about the anger of Stan's psychiatrist, the doctor-patient relationship, and power.

We begin with the anger. Stan is very specific about this as the motivating factor in his psychiatrist's action:

'. . . it was an anger reaction," he says. But Jules Henry has reminded us of the complexity of anger: ". . . it is merely linguistic poverty that makes us say 'anger' when we are really talking about amalgams of feeling in which the angry feeling is only one factor." [6] What additional factors, then, were involved in this man's anger? Can we ascribe it to an argument he had had that morning with his wife? Was his underwear uncomfortable? Had a friend passed him on the street without greeting him? We cannot know, of course; any of these things are possible and it might well be that, given other circumstances predisposing the man to a better state of mind at the moment he confronted Stan, he might not have committed him to the hospital. Of such happenstance is life made. But whatever may or may not have contributed to his feelings, we know what precipitated his anger with Stan: Stan's refusal to comply with his decision. Stan defied him. He asserted his independence. And this made the psychiatrist angry.

We can, I think, take heed of Jules Henry's *caveat* and distinguish certain qualities in this anger, even without knowing the man's mood. Stan refused to obey what was implicitly an order. "I'm going to keep you here" translates easily enough to "You *will* stay here," and to the psychiatrist it must have been a simple statement of fact: that is the way it is going to be. He must have taken Stan's compliance for granted, just as doctors take a nurse's or an aide's compliance for granted when they order medicine or a bath for a patient. Doctors give orders constantly; we have only to refer to the familiarity of the term "doctor's orders" to demonstrate this. It does not normally occur to them that people might defy them. In the context of the doctor-patient relationship the doctor is clearly in charge; he is the authority figure, the responsible expert, while the patient is his ignorant and unwell supplicant. Talcott Parsons describes all this very thoroughly in his discussion of medical practice, and the practice of psychiatry is in our society, for the most part, merely an extension of medical practice.[7] The patient, who does not know what is wrong with him and therefore cannot help himself, goes to the doctor for help and as part of the bargain submits to the doctor's authority. This superior-inferior pattern holds for most healing relationships, including most forms of psychotherapy, even when the doctor is not a psychiatrist (not a "doctor," in other words) but some other kind of psychotherapist. Built into the relationship between Stan and his psychiatrist, then, was a certain kind of power, the power which derived from the psychiatrist's role as what Jerome Frank calls a "socially sanctioned healer." [8]

By definition, however, this power is not personal but structural. That is, it derives from the structure of the doctor-patient relationship, which is socially defined, and not from any personal qualities the doctor himself may have. And there's the rub. Doctors are only human beings. Many of them obviously do not have the charisma, they do not radiate the sense of strength, the sense that they are wise and good and that they know whereof they speak, which constitutes genuine personal power. Indeed, perhaps very few of them, very few people in any profession, radiate this personal "sense of significance," as Rollo May defines it, this "ability to affect, to influence, and to change other persons." [9] So an obvious gap exists between the actual personal qualities of many doctors and the qualities they are supposed to possess by virtue of their status as doctors.

The rub is that, to a great degree, it is by his qualities as a man—his personal power—that the doctor cures. Much of the doctor's therapeutic effectiveness depends precisely on his having a certain personal influence or personal power over his patients. He must seem to them to be sure of himself, to be wise and good and caring. He must seem like a genuine authority: a Director.[10]

Now in physical medicine this is usually not a serious problem. Most patients stricken by physical disease seem to accept their doctors on faith, and by this faith, quite often, they are healed. Doctors call this the "placebo effect," and it seems to work regardless of the doctor's qualities as a man as long as, to the patient, he seems to know what he is doing. As long, that is, as the patient continues to believe in him. But in psychiatry it doesn't work that way. In psychiatry patients interact with their doctors in somewhat different ways. The patient talks about his problems, problems which are deep and personal and affect not simply his body but his whole being, the way he feels and thinks and the way he relates to other people. To be helpful the psychiatrist must respond to all this, and he must respond as a person, not as a technical expert.[11] Of the two, the psychiatrist is supposed to be "the one who knows better how to live" [12] and, by responding openly and displaying his personal qualities, by actually being wise and good and caring, to teach the other to emulate him. As we will see later on in this chapter, the psychiatrist is unlikely to be effective, he may instead do harm, unless he actually does possess these personal qualities, this real power.

In this light let us look again at what happened between Stan and the psychiatrist. Let us suppose that before this time they had had a good relationship, a long-term, semipaternal relationship like that between uncle and nephew. And it had helped Stan. Whatever our own feelings about shock treatment, Stan thought he had been helped and he thought the relationship was good. But suddenly, without warning, the psychiatrist reverted to the role of doctor, giver of orders, Director, and unilaterally ordered Stan to stay in the hospital. At once the relationship collapsed. By reverting to status, to authority, the man had revealed his actual personal powerlessness: his failure over months and years to stop the cycles of

overwork and depression, his fear that he could not persuade Stan to comply and must resort to doctor's orders,
his need to rely on hospitalization to control Stan. And
by refusing to comply with this order Stan revealed that
he, finally, also recognized the truth. This man lacked the
power to cure.

We can begin now to see through the doctor's anger.
He was defeated. He was less of a man than he was supposed to be. And it was revealed by his own foolish act,
his own arbitrary decision. All at once the gap we mentioned earlier between his actual powerlessness and his
status opened up beneath his feet. He grew uncertain
about himself, he felt futile, frustrated. Anger became a
protection for his own inadequacy; he hid behind it as
behind a wall. Finally he became self-righteous, as people
always do in such a situation. And as he argued with Stan
the anger and the self-righteousness grew even to the
point where he was ready to do violence.

Perhaps we ought not to blame this man too severely.
Doing psychotherapy successfully may be one of the most
difficult and demanding occupations in the world. It must
be especially difficult for a psychiatrist, who is trained as
a doctor and enjoys the status and authority of a doctor,
to abandon this role and interact with his patients as one
person to another, proving in intimate long-term contact
that he does indeed "know better how to live" and can
thereby help them. To abandon status means to run the
risk of revealing your own helplessness, your ignorance,
your actual powerlessness. Not many psychiatrists are willing to take such chances. In fact, the dominant model of
therapeutic interaction in this country, psychoanalysis,
specifically *forbids* the psychiatrist to abandon his status.
In psychoanalysis the analyst *must not* reveal anything
about himself to the patient, must instead become a "mirror" or "blank screen" on which the patient projects his

unconscious wishes and regressed "object relations." Any abrogation of this therapeutic mode represents a gross fault in psychoanalytic technique.

The psychoanalytic mode is a radical extension of the traditional role-playing of the doctor-patient relationship, which, as Talcott Parsons describes it, requires the doctor to maintain an "affective neutrality" toward his patients. He cares about them, yes, but in a disinterested, "professional" way. Psychoanalysis has elevated "affective neutrality" to dogma. Which conveniently protects psychiatrists from revealing themselves as people.

We shall discuss this matter later in relation to the way psychiatrists maintain their power in the mental health system. Right now I want to finish talking about anger. There is a school of psychiatry which does allow the therapist to become angry and allows him other feelings, too. I mean existential psychiatry. This school gives up its objectivity and neutrality in favor of active involvement with the patient, and it seems to be slowly gaining adherents in American psychiatry. In existential psychiatry the therapist attempts to move into the patient's world, see things as he sees them, share his experience and "be with" him in his uniqueness. It favors a nonjudgmental relationship of equal to equal, rather than the superior-inferior relationship of ordinary psychiatry. The patient's understanding of his experience is as valid as the doctor's. Therefore, as Leston Havens observes, *"Everything the patient says is to be taken at face value."* Havens goes on to explain:

> It is at this point that existential psychiatry loses what friends it has in the medical, behavioristic, and psychoanalytic . . . communities—all of which are wedded to the search for hidden processes. The existential method dictates not only the acceptance of appearance but also the bending of clinical attention to

identifying with these experiences, to accepting the
patient's point of view, and to living as fully as possible
in that point of view.[13]

Rank heresy to a psychoanalyst. But use of this therapeutic
mode encourages the therapist to be simply a human
being with his patient and open the door to expression
of feelings on the therapist's part.

An existential psychiatrist runs the risk, then, of
losing his temper. In a famous case in the early development of existential psychiatry just this happened. The
psychiatrist, Eugene Minkowski, for various circumstan-
tial reasons was forced to live with one of his craziest patients for a period of two months. Because the two men
were in continuous daily contact with each other for this
period of time there could be no question of maintaining
the formalities of the traditional doctor-patient relationship even if they had wanted to. Living together, they had
no choice but to respond to each other simply as people
who shared a bathroom, shared meals, shared time. It
proved to be a great trial to Minkowski. His patient was
an extremely unpleasant man who believed that "all the
refuse, all the waste of the whole universe, is put aside for
the purpose of being put into his stomach at some time."
Obsessed with this idea, the man interpreted everyone's
actions in its light, blamed people for making refuse, for
smoking which made ashes, for eating which made both
garbage and feces and urine, for using a watch, since the
cogs, the hands, the springs were all eventually meant for
his stomach. He complained constantly, accused Minkowski of collaborating in the "refuse policy" directed at him,
and called him a murderer. Finally Minkowski could
endure no more and lost his temper.[14]

But what a difference there is between the meaning
of Minkowski's anger and the anger of Stan's psychiatrist.
Minkowski did not respond as if the patient were threatening his power over him. Power was not at issue at all.

Minkowski had opened himself to this man, been to him as one man to another, and thereby gave up the possibility of maintaining power over him. The result was that he could use his own emotional reactions to learn something about his patient and enter his world more deeply. As he himself puts it,

> We cannot maintain a medical point of view 24 hours a day. We react to the patient as do other people around him. Compassion, gentleness, persuasion, impatience, and anger appear in turn. Thus, in the above circumstances, I not only observed the patient but had the possibility of projecting his psychic life on mine at every moment. It was like two melodies being played simultaneously; although these two melodies are as dissonant as can be, a certain balance becomes established between the notes of the one and the other and lets us penetrate further into our patient's psyche.[15]

With Stan's psychiatrist power was specifically the issue; his status and authority were being questioned and he had no choice but to exercise the only actual power he had left to him, the power to commit Stan to a mental hospital. Otherwise he would openly have had to admit defeat. His anger then was not an avenue into the workings of Stan's mind but a desperate attempt to deny that Stan's mind *could* work on a level equal with his.

As human beings we are all entitled to our anger. But only psychiatrists, it appears, are entitled to act upon their anger and do violence to others. The rest of us must restrain anger, however legitimate it may be, or suffer the restraints of the law. We have been talking about power; violence is not genuine personal power, the kind of power that actually affects or changes another person, but the resort of those who do not have genuine personal power. I refer again to Rollo May:

> Deeds of violence in our society are performed largely by

those trying to establish their self-esteem, to defend
their self-image, and to demonstrate that they, too, are
significant. . . . Violence arises not out of superfluity
of power but out of powerlessness.[16]

May's observation needs no elaboration. Despairing at his
actual powerlessness to help and heal, maddened by the
exposure of his failure as a psychiatrist, Stan's doctor
committed him to a state mental hospital against his will.
So psychiatrists enjoy an option no other medical specialist has. When their genuine therapeutic power fails, psychiatrists may fall back upon violence and put their failures permanently out of sight.

We cannot say that this episode represents a paradigm for how people get committed to mental hospitals.
Nor can we accuse psychiatrists in general of being weak
personalities who must resort to institutionalized violence
in order to control their patients. I personally know too
many psychiatrists with strong, charismatic personalities
to make such an accusation. We can, however, make two
important observations on the basis of Stan's story. The
existence of psychiatric power—I mean the status power
inherent in the doctor-patient relationship—is fully consistent with the existence of state mental hospitals. Psychiatrists often talk about the doctor-patient relationship
as something good in itself, a kind of sacred fount of
healing powers, greatly superior to what obtains in the
large public mental hospital, where bureaucratic relationships are the norm. But the one cannot exist without the other. Take away the state mental hospital and
you take away much of the meaning of the psychiatrist's
status, a status implicitly dependent on his ability to commit you to the hospital if in his opinion you get too crazy.
He is the "socially sanctioned healer," yes, but he is also an
agent of social control. With his unique legal authority to
put people away, he is the first line of social defense
against the threat of insanity. Psychiatrists do not talk

about this aspect of the doctor-patient relationship, but they rely upon it heavily to maintain their power.

It follows that as long as the state mental hospitals exist they will continue to serve as the repository for psychiatry's many failures. If a psychiatrist cannot hack it with a patient or if he gets angry with him or doesn't know how to handle him or just gets tired of him and wants to unload him, he has that option: commit him to the mental hospital. In a sense, then, *all* paths through the mental health system lead inevitably to the state mental hospital. No matter where you enter the system, if you are recalcitrant enough or crazy enough, if you cannot or will not cooperate, cannot or will not be "cured," someone is going to put you away.

II

The doctor-patient relationship which Stan's doctor abused is the only relationship many people have to the mental health system. As of July 1, 1971, the American Psychiatric Association counted 23,819 psychiatrists in the United States.[17] About 40 per cent of all psychiatric working time is spent in private practice.[18] A recent report by the APA suggests "that roughly half of about 5,000,000 persons who seek, each year, psychiatric care in the United States, seek and receive it from private practitioners." [19] Unfortunately we have no figures on what happens to all these people, how long they stay in treatment, what their diagnoses are, how many of them wind up in mental hospitals. But it seems clear that a large proportion of the patients in the mental health system are in it only to the extent of being under some psychiatrist's private care.

Without figures—there is no national reporting system for private psychiatric practice—it is difficult to know much about how the private practice of psychiatry works. The APA would have us believe that private practice is not a conduit to the mental hospital; [20] and perhaps not many psychiatrists do refer patients directly to state mental hospitals. On the other hand, they do frequently refer them to other psychiatrists, to outpatient clinics, and to community mental health centers. Even more important, they reject many people who come to them for help. Once again, we have no figures, but it is well known that psychiatrists are selective about the patients they accept for treatment. They greatly prefer patients who are fully oriented to "reality," moneyed enough to pay their bills on time, and articulate enough to talk at length about their problems. In other words, psychiatrists like bright, neurotic, and interesting middle-class people; given a full schedule, that is the kind of patient a psychiatrist is likely to make room for. Psychoanalysts are even more choosy in this regard. Few in number, prestigious, the appointed guardians of the Freudian faith, psychoanalysts tend to get the patients with the most interesting and challenging neurotic syndromes of all and the most money and time to spend analyzing them. Psychoanalysts skim the cream of the patient population, and the patient population knows this. You have no status in some circles unless you have been in analysis.

No other medical specialty, we should note, so blithely indulges its own ignorance. Every medical doctor rejects patients, certainly, sometimes because he is too busy, sometimes because the patient is in somebody else's care (professional courtesy), sometimes because the patient's illness does not fit his specialty, and often because the patient has no money. But he will not reject him for the express reason that he is too sick. A psychiatrist will. If someone is crazy enough that treatment is likely to be long, difficult, and unsatisfying, a psychiatrist is unlikely to accept him as a patient. We do not know how large it is, but there is a definite abandonment factor in psychiatry: whether by referral or outright rejection, the psychiatrist abandons to their fate the craziest of those who come to him.

Most often, perhaps, abandonment is by referral. In a survey conducted in the early 1960's, William Ryan explored the "referral jungle" in Boston and discovered some highly interesting facts about patterns of psychiatric practice. A surprising two out of three of the patients under the care of private psychiatrists in Boston were young women between the ages of 20 and 34. Most of the patients under private care lived in the same general area of Boston (an area comprising 7 per cent of the population accounted for 70 per cent of the patients), were in the top social and economic levels of Boston society, and were not seriously crazy: "Only about one patient in five is diagnosed by his psychiatrist as psychotic or even borderline psychotic, the great majority being seen as suffering from chronic neurosis or character disorder." [21] We can see plainly enough from this data the kinds of patients psychiatrists prefer: young, well-off, well-educated women with relatively mild emotional disturbances. The most prestigious psychiatric training hospitals, places like the New York Psychiatric Institute in New York City, which is affiliated with Columbia-Presbyterian Medical Center, or the Menninger Foundation in Topeka, Kansas, generally reflect this preference; their patient populations are heavily weighted with the young, the middle class, and women. Patients who do not fit into these categories tend to get shunted elsewhere, into the referral system. Ryan discovered that about seventeen thousand Boston residents in any given year are referred by the first source of help they apply to to some other source of help. Of this number some eleven thousand are directed to "outpatient psychiatric resources," that is, clinics. Of these eleven thousand, however, only twenty-five hundred actually apply to the second source when they are turned away by the first.[22] The vast majority of those referred

out, in other words, experience referral as rejection and
never show up at the second source of help.

Who are these abandoned people? Not too surprisingly, they tend to be those with the least ability to cope
with the referral process. If you are functioning reason-
ably well in the everyday middle-class world of bank accounts and baby-sitters, if you know how to apply for a
job and how to get a divorce, you are likely to know how
to follow up on a referral and get some kind of help for
yourself, even if it isn't the psychoanalysis at the William
Alanson White Institute that you hoped for. But if you
are crazy and disorganized and can't get yourself together
well enough to make another appointment, or you are
too poor to hire a baby-sitter again, or you don't trust
psychiatrists anyway and this refusal confirms your distrust,
or most probably if you are all three together, the referral
process is bound to do you in; you have, in effect, been
abandoned, and if your circumstances or your condition
deteriorate enough to come to the attention of the police
or a welfare worker you will probably wind up in a mental hospital.

What Ryan documents in his Boston survey is a kind
of filtering system which funnels poorer and crazier people toward the mental hospital. We might describe it as a
hierarchy of services with psychoanalysis at the top, other
psychiatrists in private practice just below them, followed
by outpatient psychiatric clinics, specialized clinics such
as child guidance centers, social work agencies, public
health agencies, and so on down the line to the public
mental hospital. (I have not mentioned community mental health centers, as I would like to reserve discussion of
them to a later chapter devoted to alternatives to the system I am describing here.) If we imagine the system as a
crude sort of filter we can see that at each level of the
hierarchy the system selects the "best" patients and refers
the remainder to the next level down. The "worst" pa-

tients, constituting the bulk of those who seek help or otherwise find themselves, willingly or unwillingly, in the mental health system, come to rest at the bottom, in the public mental hospital, where the facilities, the staff and staffing ratios, and the "treatment" are also the worst.

None of this is in any sense news. The referral system in Boston at the time of Ryan's survey is the same referral system to be found in cities all across the United States, and it is well known that it works to exclude people who are not functioning, white, and middle class, preferably women, with clearly defined (i.e., "neurotic") problems. Even the American Psychiatric Association admits as much.[23] This system does not serve the people who apply to it; it serves itself. As Daniel J. Levinson puts it in a commentary on Ryan's survey,

> The outpatient clinics and psychiatrists in private practice have a small, highly restricted clientele. Even in state-supported clinics, where fees are graded by income, the poor, non-white, less educated, and more severely impaired are rarely referred and even more rarely offered treatment. Referral of patients from one facility to another is handled in a relatively inefficient and irresponsible manner. The goal and spirit of referral are more to get rid of a troublesome case than to provide needed help. Most facilities have no sense of responsibility for the patients they refer elsewhere and no system of follow-up to make sure that the referral was successful. Large numbers of prospective patients get lost in the lacunae between facilities.[24]

That sums it up. Where the mental health system is not overtly coercive—and the referral system is not coercive in the sense that Stan's psychiatrist was—it is irresponsible. No happy medium seems to exist between these twin poles of coercive psychiatric power and irresponsible psychiatric indifference.

The situation in Boston has not improved appreciably since the time of Ryan's survey; most of the conditions he described still obtain. A study conducted by the Task Force on Children Out of School in 1971–72 found large-scale abandonment of children needing psychiatric services and a refusal to take any responsibility for the situation on the part of the state officials who, under Massachusetts law, were responsible for providing those services. One woman made a list of all the people she had seen and the agencies she had been to seeking help for her autistic son. Before her search ended she had tried some twenty-eight separate individuals and agencies including specialized camps, schools of all types, state agencies ranging from the Department of Mental Health to the Department of Welfare, university clinics, private physicians, a mental health clinic, a comprehensive community mental health center, general and specialized hospitals, and various politicians. The child was evaluated, referred out and simply refused help many, many times. He wound up in one of the most depressing mental institutions in Massachusetts: Boston State Hospital.[25]

At the Walk-In Clinic of the Massachusetts Mental Health Center in 1970–71 over three thousand people applied for outpatient treatment. The great bulk of them were turned away. The Center's *Annual Report* for that year states that ". . . there is outpatient time on an individual basis for only some 150 to 200 patients." [26] Another two hundred or so are accepted for group therapy. Although it has "full" responsibility for a geographic catchment area which includes some two hundred thousand people from both the wealthy suburb of Brookline and much of the black ghetto in the Roxbury section of Boston, the Center is basically a teaching institution staffed largely by psychiatric residents, who are fledgling psychiatrists learning their trade. I do not think I am being cynical in assuming that most of the four hundred or so people who do receive treatment are chosen for their usefulness as teaching material; that is what happens at teaching hospitals everywhere. But what becomes of the rest of those three thousand people, the ones who are not interesting and instructive "cases" for the residents to practice on? "Many patients are seen on a short-term basis to resolve immediate issues, many are referred to other clinics, and others must be told that treatment is not immediately available." [27] In other words, most of them are abandoned.

As Ryan makes clear, it is not for lack of mental health personnel that this system abandons so many people. Boston is more richly endowed with psychiatrists, clinical psychologists, social workers and other mental health pros and semipros than any other city in the United States except maybe New York. The Massachusetts Mental Health Center is known countrywide as a leading psychiatric institution; I have been there, it is crawling with staff. It is one of the few psychiatric facilities anywhere where you actually see psychiatrists on the ward, even if they are only residents. No: this institution does not need, most psychiatric institutions do not need, more staff. What they need is a total reevaluation of their structure and function. The referral system works hierarchically, filtering people down from the best to the worst facilities as their disturbances, their income, their general status become increasingly marginal, because the mental health system as a whole is structured as a hierarchy the basic function of which is not service to people but the preservation of its relative powers.

In practice, then, the referral system operates not as a service system but as a system of exclusion, and that is how most people experience it. I remember talking to one ex-mental patient who described how her mother had ferried her around New York City to one psychiatric facility after another looking for help. It took months of calling and referrals, a visit to a private psychiatrist (who prescribed a tranquilizer and abandoned her), and a considerable amount of crazy behavior (which psychiatrists call "acting out"), including a trip to a police station where she went to confess her "guilt," before a Park Avenue psychiatrist was able to admit her to Hillside Hospital in Queens, a private mental hospital.[28] Her case is typical, and she would have to be considered a "good" patient: young, white, female, well-educated, highly intelligent—but lower-middle-class in terms of income level (she got into Hillside on Medicaid). Consider what happens to a "bad" patient, a black man, say, with paranoid delusions that the police are after him. He may go to one clinic, possibly even two, and be turned away because he is "not a good candidate for psychotherapy"; or he may show up at the emergency room of the nearest hospital, where, if he gives signs of being troublesome, they will immediately ship him to a state mental hospital under emergency hospitalization commitment procedures; or he, too, may wander into a police station to confess his "guilt" but, because he is not young, white, middle-class, and well-educated but a middle-aged black with no education beyond the eighth grade, they will also immediately ship him to a state, county, or city mental hospital—if they don't lock him up first while they check out the "crime" he thinks he is "guilty" of. So one way or another, his paranoia will have been fulfilled. Wherever he happens to enter the system, in other words, he will rapidly settle to the level implicitly reserved for people of his status (or lack of it) and severity of disturbance: the bottom.

All of this stands far removed from the image of its service system which psychiatry tries to project. The professionals in places like Boston and New York with their plethora of psychiatric facilities, agencies, clinics, and private practitioners like to think of this agglomeration as a vast network in which everyone, through the referral process, eventually receives treatment. They talk about the "gatekeepers," the people in daily contact with the public, people like the clergy, the police, public health nurses, welfare workers, who identify psychiatric cases as psychiatric and channel them into their proper service paths. Obviously the system does not work that way. "A network," says Alfred J. Kahn, a specialist in the organization of social services, "must give major attention to channeling devices and must consider carefully the point at which each case leaves the general helping doorways that offer access to many services and enters a specialized helping channel." [29] The mental health system gives no attention whatsoever to "channeling devices." A study of services in the northern half of Westchester County, the wealthy county north of New York City, found that in psychiatric emergencies the police and ambulance drivers were taking people more often to Harlem Valley State Hospital than to the county hospital at Grasslands, even though Grasslands was closer, simply because admission procedures at Harlem Valley were less complicated and took less time.[30] Two things are notable about this finding: first, the police and ambulance drivers, not mental health professionals, are making difficult and fundamental decisions about how serious an emergency it is, i.e., whether it requires hospitalization of the person, or whether something less dramatic would suffice; and second, they are the ones making the "referrals" to psychiatric facilities, deciding which facility is more suitable—on the basis of their own convenience. This is one small example among many. The channeling devices are haphazard; the "gatekeepers" are untrained in psychiatric niceties and unaware of the decisive role they are playing; the network does not communicate part to part. The left hand does not know what the right hand is doing, and everywhere the crazies are abandoned.

III

We need not accumulate further evidence about the workings of the referral system. No ingenuous professional would deny the points we have made. The system works irresponsibly. Referrals are not followed up. People, especially the craziest people, are refused the services they seek. A service hierarchy sorts patients into their own socioeconomic and/or disturbance hierarchy. Psychiatry spends half its working time taking care of not very disturbed middle- and upper-class people in private practice. This story is not unlike the story in other social services: physical medicine is not that much better organized. But perhaps because the story is so familiar it breeds contempt. The mental health profession takes little interest in these matters, and little effort has been put into constructive change. To be sure community psychiatry, embodied in federally-funded community mental health centers, was supposed to correct this situation, taking care of those, especially the poor, whom the referral system neglected. But that has not happened, as we shall see in Chapter VIII. In a small way we have seen it already. The Massachusetts Mental Health Center meets the federal standards for a comprehensive community mental health center; indeed, its Director, Jack Ewalt, was a prime mover in the community mental health center movement.[31] The Massachusetts Mental Health Center, as we have seen, also abandons people.

In order to change the referral system, in order to make sure that those who want and seek help do not get lost in the gaps between doctor and agency, agency and hospital, some of the basic structural features of the mental health system would have to be changed. For the referral system is not a separate entity within the larger mental health system, not a patch thrown over its inadequacies, but a natural consequence, a logical conclusion, we might say, of the way the mental health system as a whole is organized.

It is difficult, however, to talk about this structure. The structure of the system is *implicit;* it does not stand out upon inspection but has to be uncovered. It is not like the structure of a school system or the sausage market which, however complicated, can be diagrammed. Its structure is implied, rather, in the way it operates, in its ideology, in its history; the only comparison I can think of is to the structure of the mind. Let me avoid complicating further an already highly complicated subject. I will simply state categorically that the system is a superstructure founded upon the doctor-patient relationship. Most other elements of the system, including the referral process, are intended in the final analysis to serve and preserve the basic doctor-patient relationship and its prerogatives—such as the right to get angry at a patient and commit him to a mental hospital.

We can see this fairly clearly, I think, if we examine the hierarchy of services in the referral system. At the top of this hierarchy stand the psychoanalysts, the small prestigious group who get the "best" patients. Psychoanalysts constitute a very small proportion of the number of psychiatrists as a whole, certainly less than 10 percent, perhaps closer to 5 percent. Their prestige is much greater than their numbers, however; they tend to get the best jobs, and they make considerably more money than other psychiatrists. They write more books and are better known both publicly and within the profession than other psychiatrists.[32] In short they have the best of everything; unquestionably they dominate psychiatry.

This dominance is the expression in practical terms of the dominance of Freudian theory in modern American psychiatry—we might even say in American life generally. (We have no time to talk at length about Freud's theories; there are already enough books on the subject.) Nathan

G. Hale, Jr., in his book *Freud and the Americans,* has
documented the growth of Freud's influence in America
more thoroughly than anyone.[33] What has always been
notable about it is the warmth with which American psychiatry received Freud, as distinguished from the hostility
he aroused in Europe. Indeed, psychoanalysis hit the
American psychiatric profession with the impact of revela-
tion; beginning with the eminent James Jackson Putnam,
a highly respected professor of neurology at Harvard
Medical School, the effect throughout psychiatry was like
conversion to a new religion. Freud's American followers
became zealous advocates of the psychoanalytic faith and
they spread his ideas rapidly through American culture.
The fact that Freud's explicitness about the primacy of
infantile sexual urges in human motivation coincided with
a general cultural attack on Victorian morality added to
the influence of his ideas. Then in the 1930's the immigra-
tion of refugee European analysts into the United States,
among them some of the most eminent names in psychoanalysis, cemented the dominant position of Freudian
theory in American psychiatry.

In talking about Freud's influence we must distinguish between two Freudian models: his metapsychology
or model of the mind, and his model of treatment. Freud's
metapsychology is widely known, if not as widely accepted,
in American culture. It has been enormously influential
in intellectual circles, particularly in the arts; it is pene-
trating the study of history as it has already penetrated
sociology and, to a lesser extent, political science. To some
extent we all know Freud; we know, that is, what people
mean when they talk about the unconscious, childhood
sexuality, the id, ego, and superego, and such psychological
mechanisms as projection, repression, and denial. Benjamin Spock incorporated Freudian ideas into *Baby and
Child Care* and millions of American children have been
raised on them.

The influence of Freud's model of treatment, however, has been confined largely to psychiatry. Reading Freud it is difficult to separate the two models. For Freud, his "talking cure" was the primary means of access to the mind. His patients lay on the couch for an hour every day and free associated whatever came into consciousness; eventually, through the analysis of dreams, resistances or blocks, and the development of the "transference neurosis," everything was revealed: the infantile genesis of the patient's troubles, the relative strengths of ego and id, the unconscious fantasies. It was all there, the whole mental structure. But American culture as a whole has been less interested in how Freud achieved his understanding than in what he understood. Very few people, after all, experience psychoanalysis firsthand. The cultural influence of psychoanalysis as a treatment for mental disturbance has therefore been far less pronounced than the influence of Freud's more generally applicable theories about mental functioning.

Within psychiatry, however, the psychoanalytic treatment model has had a heavy impact. Not only do budding psychiatrists learn about the id and the ego in seminars and lectures, they learn to do psychotherapy by practicing on carefully selected patients as well. And the psychotherapy they do is solidly based on the Freudian model. Very few of them will go on to become psychoanalysts; the training is absurdly expensive and long. But they will observe the power of psychoanalysts in their training environment, the prestige they enjoy, the emoluments. And they will come to understand that to a great degree their power derives from their sworn fealty to the Freudian treatment model and the strict control which the psychoanalytic brethren exert over psychoanalytic practice within that model.

We have already talked about certain aspects of the Freudian model in relation to Stan Hamilton's case. We can summarize its principal features quickly here. The basic relationship is one to one: the doctor and his patient.

The patient talks, the doctor listens and tries to understand what the patient's talk reveals, what is "really" going on in the patient's mind. But it takes a very long time to understand this, so psychotherapy must be long-term, and in psychoanalytic practice it is not unusual for treatment to continue for five or six years or even longer, an hour a day, three days a week. The doctor's silence during all this time is more than just a listening process, however. He seldom answers direct questions and he never reveals anything about his personal life; he is a "blank screen," we will recall, upon which the patient projects his own feelings, his fantasies, his desires.

Over a period of time, because the patient knows nothing about the doctor, who always retains his "affective neutrality," he comes to relate to him as if he were someone problematic from his own past, usually a mother or father who provided too little love or too much, who was too punishing or not punishing enough, who tried to toilet train him too early or who weaned him too late. The patient's relating to the doctor in this unreal way is called "transference," and cure in psychoanalysis is not possible without it; the transference is the central psychoanalytic experience.[34] Some people cannot effect a transference, however. Their disturbances go very deep, both in the sense that the genetic origin of these disturbances is early in life and that the break from reality has been profound and total. In a treatment situation they withdraw from all contact with the therapist and retreat into their own private world. Their disturbances are called "psychotic" rather than "neurotic." The capacity of these people for "object relations"—relations with other people—never developed properly, and in their narcissism they therefore have no pattern of "object relations" they can transfer onto the therapist. Hence "psychotic" people are not good "candidates" for psychotherapy.

Things begin to fall into place. Most psychiatrists do not practice psychoanalysis, but they do practice psychotherapy taken more or less faithfully from this model. They see their patients for an hour—fifty minutes, to be precise—not three times a week but probably once, in some cases twice. They see them alone, one to one. They see them over a long period of time, not five or six years but quite often for a year, perhaps even two. They do not maintain an analytic silence but they expect the patient to do most of the talking and most of the work. The relationship is not equal; the doctor is supposed to know everything about the patient, the patient is not supposed to know anything about the doctor. And finally very few psychiatrists attempt to do psychotherapy with "psychotic" people.

As we have already seen, this is precisely the way virtually the entire mental health system outside the mental hospital operates. The one-to-one doctor-patient relationship is *the* therapeutic mode of choice. People who want help are "candidates" for therapy and must demonstrate their suitability for it before they are accepted; the intake procedures at most psychiatric clinics serve in effect as a suitability test. All other people, especially very crazy people such as "psychotics" or others who would not function well in this setting, are referred out, *i.e.*, abandoned, or they find themselves on a referral ladder which descends abruptly into the mental hospital. Frequently these other people who are not suitable for psychotherapy are the poor, blacks, white ethnic types, people with little education, inarticulate people; because they are not "good candidates" they find themselves on this ladder, the "psychotic" label duly attached, much more often than white middle-class Americans with the education and the money to spend on psychotherapy.

The abuses of the referral system, in short, are a direct consequence of the dominance in American psychiatry of the Freudian model of the doctor-patient relationship.

There have been many apostates from the Freudian

faith, and it could be argued that Freud's treatment model no longer dominates the scene to the extent that it once did. This is only partly true, however; or it is true more on the intellectual front than the therapeutic front. The intellectual battles between Freudians and neo-Freudians and Jungians, Freudians and Adlerians and all the rest are still actively raging. But we are not talking about an intellectual situation, we are talking about the mental health system. Jung's works are available in bookstores everywhere and he is widely read, but the number of genuine Jungian analysts at work in the United States today may number no more than the fingers and toes on one man's body. They are scarce. So, relatively speaking, are analysts who follow Karen Horney or Alfred Adler. These people have influence, but it is an intellectual influence with little effect on the doctor-patient relationship we have described.

Of course, attacks have been made from other quarters specifically on the doctor-patient relationship. Carl Rogers advocates a client-centered relationship in which the therapist abandons his objectivity and "affective neutrality" and becomes the client's active emotional sponsor. Carl Rogers is a psychologist, however, not a doctor: the difference, as we shall see shortly, is crucial. Gestalt therapy as practiced at the Esalen Institute and similar humanistically oriented centers can hardly be said to support a traditional doctor-patient relationship. Once again, however, Gestalt therapy is not based in psychiatry, and this and many other therapeutic schools—transactional analysis, bioenergetics—exist somewhat outside of or in addition to the mental health system.[35] I do not want to dismiss them out of hand; it is just that they are not our subject. For all their interest, there can be no doubt that within the mental health system as it is presently constituted, which is a system under the firm control of psychiatry, the Freudian models both of therapy and of the mind's structure still reign supreme. As Arnold Rogow puts it:

. . . no body of doctrine has appeared, as yet, to take
the place of psychoanalytic theory, and . . .
notwithstanding the importance of the so-called drug
revolution and other therapy innovations, the main
theoretical influence in psychiatry continues to be the
teachings of Freud and his followers.[36]

What is truly odd about this situation is that psychoanalysis as a method of treating emotional disturbances is
so ineffective. You have to wonder why psychoanalysts do
not sit in their glove-leather Eames chairs and blush all
day long. In 1952 the British psychologist H. J. Eysenck
published figures showing that the rates of improvement
and outright cure claimed for psychoanalysis were no better than the rates of what is called "spontaneous remission"
—improvement and cure among *untreated* cases—in control groups of people with similar neurotic complaints.
The battle has raged heavily back and forth since that
time; Eysenck is still publishing data supporting his case
against psychoanalysis, and psychoanalysts are still publishing rebuttals. Which indicates that Eysenck touched a
nerve. In a report on his careful review of the vast literature on the outcome of all types of psychotherapy, Allan E.
Bergin can only use words like "modest" and "moderate"
to describe the positive effects of psychotherapeutic treatment of whatever persuasion. More significantly, he finds
that this weak positive effect is nearly matched by negative
effects. Nearly as many people *deteriorate* in psychotherapy
as improve. Furthermore, what positive effects he does
find he traces to a minority of the therapists in question.
A few highly successful therapists, he says, account for
most patient improvement.[37]

In any other enterprise calling itself "scientific" data
such as this would send the entire profession into agonized
reappraisal of its foundations.

Let us give credit where credit is due. Freud himself,
always more intelligent than the school he founded, was
by no means uniformly sanguine about the therapeutic

effectiveness of psychoanalysis. In his well-known paper on "Analysis Terminable and Interminable," written toward the end of his life, Freud deals at length with the various factors which militate against effectiveness in psychoanalysis. Among them he mentions the deficiencies of psychoanalysts:

> It looks as if a number of analysts learn to make use of defensive mechanisms which enable them to evade the conclusions and requirements of analysis themselves, probably by applying them to others. They themselves remain as they are and escape the critical and corrective influence of analysis. This seems to confirm the dictum of a writer who warns us that it is hard for a mortal who acquires power not to misuse it.[38]

This last remark is especially suggestive. In the same volume which contains Bergin's assesment of the research on therapeutic outcome, Truax and Mitchell write that the qualities which seem to characterize the few highly successful therapists who account for the improvement rates seem to be fairly uniform. The successful therapist, they find, exhibits "genuineness" or nondefensiveness in his encounter with patients: ". . . he is a real person in an encounter presenting himself without defensive phoniness, without hiding behind a professional facade or other role." [39] He also exhibits a "nonpossessive warmth" toward the patient and something the authors call "accurate empathy": the ability to get inside the other person and intuit where he is moment by moment, to read his feelings accurately and empathize with them. This sounds like a description of the existential relationship we talked about earlier; [40] it is certainly far removed from the highly intellectual and rather remote stance which most psychoanalysts adopt—a stance which, as Freud suggests, maintains the analyst's defenses intact but does not do much for his patient.

Even if psychotherapy did effectively treat those it undertakes to treat, it is by no means clear that it ought to retain anything but a minor, subsidiary role in the mental health system. Being confined on theoretical grounds to "neurotics," a diagnostic classification the private practice of psychiatry seems designed to reify, it automatically abandons crazier sorts of people to the mental hospital, as we noted earlier. It similarly abandons the poor, the uneducated, the nonverbal. Taken together, these "unsuitable" sorts of people probably constitute the bulk of those wanting and seeking some form of help for emotional problems. Yet in the face of its obvious inadequacy as a helping instrument for vast numbers of people, psychotherapy has not lost its grip on the mental health system.[41] In November, 1972, I interviewed Milton Greenblatt, then Commissioner of Mental Health for the State of Massachusetts, and he referred to recent studies on the efficacy of psychotherapy with which he was familiar:

> Two major studies—I happen to have written the introduction to both of those books—on the value of psychotherapy in the chronic schizophrenic, in the schizophrenic ill two years or more, . . . show that psychotherapy is less valuable than drugs, than even shock treatment, and so on. And it doesn't add much to drugs when the two are combined.[42]

Yet Greenblatt himself admitted to still doing some psychotherapy even while serving as Commissioner: ". . . even I see a patient or two every week, and I think I do them some good. Yes, we comfort, and we help them through their crises, and we give them a little self-esteem and all that sort of thing." A few moments later he said: "Psychotherapy is the central pillar of psychiatry in that the greater psychiatrist is the more sensitive to human interaction and understands it all." In the mind of this highly respected psychiatrist, then, exists an unmistakable contradiction. He is thoroughly familiar with data on the virtual worthlessness of psychotherapy for those who need help most (not to mention the "neurotics" seen in private practice) and who presumably ought to be psychiatry's main concern. Yet psychotherapy remains for him the model of psychiatric treatment and he continues to practice it himself. What madness is this? It is the madness of a mental health system based on fundamentally elitist notions of who deserves treatment and who does not. As Greenblatt himself revealed:

> Only a certain number of selected people need the depth analysis and can profit by it. There are others who, you throw any amount of light on their unconscious, and they're still, if I may say so, second-rate people in terms of the fiber of their neurological make-up, which expresses itself over time; for after three to five years that you put them together in psychotherapy, they'll still decline to their natural level.[43]

I said earlier that the mental health system is a superstructure founded upon the doctor-patient relationship. It is, of course, highly relevant that psychiatrists are trained as physicians first, before they receive their psychiatric training. Anyone at all knowledgeable about Freud knows that there is no self-evident connection between his theories and the body of knowledge we associate with physical medicine. The connection lies in the realm of practice: both stand firmly, furiously, upon the sacred ground of the doctor-patient relationship. Or to put it another way, psychiatry borrows from medicine the power and the prerogatives that belong to the doctor of medicine. Psychiatry borrows his status, the myth of his magical curing powers, and his income. These structural connections between psychiatry and medicine are more important, I believe, than the "medical model" of mental disorder which Szasz and other critics have beaten to death. I doubt whether many but the most conservative, old-line psychiatrists believe that "mental illness" is a disease entity in the same sense that diabetes or pneumonia is, or even that it is very helpful, except for public relations purposes, to call it "illness" at all.[44] Psychiatrists who defend the medical model, who make the analogy between mental and physical illness, are really defending the power that their position as medical doctors lends them. The M.D. automatically places them where a Ph.D. in psychology does not: at the top of the professional pecking order. That, of course, is definitely worth defending.

This is in spite of the fact that psychiatrists generally receive much poorer training than psychologists. Consider how the psychiatrist becomes a psychiatrist. He spends four years in medical school where he may read one psychiatric textbook, be exposed a few times to interviewing techniques, and interview a few patients himself. On the basis of this minimal experience he makes a choice of psychiatry as a career, but he still receives no psychiatric training; instead he must spend a year as an intern in a general hospital doing all the things interns do, which are everything but psychiatry. Then, only after he is qualified for a career in general medicine, does he finally enter his specialty. Immediately, as a first-year resident, he is thrown into practice on the wards of some large psychiatric facility. It is unquestionably practice: he will be the first to admit that he doesn't really know what he is doing. For the next three years he will continue practicing in this way while learning in seminars and lectures something about the work of Freud, perhaps about the neo-Freudians such as Hartmann and Erikson and such other theorists as Harry Stack Sullivan.[45] What he learns of the more advanced developmental science of people like Piaget and Bruner, of the behavioral school from Watson on down, of Gestalt theory from Koffka and others on down, of the contributions of the Structuralists, of sociologists like Goffman, Birdwhistell, and so on, all very pertinent to an understanding of behavioral disorders in man, he will have to learn on his own.

Contrast this to the education of a Ph.D. candidate in psychology. He will or ought to be familiar with most, if not all, the above-named writers, as well as the work of Freud and his followers. If he goes into clinical psychology he will receive a good deal of clinical training besides; that is, he too will do psychotherapy. He may not do as much of it as a resident in psychiatry, but he will do it with a much broader intellectual background. But because the mental health system is based on the practice of medicine, that is, on the doctor-patient relationship, the superiority of his training will mean little when he graduates. The medical structure will place him second in command on the typical "treatment team," which consists of a psychiatrist at the top, a psychologist below him, and below that a psychiatric social worker. The levels of income will match the hierarchy. Needless to say, this hierarchy is not a meritocracy; the psychiatric social worker may in fact be a better therapist than either of the other two, be warmer, that is, more genuine in his (more frequently her) relations with other people, better able to empathize. Indeed, someone at the very bottom, some volunteer, a psychiatric aide, a nurse, perhaps even the secretary who gives people their clinic appointments, may be a better natural therapist than any of them. But it won't matter. The power structure will remain intact.

Two psychiatric prerogatives preserve this hierarchy. Psychiatrists are the only ones in the hierarchy who can sign commitment papers and put someone in a mental hospital. And equally important, perhaps more important, psychiatrists are the only ones who can prescribe drugs.

These are controlling factors in the movement of psychologists (and psychiatric social workers) into private clinical practice. If a psychologist wants to prescribe drugs to his patients he will have to affiliate with a psychiatrist. This often involves working in an adjoining office, taking referrals from the psychiatrist, or simply working *for* him on a salaried or fee-splitting basis. His only other choice is to practice without resorting to drugs, a definite liability in a culture where drugs—pills—are the preferred treatment for every complaint. Either way he loses, and that is precisely the way the psychiatric profession wants it. Listen to the voice of the turtle:

> The medical profession fully endorses the appropriate utilization of the skills of psychologists, social workers, and other professional personnel in contributing roles in settings directly supervised by physicians. It further recognizes that these professions are entirely independent and autonomous when medical questions are not involved; but when members of these professions contribute to the diagnosis and treatment of illness, their professional contributions must be coordinated under medical responsibility.[46]

It seems worth noting that psychiatric—*i.e.*, medical —control over the mental health system extends upward as well as downward. In the United States you cannot become a psychoanalyst, officially endorsed and approved by the American Psychoanalytic Association, until you first become a doctor. Some people believe that it is this fact which accounts for the rigidity and sterility of psychoanalytic thought in this country. The most creative psychoanalysts have generally been Europeans, people like Erik Erikson, Anna Freud, Ernst Kris, Franz Alexander, Hartmann, Winnicott, Hans Sachs, Otto Rank. A great many—half of those here named—are or were lay analysts, not physicians. It is well known that Freud, although a physician himself, fought for lay analysis and believed that psychoanalysis should establish connections with the arts, psychology, history and anthropolgy and should recruit analysts from all these fields. He wanted psychoanalysis to become a genuine science of man. In America his position on the subject has been ignored. Only rebellious psychoanalytic institutes like the William Alanson White Institute in New York, where Rollo May, a psychologist, practices, teach psychoanalysis to nonphysicians, and the American Psychoanalytic Association naturally refuses membership to their graduates. The Freudian treatment model lives on, but psychoanalysis is dying in the United States. Fewer and fewer bright young candidates are being attracted to it. Even the influential analyst Judd Marmor is turning away from it.[47] Eventually, perhaps, everyone will turn away from it.

The mental health system will not change without a profound alteration of its basic structure. That means breaking the grip of medical control. As long as the doctor-patient relationship, as embodied in the Freudian psychotherapeutic treatment model, is perceived as the primary mode of treating something egregiously called "mental illness," medical control will endure and the system will not change. If other methods of treatment, other models of helping relationships among people, achieve equal status, the system will change. At the moment, however, change seems unlikely. When you attack psychiatric control of the system you attack one of America's great business enterprises. At once all talk of psychiatric responsibility, the treatment team, hierarchies within and among agencies becomes subordinate to considerations of money: who makes how much salary. Who gets the biggest consultants' fees. Who is named the "senior investigator" in a research project. On these grounds psychiatry will fight to the last man.

We ought to know what they are fighting for. Psychiatrists earn anywhere between thirty-five and fifty dollars per hour in private practice, as distinguished from perhaps thirty dollars an hour or less for psychologists, twenty-five dollars an hour or less for social workers.[48] Their median net income per year (as of 1966) came to about $29,000; now it must be closer to $40,000.[49] Different sources disagree on psychiatry's relative standing, in terms of income, among other medical specialties; a 1966 source places psychiatry fifth among ten specialties, while the AMA more recently placed them seventh among eight, just above pediatrics.[50] Apparently there are no reliable figures. Nevertheless, psychiatrists obviously make a lot of money and a lot more than other professionals in the mental health system; no one questions that fact. About two-thirds of American psychiatrists, by the way, work for institutions, but most institutions allow them to supplement their salaries by taking private patients on the side: witness Milton Greenblatt.

Many psychiatrists in private practice make more than the usual amount of money by concentrating their efforts on so-called medical treatments rather than psychotherapy. A case in point is ECT, or shock treatment. Shock is considered one of several possible treatments for severe depression. Most psychiatrists charge about the same for one shock treatment as they charge for an hour of psychotherapy, say forty dollars a shock. The difference is that shock can be administered in less than five minutes. The script usually runs like this. A psychiatrist is affiliated with a general hospital or perhaps a private psychiatric hospital, of which there are about 160 in the United States. Half of these are proprietary—run for profit. He checks his "depressed" patient into the hospital for a series of shock treatments, eight or ten perhaps, run over a period of two weeks or so, or as long as the patient's insurance policy holds out. He will often have a number of patients in the hospital at the same time, making things as convenient as possible; he drops in on shock days and spends perhaps an hour administering shock, a complicated technical procedure which requires him to push a button.[51]

At forty dollars a shock, that works out to quite a bit of money. He makes even more, of course, if the hospital is proprietary and he is one of the owners. And the whole process leaves him plenty of time to play golf.

If this description sounds cynical, forgive me. It is just that the whole situation is unredeemably contemptible. The doctors will defend themselves: "Shock treatment works! People get better!" Maybe. No one knows what damage repeated shock treatments do to the brain; all anyone knows definitely is that they do affect your memory. Psychiatrists who are fond of shock treatment theorize that it wipes out the memory of the unpleasant events that are troubling you. Others, however, theorize that depressed people are actually extremely angry people who have turned that anger against themselves: a theory which calls for another treatment strategy entirely. In any case I have interviewed plenty of mental patients who have been through shock treatment, and they talk about it as if they had survived some special brand of torture. None of them thought it had helped them. And no treatment in medicine is so blatantly abused for the profit of doctors. In 1971 the classification "depressive disorders" accounted for 41.6 percent of the admissions to private psychiatric hospitals in the United States, as opposed to a mere 20.7 percent diagnosed with "schizophrenia." [52] And this incredibly high percentage of "depressive disorders" noted for 1971 represents a steadily rising trend. In state and county mental hospitals, on the other hand, "depressive disorders" accounted for a mere 8.8 percent of the admissions, while "schizophrenia" accounted for 38 percent.[53] These latter figures are considered to be close to the actual relative incidence of these two disorders in the population. (Most state and county mental hospitals, it should be noted, no longer use shock treatment.) What is going on here is unmistakeable. Some psychiatrists are diagnosing more and more people who are *not* "depressed" as "depressed" in order to give them shock treatments and make more money. The figures tell the story; obviously they are resorting to shock in their own private hospitals more and more often. There are just not that many "depressed" people. It is impossible to be objective about this sickening fact.

Psychiatry is now attempting to fortify its financial position in the mental health system by persuading the Government to include it in proposals for national health insurance. Traditionally insurers have been reluctant to provide much if any coverage for "mental illness." For obvious reasons: hospitalization has in the past tended to be indefinite; people leave the mental hospital only to return repeatedly; no real "cure" is known for "mental illness"; and finally, insurers have found that when they do provide coverage for "mental illness" people abuse it.[54] In recent years insurers have begun to provide more coverage, but it is always more limited than the coverage for physical illness. A typical Blue Cross/Blue Shield plan will pay for 120 to 125 days of hospitalization for a physical illness, less the usual deductions, but only thirty–thirty-one days for a "mental illness," and this only in general hospitals. If the patient is rehospitalized within a year, most plans will not pay for it. There is much more coverage, by the way, for inpatient shock treatment than for outpatient psychotherapy. Coverage in most plans for outpatient psychotherapy—that means therapy with a private psychiatrist—is limited, when it is covered at all, to 50 percent of the cost of a limited number of visits, with other restrictions on fees and on maximum benefits payable.[55]

For years psychiatry has been campaigning to extend the benefits available for "mental illness" under all types of insurance programs. Now that some form of national health insurance seems inevitable, the campaign has been extended to Congress. In a recent bill to encourage the establishment of Health Maintenance Organizations, which are loosely-knit health care organizations providing "comprehensive services to a voluntarily enrolled membership at a pre-paid fixed fee," [56] coverage for up to twenty outpatient visits to a psychiatrist—several months of psychotherapy—was made a *basic* benefit.[57] That means that an HMO must provide this coverage to get Federal funding under the bill. The American Psychiatric Association claims credit for this victory. In proposals for national health insurance the APA is not doing quite as well. The original Nixon Administration bill provided no mental health coverage at all; the present bill provides unlimited coverage for outpatient visits to community mental health centers but will cover only fifteen visits to private psychiatrists. That is definitely not what the APA has in mind; the Association wants the greatest possible coverage for private psychiatry, not public. It is therefore busy "educating" members of Congress and the Administration on the necessity for what it calls "equal coverage for mental illness." (It isn't hard to imagine what would happen to these lobbying efforts if psychiatry's base in medicine and the medical model came under serious public challenge.) "Equal coverage for mental illness" will no doubt drive the cost of this insurance out of the reach of most poor people.[58]

I do not think I have drawn an outlandish caricature of the psychiatric profession as it exists outside the mental hospitals. Not all psychiatrists are money-hungry, not by any means: let me be quick to grant that fact. Many are warm, genuine people—good therapists, in other words— who despise those of their brethren who abuse their power. Psychiatry even has its own radical fringe, men like Paul Lowinger whose avowed purpose it is to destroy the APA and all other symbols of psychiatric power completely.

Nevertheless, many other psychiatrists, far too many, are not warm, genuine people and good therapists but simply businessmen out to make a buck in the nearest available racket. Still others are cynical or sadistic or worse. As people, that is, they run the spectrum. For largely historical, i.e., accidental, reasons—reasons we touched on in the first chapter—these people, the businessmen and the genuine helpers alike, have been granted unparalleled power: power both to commit other people to places of confinement, there to perform subtle and unsubtle atrocities upon them, and to run the mental health system to their own (largely financial) ends. I will say it repeatedly throughout this book: *no person should have such arbitrary, unlimited power over another.*

We are always going to have some sort of mental health system. But nothing says it has to be the sort we have now. The target of this book is psychiatric power, which degrades both its victims and its abusers and vitiates whatever therapeutic effectiveness the system may actually have. "It is hard," says Freud, "for a mortal who acquires power not to misuse it." Psychiatrists ought to tattoo those words on their brains.

IV
Mental Hospital:
The Commitment Experience

When the liberty of the subject only concerns the liberty
to do *good,* it ceases to be liberty.

Stacy Aumonier, *Odd Fish*

I

While doing research for this book I have met or
corresponded with some remarkable people. But none, I
think, may be quite so remarkable as the young woman
I shall call Sarah. Sarah belongs to that small, elite group
who have survived concerted, systematic, and extreme attempts to break their will. Will is not an entity to which
most psychiatrists would grant recognition; it is one of a
whole class of attributes—determination, courage, spirit—
which, as names for "real" mental characteristics, lack the
scientific respectability of other names like ego and id or
borderline schizophrenia.[1] But in the nonpsychiatric world
in which most of us live Sarah stands out as a woman of
what we can only call spirit, determination, and courage,
a woman bent on preserving her free will under the most
adverse circumstances. She surely possesses those attributes
psychiatry wants to deny. In fact, perhaps we can read into
psychiatry's attempt to subdue Sarah's will a symbolic
attempt on the will of man as a whole. Perhaps not: I
don't want to be sentimental about what happened to her.

In any event Sarah survived extremes of psychiatric "treat-ment" that would have destroyed most other people, cer-tainly including myself.

When she was nineteen Sarah's mother and father took her to the Menninger Foundation in Topeka, Kansas, for treatment. By her own accounts she had "had lots of emotional problems in my youth and adolescent years," yet she had graduated from high school in California with honors, she had spent a summer in Europe on an exchange program, and she had had an active social life. Her main problem sounds like the problem many parents of many teen-age children are familiar with. She was rebellious. Apparently she was also too active sexually by their stan-dards. Unable to deal with the problem themselves and having a great deal of money, they brought her to the Menninger Foundation, where she signed herself in, with "no idea what I was getting into, and no choice anyway." She spent the next three and a half years there.[2]

The Menninger Foundation may be the best-known private psychiatric facility in the world. It runs a psy-chiatric school which has produced over one thousand psychiatrists since World War II, 4 percent of the nation's total.[3] It has a finger in all the current therapeutic pies; it helps staff a clinic in the slums of East Topeka, does research on biofeedback mechanisms, and runs a rap-group program for local young people in addition to its traditional inpatient and outpatient services.[4] One of its staff members, Dr. Herbert C. Modlin, a champion of community mental health centers, recently ran for Presi-dent of the American Psychiatric Association. Its grounds are lovely, the occupational therapy department has the best equipment money can buy, the greenhouse is of commercial quality. Quality is the word at Menningers. Treatment is based on long-term intensive psychotherapy along the now familiar lines of the Freudian model (al-though psychoanalysis itself is offered only to outpatients).

A stay of three and a half years is not unusual by Menninger standards, and, according to Sarah, "you have to
guarantee that you can pay for at least 3 years of treatment before they accept you." Mostly these days they are
accepting young people brought there, like Sarah, by their
parents; 70 percent of the patients are under thirty.[5]

Contrary, perhaps, to her parents' expectations,
Sarah's rebelliousness did not automatically evaporate
simply upon admission to the Foundation. They run
things at Menningers as they run things at most mental
hospitals, on a privilege system in which, as in the old
days of moral treatment, you must earn the right to be
accorded status as a person by showing that you are "responsible": by submitting, that is, to the authority of the
Director and those to whom he has delegated his powers.
But rebellious Sarah would not submit:

> If you don't do as you are told you don't get any
> priveleges you don't get to go to the dining room or go
> outside, or have visiting priveleges etc. I was always
> being restricted to my room. They would unlock the
> closet and give me ten minutes to get dressed, use my
> toothbrush and then she would lock it on doctors orders.
> As if I couldn't handle a closet. Then you would have
> to sort of bargain your way up to getting the privelege
> of an unlocked closet by cooperating.

Sarah already believed herself to be a competent human
being, and the kinds of things the hospital expected her
to do in order to earn privileges were in her view beneath
contempt:

> In the 3 and one half years I was there I did not
> participate in a single activity for 2 and one half years.
> Mainly because I refused to go. One time two aides
> literally dragged me down the hall to gym activity but I
> kicked and screamed so loud the doctor decided it
> wasn't worth going through that scene every day to get

> me to an activity. I couldn't stand being put like a child
> in a little group and supervised by the aide like a two
> year old. I wouldn't dream of going to project group: in
> that group you have to get up at 7:00 in the morning and
> saw logs in the snow. It is supposed to be therapeutic
> for people that have a lot of anger. There are patients in
> that group for years and they hate it. I don't see it's
> done them any good. Other patients are stuck in the
> craft shop and *forced* to sand on a bowl for 8 hours a day.
> Or hook a rug for hours at a time against their will.

The activities she is talking about here belong to
something the Foundation calls milieu therapy, which is a
Menninger specialty. As the Menningers practice it, the
patient's physical environment, his daily ward activities,
and his contacts with lower-echelon staff are all "prescribed" according to the patient's particular intrapsychic
problems and needs.[6] If a patient is "acting out" sexually
and is openly rebellious, as Sarah was, her "prescription"
might conceivably include tasks that would channel the
anger supposedly at the root of her rebelliousness into saw-
ing wood, while at the same time all contacts with male
patients would be discouraged. The doctor would instruct
the staff, meanwhile, how to behave toward the patient,
whether to be warm and sympathetic or distant and reserved, whether to harangue the patient or leave him
alone, all according to the patient's presumed needs. In
this way the patient's entire environment would artificially
take on a posture therapeutic to the patient twenty-four
hours a day.

Sarah refused to follow any prescription, however,
and it made things hard for her:

> I had a rough time at Menningers because my personality
> would not allow me to "go along with the program"
> and so I fought it in every way. I realize I brought upon
> myself the staff's anger and all the consequences, but I
> am not a person to be pushed around and do things I do

not believe in. The only positive assertion of myself
was to say *No* and I just had to reject all their
"treatment." "Treatment" is like a magical word that
floats around Menningers. There is no treatment going
on in there. They just teach you how to become more
and more dependent on them.

Confined to her room for long periods of time, not allowed
such "privileges" as eating with other patients or talking
to them, choosing her own clothes or even having access
to her closet except for those ten minutes, she began to
become the nonperson the hospital assumed her to be:

> It was hard to believe myself in the situation in
> Menningers after about the first year there, that I was not
> able to dress myself, I could not and would not take a
> bath by myself, and I was afraid to leave my room and
> walk down the hallways. The aides would come every
> morning, and run a damp towel across my face and
> proceed to put on my bra and panties and dress me, while
> I just was like a lump of a body with no strength or
> desires hardly to live anymore.

Accorded the status of a thing, she became one. Psychiatrists call this regression; the patient returns to an infantile state of dependency. In Sarah's case, however, the
true act of dependency would have been to "go along
with the program." Her regression was the last tactic
available to her in her refusal to submit. Except that
Sarah, never one to do things halfway, "acted out" her
regression just as she had "acted out" all her other ways
of rebelling. For Sarah, in other words, tactics were more
than tactical; she lived her regression.

But it didn't last. After a year or so she reached a
compromise with herself and began consciously to manipulate her doctor and the hospital. She wouldn't talk to her
doctor about her emotional problems:

> Not that I wouldn't have liked to talk to him, I tried but

he just wouldn't hear where I was coming from, and I couldn't get through to him on anything relevant to my needs or problems, so when I did talk to him it was just to get my way or another privilege.

She managed to persuade him to give her a grounds pass, which finally allowed her to be out and around, on her own, from eight in the morning until ten at night. She used that privilege to have affairs with some of the black male aides. She also had a boyfriend in town who used to pick her up in the afternoon when she could slip away without being seen and take her to a pool hall.

I managed not to get caught for about ten months, and then one day I did get caught and once more I was restricted to my room and on trays and lost all my privileges again. The closets were locked again. So you see, treatment was something of a farce, it was more me trying to outsmart them and they trying to contain me.

She understands perfectly what was going on. She was trying her best to obtain some freedom of action on her own terms, while the hospital was intent on making her accept freedom as a reward granted only on the hospital's terms. It is indeed farcical to call such a battle of wills "treatment."

The farce went on for three and a half years, however, and that is a long time. It is almost equivalent to a college education; and under normal circumstances Sarah would have been going to college during just that time. But instead of being in a situation where she could learn and grow she found herself fighting for her very sense of herself as an autonomous human being, for what we can only call her identity, for Sarah, a person of such and such a character, somewhat crazy at times, like all of us, but very much her own person. "I am not a person to be pushed around and do things I do not believe in," she proudly states. "The only positive assertion of myself was to say *No.*" On that basis, on resistance, she built an admittedly difficult life, but a life she could call her own.

To a psychoanalyst, however, resistance is nothing but a manifestation of the patient's "disease." The approach to treatment at the Foundation is basically psychoanalytic, and it is instructive therefore to look at Sarah's resistance in that light. Sarah resisted "treatment" in all its forms and all such resistance, in the framework of psychoanalysis, arises from the ego's resistance to "cure." What this actually means is that the person the patient is, his personality, his "character," does not change easily or willingly. The person holds on to his "neurosis" or his "psychosis" because in a fundamental sense he *is* his "illness." To get rid of the "illness" means to give up all the defense mechanisms, the "symptoms," the whole structure of compromises the patient has made between his instinctual demands and the contradictory demands of the social world, and these compromises, in the psychoanalytic (and by extension the psychiatric) view, *are* the person. Thus psychiatry speaks of the neurotic and the schizophrenic, the manic-depressive, the hysteric, and not of the person *with* neurosis or schizophrenia or whatever. To "cure" the "illness," psychiatry must therefore restructure the patient's entire personality. And the patient always resists. Analysts expect resistances, in fact, and analyzing them is one of their basic techniques.

In traditional psychoanalysis the resistance is a resistance encountered in free association. At some point, as the patient lies on the couch and relaxes and the repressed impulses slowly rise up to consciousness, he may unaccountably falter, hesitate, then fall silent. He has broken the fundamental analytic rule of saying whatever comes to mind. Suddenly he has nothing to say. His defenses are at work and he is refusing to remember some key to the whole neurotic structure; he *cannot* remember, memory is no longer in his power. This silence may last for weeks, even months. But with many patients something else happens; inside the office they are silent but outside, in their lives, they begin to "act out" the unconcious impulses, the fantasy with the unspeakable name. They may become aggressive and attack someone without provocation, verbally or physically, leave their wives and take up with other women, quit jobs, or do something else totally out of character. They talk about it to their analysts, of course, and the analysts then know how to proceed, for "acting out" is as much material for analysis as dreams or slips of the tongue. "Acting out" is therefore intimately related to resistance, they are two sides of a coin, and many analysts implicitly or explicitly encourage their patients during periods of resistance to engage in "acting out" behavior in order to have something to analyze.[7]

The relevance of this piece of theory for Sarah's situation is clear. Ultimately psychoanalysis aims to destroy the patient's resistances entirely and expose his unconscious to full view. Sarah was not in analysis. But the Freudian paradigm rules psychiatry, it explains everything, and it is possible by applying the paradigm to Sarah to see her whole life at the Foundation as merely the flip side of her resistance to treatment, everything she did there, from sleeping with the black aides to running off to play pool, as the "acting out" of unconscious impulses. That is in fact how many psychiatrists see the lives of adolescents generally, as a period of crisis accompanied or caused by the "return of the repressed" infantile wishes and impulses, which the adolescent "acts out." We do not know what Sarah's doctor thought of her, but the theoretical weathervane at Menningers points steadily toward Vienna, and it seems safe to imagine him putting her resistance to treatment into the endless perspective of psychoanalysis. If her father could afford the "treatment," he could afford to wait. *Someday*, if the hospital kept the pressure on her long enough, and milieu therapy was de-

signed to do just that, the strength of her resistance, which
was the strength of her personality, which was the strength
of her "illness," would begin to crumble. She would sur-
render eventually. Three and a half years was as nothing
in that endless perspective. In another three and a half
years, she might actually talk to her doctor.

The hospital did keep the pressure on, and the pressure took its toll. Sarah did not give in, but she began—
who wouldn't?—to have doubts about herself.

> At one time Mrs. X who was a head nurse told me that
> I was the worst patient on the floor. She and other nurses
> and aides were always telling me that I was so ill that
> I would never be able to live outside of an institution.
> All these people and the circumstances and the
> restrictions and loss of freedom and ability to make my
> own decisions started to put doubts in my mind. I would
> ask doctor Y if I would ever get well. They never told
> me what my illness was. Dr. Y made it sound like I had
> this mysterious curse, dreaded illness and disease upon
> me, and was so vague about it and he offered no hope of
> ever overcoming it let alone a clue of what the problem
> was. And when my parents would come and visit me
> he would tell them in front of me like as if I had a ugly,
> almost impossible to treat, complicated "illness" a
> very grave matter. My parents would sigh, like it was the
> end of the world.

She begged her parents to get her out of there, but to no
avail. "My parents were thoroughly snowed by the impressive Dr. Y and the Menninger reputation." Sarah was
in a box.

Except for one factor. Kansas, like every other state,
has commitment laws. The law in Kansas states that a
voluntary adult patient, which Sarah was, could sign herself out of a mental hospital with five days' written notice.
While she was in the hospital Sarah had reached and
passed her twenty-first birthday; she did not need her

parents' permission to check out. So after three and a half years, despairing of any other means to gain her release, Sarah wrote the hospital authorities and informed them of her intention to leave five days hence.

More "resistance" on her part. Sarah had been resisting so long, we have to assume that the hospital simply did not take her seriously. The five-day period is intended to give the hospital time to institute formal involuntary commitment proceedings if it wishes. The Menninger powers that be let the five days pass without taking any action at all. On the fifth day, they locked Sarah up in seclusion and assigned an aide to watch her and make sure she didn't run away.

By now, however, Sarah had developed all the cunning of a cornered rat. Sarah managed to run away in spite of her guard. She got as far as the house of a friend some forty miles away. Her doctor found out where she was hiding and drove out with an aide and brought her back to the hospital. The best construction we can give the hospital's action is that they must have thought that fulfilling their "responsibility" for Sarah meant taking her back against her will. But in fact the hospital was acting in open contempt of the law. I would hesitate to call it kidnapping, yet the hospital had taken no action on Sarah's five-day letter, and she was therefore legally free.

But the legal protections most of us take for granted are rarely accorded to mental patients. Sarah was not finally released until the Menninger people received permission from her parents to release her, even though she had come of age.

On her own for the first time in nearly four years, Sarah set up house in nearby Kansas City with a black man she had met on the bus the first time she escaped. He was an escapee from Topeka State Hospital, which is just down the road from the Menninger Foundation. They

seem to have fallen in love and, according to Sarah's affidavit before a special committee of the Kansas legislature
investigating the commitment laws, they were even talking about getting married.

Sleeping with black aides ("acting out") is one thing,
but for the white daughter of wealthy parents to marry a
black man is something else altogether. In Kansas the law
states that any reputable person can petition the court
—the county probate court, to be precise—to have anyone
else committed to a mental hospital for "evaluation." The
reputable person need only state that he thinks someone
is "mentally ill"; the judge may then issue an order of
protective custody and send the police to bring the person
in. The law does not even require a statement from a
doctor concurring with the petition (or, conversely, reporting that the subject refuses to be examined), although a
judge may ask for such a statement; it is left to his dis-
cretion. When Sarah's parents heard that Sarah was living
with and planning to marry a black man they flew to
Kansas to confront them. Sarah believes her father ar-
ranged things with the local probate judge before they
even came to see her:

> I believe my father talked personally to Judge A. In my
> apartment my Mother & Father myself and Sam F_____
> were all together talking about my situation—Sam
> F_____ told my father—Please leave us alone—I love
> your daughter, I have been with her for 2 weeks and I
> haven't seen any indications of mental disturbances,
> my mother said to Sam—Sarah is very ill, she can't
> function, she's incompetent etc. and while we all argued,
> I saw my father pick up the telephone and place a call.
> In no time after he had placed the call—a police car
> came to the apartment—and two huge armed policemen
> knocked on my door, and they put handcuffs on me and
> put me in the police car and took me to the . . . jail
> and I was put behind bars for 4 hours, waiting for some

one to be available to drive me to Topeka State Hospital
—under protective custody.

After three and a half years of "treatment," two weeks of
freedom abruptly ended. Already Sarah's life is not the
life most of us want to imagine for our sons and daughters.
But Sarah's ordeal was just beginning.

When she was finally taken to Topeka State Hospital
a group of staff members gathered and gave Sarah what
we are already familiar with: a reality test. It must have
been fairly extensive, for it took about an hour. Then,
says Sarah,

> After about an hour with the staff they let me out of the
> room—I started to walk slowly down the hall when a
> nurse came from behind me, put her arm around me and
> said: "You're upset"—I turned around and looked at
> her, and then a whole squad of aides marched me down
> to the end of the hall—they stripped me naked except
> my panties—in the presence of male aides—Mr. C_____
> was present—and they put me in a seclusion room and
> locked the door.

Seclusion rooms in Kansas hospitals, as in most mental
hospitals, are equipped with a mattress and nothing more;
sometimes even the mattress is taken away. In this case,
however, there was a mattress on an iron bedstead. Sarah,
who was not upset when the nurse told her she was, now
became so.

> My first reaction was of anguish and despair and I
> one-time pounded the door with my fist and cried out
> pleadingly "Let me out!" No sooner had I uttered these
> words than I heard the rustle of keys at the door: and
> then they all came in with heavy restraints and chained
> me to the bed spread-eagled by my wrists and ankles in
> a very rough way: and one of the aides threatened me
> personally that she would knock the shit out of me if I
> gave any opposition—they locked the restraints with a

key and left me all night like that with the light burning
on all night in my eyes.

This is a true story. I have talked to other patients who
were on that ward with Sarah, and they verify what she
says. Incredibly the hospital staff left Sarah in that position, tied spread-eagle to the bedstead, the light burning
all night, wearing nothing but panties, for three weeks.
They let her up once a day to go to the bathroom.
When they fed her they untied one hand so that she could
roll halfway over on her side and feed herself awkwardly
from the tray. At the end of the three weeks they let her
loose altogether, but they did not let her out of the seclusion room for nine more months. Nothing else changed,
she still had no clothes, the light still burned all night
long, she had nothing to read, nothing to do, no one to
talk to. She was not allowed writing materials. During this
period she was committed indefinitely to the hospital,
although her doctor never visited her, spoke to her, or
communicated with her in any way in that time. After
nine months she was allowed out of her room, but only
on condition that she would do menial hospital labor, to
wit: she was "forced to scrub corners of the floors with a
toothbrush."

Men and women endure incredible tortures for the
sake of some vague but vital principle. James Mulligan,
an American prisoner of war in North Vietnam, was kept
in solitary confinement for twenty-six months in one
stretch; he was physically tortured, he wore leg irons for
sixteen months. When asked why, why he endured all this
rather than make a propaganda statement which would
have had no meaning anyway, he answered, "It's a moral
question—you stand up for your rights as a human being." [8]
It is indeed a moral question, a question which transcends
all considerations of psychology. Though he bomb North
Vietnamese villages a man does not forfeit his rights as

a human being. Though a person be "schizophrenic," whatever that means, eating dirt off the floor, exposing himself on the street, shitting on the living room rug, regressing, in other words, all the while denying his "illness" and resisting "treatment," yet he retains his rights as a human being. But in mental hospitals in Kansas, in New York, in Massachusetts, Ohio, and California, everywhere in the United States, what was done to Sarah has been and is being done to others right now. Sarah's "offense" was that she wanted to marry a black man. Others' may be that they talked to themselves on the street or threatened to commit suicide. For these "offenses" they are stripped of their clothes and their privacy, subjected to systematic indignities, deprived of their liberty. They are treated like animals, not human beings. It is a moral question, a question of basic human rights. No one has the right to treat another human being that way.

Sarah survived her "treatment." She escaped from Topeka State Hospital in 1972. She now lives in California where she is belatedly attending college. She has already had her education, however, an education in courage, in determination. Sarah may well be unbreakable. She has certainly paid her dues.

Sarah believes, incidentally, that her experience at the Menninger Foundation was worse than her experience at Topeka State:

> As compared to my experiences at Topeka State, Menningers was much more destructive and painful through its more subtle yet undermining techniques. In the state hospital faced with a harsh reality you had to work hard physically and otherwise to keep up with it. Menningers on the other hand led to a total disintegration of personality and personal autonomy.

But not a total disintegration: that is clearly wrong. When the psychoanalysts talk about "resistance," they acknowl-

edge "the existence of a residue." After they have penetrated the depths of someone's personality, explored all
of a person's defense mechanisms and analyzed away all
the resistances, something still remains:

> For Freud the question of *who resists* remains open and
> vexed. There is no getting around the fact that beyond
> the ego, 'which clings to its anticathexes', there lies a
> final obstacle to the work of analysis—a fundamental
> resistance about the nature of which Freud's hypotheses
> were at variance, but which, in any event, cannot be
> placed in the category of defensive operations.[9]

I am deeply tempted to claim for this "fundamental resistance" the status of that basic human quality I would
like to call "spirit." I would like to say that it represents
some ultimate in a person which psychiatric "treatment"
can never reach, much less restructure. "Yet, we truly shy
away," says Erik Erikson, "from any systematic discussion of human strength."[10] Perhaps it is better not to
name it; perhaps we should make no claims but merely
stick to the evidence of Sarah's experience. Sarah collapsed
under the pressure sometimes, but never totally. Always
there remained to her some quality, some "fundamental
resistance"; and this nameless human quality was her
salvation.

II

Sarah's imprisonment and torture at Topeka State
Hospital ought not to be taken as absolutely typical of
practices at mental hospitals everywhere in the United
States. The situation in Kansas is unusual. It enjoys the
reputation of having one of the best mental health systems
in the country, largely because of the Menninger presence, yet in fact it has one of the worst—largely because
of the Menninger presence. The Menningers use the
state system to train residents at the Menninger School

of Psychiatry; they get much of their clinical training at Topeka and Osawatomie State Hospitals. To maintain training standards the Foundation arranges joint appointments for certain psychiatrists who work in the state system; that is, they supplement the salaries of these psychiatrists. In effect this allows the state to continue paying low salaries to its psychiatrists generally. That is, the state relies on this supplementary income available from the Menningers to attract a few good psychiatrists to Kansas, while those who are not on the Menninger payroll get the measly sum (for a psychiatrist) of about $27,000 a year.[11] Thus there are two classes of psychiatrists in the Kansas State system, high-paid psychiatrists with joint appointments at the Foundation and low-paid psychiatrists. Many of the low-paid psychiatrists are, of course, not very capable. Some of them are brutal. The state's association with the Menningers, therefore—the fact, for example, that Walter Menninger is serving as clinical director of Topeka State Hospital—lends a surface respectability to the state's mental health reputation which it does not in any sense deserve.

The Menningers know about this situation but do nothing to alleviate it. In 1968 the aides at Topeka State Hospital staged a strike aimed not only at raising their own level of pay but at showing up the incompetence of the doctors and nurses above them. The first day of the strike they locked the nursing and psychiatric staff out of the wards in order to demonstrate how a mental hospital ought to be run.[12] It is irrelevant to blame aides when brutality exists. Aides in a mental hospital are powerless; when they treat patients brutally, their behavior is only a reflection of the attitudes of those above them. Roy Menninger admits that he lined up philosophically with the aides on the issues they raised in the strike, but he refused to take a public stand. He claims that coming down on their side of the fence would have angered the

legislature and made things even harder on the aides.
Perhaps. It would also have disturbed the Menningers'
cozy relationship with the state. The Menningers clearly
want to keep this the way it is. To this end Roy Menninger is wary about discussing the fact that the Foundation supplements the salary of state psychiatrists. When
asked about it, he said:

> That is correct but that is a fact I am not eager to
> answer. Generally it is no secret, but . . . it raises—it
> has been fairly clear and is acceptable but I'm sure that
> it creates potential problems from the state's point of
> view, if in any way this is perceived as the Foundation
> somehow muscling in on the state's authority and the
> state's prerogative. It's a delicate point, it's legal and
> it's correct, but it's potentially capable of being
> misunderstood. . . .[13]

So the Menningers cooperate with the state mental health
authorities: they don't make waves. And the state mental
health authorities cooperate in turn, training Menninger
residents. This kind of "joint back-scratching," as Roy
Menninger characterizes it, has helped create a system that
can tie people to mattresses for three weeks at a time.

But, though the systematic torture Sarah endured
may be more typical of Kansas than of many other states,
the rest that happened to her might have happened anywhere. Except for the torture, in fact, Sarah's case is so
routine that we hardly notice what *is* happening to her.
Sarah's father committed her to a mental hospital on the
basis of nothing more than his allegation that she was
"mentally ill" and "dangerous," an allegation he will
never have to prove in a court of law. With minor variations the same thing happens every day to people all over
the United States. The civil commitment process which
puts people in mental hospitals is so casual in most states,
so little surrounded by traditional legal safeguards, that
even a cursory inspection would seem to reveal its mani-

fest unconstitutionality. Mental patients have never been accorded the due process rights which the Supreme Court has been careful to guarantee to defendants in the criminal law. This is not the fault of the Court. One observer, writing in 1972, points out that up until then the Supreme Court had had occasion to rule on civil commitment statutes only three times, and two of those cases concerned people convicted of crimes.[14] In recent years legal efforts to seek relief for mental patients through the courts have been increasing, and several cases seem headed for the Supreme Court now.[15] Until such time, however, as the courts do start setting limits on the states' power to commit and start demanding legal safeguards on the commitment process, it is in all likelihood going to continue to be an easy thing to put somebody away.[16] For the mistaken assumption everywhere is that it is all for the patient's own good.

This assumption is so universally held that even in states where the commitment laws do provide safeguards the law is frequently ignored. In states which call for court hearings on all involuntary commitments the hearings are largely *pro forma* affairs at which patients are seldom present. Sometimes a phone call from a hospital psychiatrist is sufficient to obtain a court order committing someone. In spite of statutory provisions, right to counsel is ignored or else the counsel is a court-appointed attorney *ad litem* who sees his primary duty as guardianship in the traditional sense, looking out for the interests of someone he assumes to be incompetent. Even when a patient's attorney does want to make a hearing an adversary proceeding, as it is in criminal cases, the judge and the psychiatrist, working together in a routine conspiracy of good intentions, usually frustrate him. I talked to one young lawyer in a small town in Kansas who as a court appointee had recently represented a number of mental patients in commitment hearings. Being young and inexperienced, he assumed that due process applied here as elsewhere, and after the hospital psychiatrist had testified as to his first patient's "mental illness" the lawyer started to cross-examine him. Whereupon the horrified judge immediately interrupted: "We don't cross-examine psychiatrists here." [17]

To his credit this young lawyer did go on to cross-examine the psychiatrist and satisfy himself, at any rate, that his patient was indeed rather crazy. But the judge was clearly not interested. The judge was there essentially to legalize the opinion of the psychiatrist. In Kansas, then, though a patient has a right to a court hearing, the commitment decision is still, to all intents and purposes, left to psychiatrists. A mountain of evidence indicates that the same is true in most other states. For years psychiatrists have been campaigning to eliminate all legal controls on the commitment process. They disapprove of hearings because they believe court appearances traumatize the patient and start treatment off on the wrong foot. They want commitment decisions left entirely in their hands.[18] The issue is phony. Psychiatrists already control the commitment process.

The Kansas commitment statute is typical of the law in many other states, and it might be useful to look in more detail at how it is supposed to work, and then at how it actually works in practice.[19] As in many states, Kansas law provides for three kinds of patient status: informal, voluntary, and involuntary. "Informal" is a seldom used status in which a patient is admitted to the hospital without signing himself in and may leave at any time without giving notice; it is similar to the admission procedures of general hospitals and it is reserved for those rare patients the hospital psychiatrists believe have enough judgment not to leave the hospital "against medical advice." The voluntary patient, in contrast, signs himself in and must give the hospital five days' written notice before he can leave. This five-day interval, as we saw in Sarah's case, allows the hospital to institute involuntary commitment proceedings if it wishes. About 70 percent of the inpatients in Kansas state mental hospitals are voluntary, according to Dr. Haines, a high official in the state mental health system.[20] This figure reflects a growing trend toward voluntary admissions which is showing up nationwide.. We must be very careful, however, about drawing the happy conclusion from this trend that psychiatry is becoming less coercive. Szasz notes that

> Truly voluntary hospitalization is virtually nonexistent in public mental institutions in the United States. In some jurisdictions patients may be admitted on a "voluntary commitment," which means that they enter the hospital voluntarily rather than because of legal coercion. However, such persons are not free to leave the hospital, and their commitment is readily converted into an "involuntary" type. The distinction between voluntary and involuntary commitment is therefore not a significant one.[21]

The distinction is only significant when the patient is really free to leave whenever he thinks he is ready to leave. In many hospitals the moment when a patient turns in his three-day or five-day or ten-day letter, whatever it may be, announcing his intention to leave, is the moment the staff threatens to institute involuntary commitment procedures unless he "voluntarily" withdraws it.[22] Most patients do withdraw their letter. Or else they never submit it, knowing they have no real chance to get out.

In Kansas the third status, involuntary commitment, is further broken down, as in most states, into several different procedures designed to meet different circumstances. Under one procedure any "peace officer" may arrest someone he suspects of being "mentally ill" and take him to a mental hospital or other psychiatric facility for observation, applying afterward to a probate court for an order of protective custody to justify his action. "Any reputable person" may also apply for such an order if he thinks someone is likely to injure himself or others, that is, that he is "dangerous." If a probate court is not available to issue an order, a doctor's order suffices for hospitalization. If the person refuses to submit to a psychiatric examination, however, a statement to that effect by the petitioner will suffice. Under certain circumstances, in other words, virtually anyone in Kansas can easily arrange to have anyone else committed to a mental hospital for observation.

And this happens, and not just to the rebellious daughters of wealthy businessmen. I know of a case where a woman was having trouble in her neighborhood; she and her husband are extremely and outspokenly conservative politically, while the neighbors are liberal, and he, although he works in the Post Office, was able to afford a large addition to the house which made it much more conspicuous and attractive than the surrounding houses. The neighbors wanted to get rid of these people—I shall call them the Warrens—and started a harassment campaign. They threw stones and broke windows, they called the children names, they tried to get Mr. Warren fired from his job. When none of this worked, one of the neighbors signed a petition to get Mrs. Warren committed to Topeka State Hospital, the court routinely signed the order, as it routinely does, and the police came, broke down the door, and took her away in handcuffs. She spent two weeks in Topeka State Hospital. Hearings are held on involuntary commitments in Kansas but there is no statutory requirement that the patient be allowed to attend. This "patient" did not attend her own hearing.[23] We have already seen something of what these hearings are like. One observer, Dr. Louis Frydman, an associate professor of social welfare at Kansas University, comments on them:

In general, cases are rarely contested, hearings before a jury [a statutory right granted upon request] are rarely requested, habeas corpus petitions and appeals to district court are virtually unknown. At the hearings proper, the presence of the patient is rarely required, seemingly with the sole exception of Shawnee County,—in Douglas, Johnson, and Wyandotte counties it is reported to occur in less than 5% of the cases. As the presence of the hospital examiners seems rarely mandated, cross-examination is often not even possible. Hearsay evidence is accepted, the examiner's findings are not regarded to be a privileged communication even though the proposed patient was never made aware of this fact, and the standard of substantial evidence, rather than evidence beyond reasonable doubt, is used as the basis for a finding of mental illness. The hospital examiner is rarely of the opinion that no mental illness is present— a request for a ninety (90) day continuation is virtually pro forma.[24]

The whole process is *pro forma*. In Kansas, if someone accuses you of being crazy, it is more or less taken for granted all the way down the line that you are guilty. And the law is not designed to protect you. The law makes it as easy as possible to imprison you, because, if you are guilty of being crazy, obviously you need "treatment": that is, restraint, seclusion, and sometimes torture.

The Warrens, incidentally, still live in the same house, surrounded by the same neighbors.

The grounds upon which commitment is supposedly adjudicated in Kansas are as hazy and imprecise as the commitment process is casual. Only people who are "mentally ill" may be committed and the purpose of the probate hearing is to determine whether or not they are "mentally ill," but the definition of "mental illness" in Kansas law is so evasive as to defy definition altogether. A "mentally ill person" in Kansas is one who is "mentally impaired" to the extent that he is

. . . in need of care or treatment and who is or probably will become dangerous to himself or the person or property of others if not given care or treatment and

(A) who lacks sufficient understanding or capacity to make responsible decisions with respect to his need for care or treatment, or;

(B) who refuses to seek care or treament. . . .[25]

This definition means that you are "mentally ill" when you are "mentally impaired" and "dangerous" and don't realize it, or, if you do realize it, won't do anything about it. In effect, you are "mentally ill" if you refuse "care or treatment." If you recognize that you are "mentally ill," on the other hand, and seek "care or treatment," you are not "mentally ill." Louis Frydman has analyzed the implications of this nicely:

> The voluntary psychiatric in-patient, having sought care or treatment is legally assumed not to be mentally ill—should he desire to leave the hospital this might well be seen as his loss of capacity to determine his treatment needs and he may thus be determined to be mentally ill . . . Once he is legally determined to be mentally ill, he cannot in all likelihood be restored to voluntary status as a non-mentally ill patient unless he acknowledges being mentally ill. One has to declare himself to be mentally ill to protect himself from being adjudged to be mentally ill. Catch 22.[26]

You cannot win.

It is taken for granted in this definition of "mental illness," which is no more vague, by the way, than definitions of the term in most other states, that "mentally ill" people are dangerous. This is an ancient idea which no amount of evidence to the contrary seems able to destroy. Old metaphors of the insane live on, they are "wild beasts" or possessed of devils, they do not feel heat or cold like normal men, they are homicidal to a man, you can never predict what they will do.[27] They commit mass murders and other unspeakable crimes. The movies, television, the newspapers perpetuate this view: ESCAPED MANIAC RUNS AMOK, KILLS FIVE; in *Psycho* Anthony Perkins dresses in drag and murders his motel guests; in California it seems they do nothing but let loose dangerous paranoid schizophrenics who immediately go home and cut off their grandmothers' heads. I know people from the city who are afraid to come out to the country because of the madmen running loose in the hills. It is a joke, but it is no joke; the mental health system lives on these myths.

The facts are that those people who have been labeled "mentally ill" are probably no more dangerous than the general population and may be less so. I say "probably" because the evidence is uncertain. Early studies on the arrest rates of people who had been in mental hospitals, compared to the rates for the entire population, found that the hospitalization group was arrested up to five times *less* often than the general populace.[28] Later studies by Rappeport and Lassen and others, however, contradict these early findings.[29] Rappeport and Lassen found that, for some crimes, discharged patients were arrested about as often as the general population, while for two, robbery and rape, they were arrested more often. But the authors urge caution in interpreting these findings one way or the other. Arrest does not equal conviction, and ex-mental patients may be more prone to arrest than other groups precisely because they are ex-patients and thereby thought to be "dangerous." We have no way of telling, furthermore, which studies, the early or the later, are more accurate. What may be more to the point in the Rappeport and Lassen findings is that treatment in a mental hospital had no effect whatsoever on arrest rates; patients were arrested as often after hospitalization as before. "Treatment" would therefore appear to have no effect on "dangerousness," real or implied.

But the whole question of whether the "mentally ill"

are in actuality more or less dangerous than the populace at large is from a practical standpoint simply irrelevant. A person is not "dangerous" until he has actually committed a crime, but no one waits around for the "mentally ill" to commit crimes before committing them to mental hospitals. Commitment is based, as the Kansas law (and the law in many other states) makes clear, on the *probability* of dangerousness. It is based, that is, on psychiatric *predictions* of dangerousness rather than on evidence of actual dangerous acts which someone has performed.

Here the facts are clear and unmistakable. Psychiatrists cannot accurately predict whether or not someone will become dangerous. In an extensive review of the literature on this subject Alan Dershowitz (a professor of law) discovered general agreement not only that psychiatrists are grossly inaccurate in their predictions, but that they are less accurate than other professionals such as psychologists and social workers.[30] What the psychiatrists invariably do, it seems, is overpredict; they are much more likely than other professionals to think people "dangerous" who are not. And overprediction, of course, puts people in mental hospitals.[31] Macdonald conducted a follow-up study of one hundred people who had been committed to mental hospitals on the basis of threats to murder someone, and had then been released. Nearly two years after the study began only one had actually killed a person.[32] The thought that you might kill someone, the fantasies you might have about it, even the verbal threat, are very different from the actual deed. When it comes to the decision to commit someone, however, psychiatrists routinely ignore this distinction. Nearly every commentator on the subject notes the difficulty, the impossibility, of predicting when someone will translate his aggressive thoughts and fantasies into action. Yet psychiatry continues to commit hundreds to mental hospitals because a few might actually be violent.

Psychiatrists are aware of this tendency to overpredict

dangerousness, but they justify it with fearful stories about what would happen if they did not. Dr. Robert Haines told me a story about a former air force pilot he had as a patient when he was in charge of an outpatient service at Topeka State Hospital. The man owned an airplane and Haines wanted to find some way to ground him, as he thought the man ought not to be flying in his mental condition. Unfortunately the law protected the man's right to fly as long as "he was not, according to our narrow definitions of mental illness, psychotic" (yes, he said *"narrow* definitions"). Some weeks later the man took his twelve-year-old son up in the airplane, it crashed, and both of them were killed.[33] Every psychiatrist, it seems, has a story like this where he was not able to control someone's behavior, usually by committing him, and something terrible happened. It is always safer from the psychiatrist's point of view to commit people and prevent the possibility of violence. When they balance the liberty of the individual against *possible* danger to the community, liberty always loses.

Overprediction also results from the legal requirement that someone be adjudged dangerous before he can be committed. If a psychiatrist wants to get someone into "treatment," therefore, in many states he must find him dangerous even if he is obviously not. From what we have learned about the casual operation of the law we might expect this to happen frequently, and it does. Rubin notes that ". . . predicting dangerousness is just a convention to get someone to treatment. Once in treatment the concept of dangerousness is forgotten." [34] In Kansas, according to Louis Frydman,

> . . . what generally happens is that the psychiatric
> examiner limits his findings to mental illness
> considerations and ignores the issue of dangerousness
> but the probate judge nevertheless assumes that the

finding of mental illness entails dangerousness and feels bound to order involuntary detention and treatment.[35]

As far as protecting the rights of patients is concerned, then, the law is transparently inoperative. What the law protects, what it *enshrines,* is the predictive ability of psychiatrists. Which may be inaccurate, as Macdonald has shown, as often as ninety-nine times out of one hundred.

What is at stake here is not only the liberty of people labeled "mentally ill" but the liberty of all of us. It is a constitutional question; the law gives psychiatrists an amazing latitude to engage in a form of preventive detention, which in criminal law is generally regarded to be unconstitutional. (That is not to say it does not happen.) [36] Unfortunately commitment to a mental hospital is a civil procedure, not a criminal one, and a mental patient is not nearly so well protected as, say, an alleged murderer. "If a sociologist," an article in the *Harvard Law Review* points out,

> predicted that a person was eighty percent likely to commit a felonious act, no law would permit his confinement. On the other hand if a psychiatrist testified that a person was mentally ill and eighty percent likely to commit a dangerous act, the patient would be committed.[37]

This invocation of statistical probabilities is interesting; I know of no psychiatrist who would be willing to lay odds of any kind on the likelihood of someone committing a crime, even the most aggressive paranoid. But without just such precise statistical standards of dangerousness psychiatry must operate in a vacuum of uneducated guesses, anecdotes about pilots who may or may not have deliberately crashed their airplanes, and an inappropriate medical attitude that it is better when in doubt to treat someone for a nonexistent illness than not to treat him and see the illness flourish. The statistical standard in

criminal law is very high; it is summed up in the phrase
"beyond a reasonable doubt." In civil law the test is "the
preponderance of the evidence." Psychiatrists do not even
apply this standard. They are ignorant of legal standards
and they ignore them.[38]

The only remedy to this situation is the law. We certainly cannot rely on the good intentions of psychiatrists.
Either the commitment laws must be changed, or they
must be challenged in the courts on constitutional
grounds. Attacks on both these fronts are now moving
forward and they are having some effect. Recent court decisions have appreciably strengthened the rights of mental
patients, both limiting the grounds for commitment and
widening the grounds for release, and specifying the patient's rights within the hospital, including the basic right
to treatment. The best-known case is *Wyatt v. Stickney*,
in which Federal judge Frank Johnson ruled that if a
state deprives people of their liberty on the basis of their
need for treatment, then the state is obliged to provide
treatment commensurate with the need.[39] The suit was
brought against the state of Alabama, by any measure one
of the worst states in the Union when it comes to mental
health care,[40] and the court not only ruled that patients
had a right to treatment, it also set legal standards for
treatment which included mandatory staff/patient ratios,
individual treatment plans, and a humane environment.
Wyatt v. Stickney is now being appealed. Another case,
Lessard v. Schmidt, also on appeal, may have a heavy impact on commitment proceedings. In this case a Federal
court found Wisconsin's commitment law unconstitutional
on a variety of grounds. The dangerousness standard was
imprecise, the court found, and it ruled that a person may
be adjudged dangerous only on the basis of a recent overtly
dangerous act or a threat to do "substantial" harm to
himself or another. The burden of proof is on the government, which must present "clear, convincing evidence" of

dangerousness; the standard to be applied is "beyond a reasonable doubt." Patients must furthermore be informed that anything they say to a psychiatrist may be held against them; they have the right, in other words, to remain silent.[41] These are important carryovers from the criminal law. It is interesting and ironic that many of the precedents in this area stem from cases where criminally insane defendants, upon completion of their sentences, or (if found incompetent to stand trial) while being held pending trial, were civilly committed to state institutions for the criminally insane for indefinite periods of time. This is a way of sentencing people to what is essentially a prison without ever trying the case, and courts have been finding the procedure unconstitutional. Thus criminals, who are "known" to be dangerous, are being granted these protections before the "mentally ill," the dangerousness of whom remains at issue.

Cases such as *Wyatt v. Stickney* and *Lessard v. Schmidt* have highlighted the legal neglect of the "mentally ill," and action in this area continues to grow. The Mental Health Law Project has held seminars throughout the United States on mental health law for the benefit of lawyers, psychiatrists and other professionals.[42] The American Civil Liberties Union has a section on mental health law headed by Bruce Ennis, a leader in the field. Ennis has been involved in a considerable number of important cases, including *Wyatt v. Stickney*.[43] Recently the American Bar Association formed a Commission on the Rights of the Mentally Disabled. According to its news releases, the ABA will "no longer conduct studies of the subject" but intends now to become involved in "action-oriented programs." [44] All of this is long overdue. One of the most useful actions lawyers can take is vigorously to represent people who have been accused of being "mentally ill" and try to keep them out of mental hospitals. The evidence shows that when lawyers are present and active during the commitment process, the rate of involuntary commitments drops sharply, in some cases almost to nothing.

Paralleling the developments in the courts, a number of states have moved to liberalize their mental health codes. Massachusettes adopted a revised code in 1971, New York in 1973, and other states have been or appear to be following suit. Louis McGarry, reviewing the law in nine states, claims that ". . . what these new statutes have in common is a comprehensive attempt to correct the deficiencies of the past." [45] "Comprehensive" overstates the case; nevertheless, some gains have been made. Massachusetts is now basing involuntary commitments on a standard of dangerousness calling for the "likelihood of serious harm," [46] and the definition of this likelihood is at least somewhat more precise than the Kansas and other statutory definitions of dangerousness. The Massachusetts law also specifies that patients have the right to present independent psychiatric testimony to their sanity at hearings. It provides for periodic review of the case after a patient has been committed. Emergency commitments are restricted to ten days. The immediate impact of the Massachusetts law has been dramatic. The percentage of voluntary admissions rose in one year from 28 percent to 78 percent. Long-term involuntary civil commitments were cut to one fourth of what they had been. And total admissions fell 12 percent.[47] Two cheers.

The new New York law is somewhat less protective of patients' rights than the Massachusetts law, but New York has a unique agency called the Mental Health Information Service whose sole statutory mission is the protection of patients' rights. MHIS is a division of the Department of Justice in New York, not the Department of Mental Hygiene. It has a staff of lawyers who work in the state's mental institutions as patient representatives. The Service was instituted in 1965 and it appears to have had a genuine impact on *court* commitments, as distinguished from the two-physician commitments which are standard operating procedure in New York. At Bellevue in New York City the percentage of court commitments dropped from a high of 13 percent in 1965, when the Service came into being, to a low of 2.3 percent in 1969.[48]

Unfortunately there is some question about the benefits of this Service. In spite of its statutory mandate, MHIS lawyers sometimes wind up recommending the commitment of patients, or else they work with the hospital psychiatrists to persuade patients *not* to contest the two-physician commitment in court.[49] These lawyers are using their own judgment about a patient's need for hospitalization, in other words, which is like adding another psychiatrist to the two who have already decided the patient is crazy. Furthermore, the Service is badly understaffed. New York has more mental hospitals, more patients, and a larger mental health bureaucracy than any other state. Many New York mental hospitals have three thousand or four thousand patients, while Pilgrim State Hospital on Long Island, the largest mental hospital in the world, has well over seven thousand. Yet the MHIS averages about one lawyer to a hospital, and some of the smaller hospitals have to share a lawyer. The job is not the most prestigious in the world, either, and the quality of MHIS lawyers leaves something to be desired. I have heard numerous stories about their indifference to patients' complaints. Working in close contact over a period of years with hospital psychiatrists, it is only understandable that they would begin to adopt the indifference of psychiatrists. The MHIS experiment, it appears, is not all that effective.

The state most protective of the rights of patients during commitment proceedings is California. Nothing like the California mental health system exists elsewhere in the United States. In view of the liberalizing trend McGarry speaks about, many mental health administrators across the country believed until recently that eventually every state would follow the California model; in fact some of the administrators I talked to were openly defensive about the deficiencies of their systems in comparison to that model. The California system came under heavy attack in 1973, however, and the state has backed off recently from its announced intention to get out of the mental health business entirely. What tack the state will take next is anybody's guess.

The California model began to take shape in 1957 with the passage of the Short-Doyle Act, which encouraged the development of comprehensive mental health services at the county level as a way of keeping people out of the state mental hospitals. The population in California mental hospitals had been growing at the rate of one thousand patients a year, the hospitals were already badly overcrowded, and the state faced the prospect either of building new mental hospitals or of finding some other way to provide services to the "mentally ill." The state decided it would be cheaper and more therapeutic to encourage the development of local services. Short-Doyle set up a fifty-fifty matching grant system whereby the state paid half the costs of county programs. These programs were to provide both outpatient and inpatient services, as in the Federal community mental health center program which was not enacted until 1963, plus a spectrum of other services. The growth of the Short-Doyle system was slower than expected, however, largely because the counties found it too expensive, so the state gradually increased its share of the funding until it now stands at a ratio of 90 percent state funding to 10 percent county.[50]

The basic Short-Doyle program was implemented in 1969 by passage of the Lanterman-Petris-Short Act, which surrounded the commitment process with unprecedented restrictions. To encourage voluntary admissions to both county and state facilities, LPS removed the traditional requirement that a patient give a three-day, five-day, or ten-day notice of his intention to leave; now a voluntary mental patient in California can leave a facility whenever he wants to. Other states call this "informal" admission and seldom use it; California prefers it over all other admission procedures. Involuntary commitment is clearly intended only as a last-resort measure. A policeman on his own, or someone else with a court order, may cause someone to be detained in a county-designated facility for evalution and treatment, just as in Kansas and other states, but for a *maximum* of seventy-two hours. To be detained beyond that time, the person must be "gravely disabled" —that is, unable because of his mental condition to provide for his basic needs—or else a danger to self or others.[51] Even then he can only be committed for a maximum of fourteen days, and he is entitled to a court hearing on this detention, during which, as the law specifically states, he may present independent expert testimony on his own behalf. After the fourteen-day detention, the facility may apply for a ninety-day court commitment, but only on the grounds that the patient constitutes an "imminent danger" to himself or others. That means that he must at the minimum have threatened himself or someone else with substantial physical harm. The patient gets a hearing in court on a ninety-day commitment order whether he wants it or not.[52]

What counts, as we saw in Kansas, is not the protections the law provides, however stringent, but the way the law is administered. In California they take it seriously. The state wants the counties to develop their own facilities and keep people out of the state hospitals, and it works actively toward that goal. It is the national pattern, as we saw in the last chapter, for local facilities of all kinds, outpatient clinics, private psychiatrists or what have you, to pass their most difficult, intractable cases along to the state mental hospital, to dump them into the state's lap. California has been trying to reverse the pattern. The state even penalizes counties for every mental patient over a contracted number they send to a state hospital; the costs involved are subtracted from the state's share of the county's cost in the following budget year. On all fronts, then, legally, financially, and administratively, the state places the burden of care upon the county.

The result of this program has been virtually to empty California's mental hospitals. In 1963 the resident population in California mental hospitals numbered thirty-five thousand souls. In March, 1973, the figure stood at a little over seven thousand, and the state projected a further reduction to six thousand by July 1, 1974.[53] From 1963 to 1973 California shut down five large mental hospitals.[54] Two of them are now junior colleges, one is a county center.[55] The figures for the state of New York make an interesting comparison; with slightly less total population than California, New York has close to forty thousand resident mental patients in state hospitals, and New York, moving against a national trend, has recently completed one new mental hospital in Staten Island and is building another in Syracuse.

Some psychiatrists have criticized the California law. According to one psychiatrist the law has tended to criminalize "mentally disordered behavior"; society has limits to the behavior it will tolerate, and if it cannot commit people to mental hospitals it will force them into the criminal justice system. He presents no figures to substantiate this, but what he says makes sense; he fails to mention, however, that many people, particularly people who have had some experience with the mental health system, prefer to take their chances with the criminal justice systems. And he admits that ". . . criminalization of mentally disordered behavior is not totally without its positive aspects." It encourages people with mental problems to recognize that society does indeed set limits to behavior, and if they step over the line they will wind up in jail.[56]

But the most vociferous criticism of the law has come, surprisingly, not from psychiatrists but from two other sources: the people who lose their jobs when a state hospital closes; and a frightened public.

The state has been closing mental hospitals for several years, but the situation became a public issue in January, 1973, when Governor Ronald Reagan announced that the state planned to close *all* its hospitals for the "mentally ill" by 1977 and *all* its hospitals for the mentally retarded by 1982.[57] Reagan's anouncement, which took the California Legislature by surprise, mobilized a variety of organizations which had not previously had anything more concrete to attack than an unannounced trend toward closing the hospitals. Organized groups of the parents of retarded children became especially active, as did the California State Employees Association, which stood to lose sixteen thousand members if all the state hospitals closed. Under pressure from these and other organizations the California Senate formed a Select Committee on Proposed Phaseout of State Hospital Services, headed by Alfred Alquist, a Senator from the Bay Area city of San Jose. The problem posed by the state's policy is especially acute in San Jose; one thousand former mental patients, most of them discharged from Agnews State Hospital when its "mental illness" section closed, live in one twenty-square-block area of the city.

The Committee held a series of increasingly argumentative hearings from May to October, 1973. A series of particularly bloody murders were throwing these laws into high relief. It seemed as if all over California ex-mental patients, or people their families thought should be hospitalized as mental patients, were going on a rampage. In May of 1973 Charles Soper checked out of Camarillo State Hospital and two weeks later shot his wife and three of their five children before turning the gun on himself. Soper's crime occurred shortly after another man,

Edmund Kemper, had murdered his mother and a friend and mutilated his mother's body.[58] Soper's mother testified at the hearings, telling how she had repeatedly attempted to get her son committed to a state mental hospital; lacking concrete evidence of his "imminent dangerousness," however, the hospital would not take him. The TV stations taped her appearance, then packed up and left, ignoring the less dramatic but more substantive issues being raised.[59] Newspaper headlines milked the subject, too: SLAYINGS MOUNT AS MENTAL PATIENTS ROAM STREETS, one read.[60] Unfortunately there was some truth in them; the state acknowledged some sixty-nine murders, suicides, and "unfortunate accidents" attributed to ex-mental patients.[61] The Senators on the Committee were getting a great deal of mail about ex-mental patients wandering around molesting children, exposing themselves, talking to themselves. People seemed to find this bizarre public behavior almost as frightening as the murders the news media were exploiting. All the myths about the dangerousness of the insane were being confirmed.

The Committee recognized that the public reaction to the dangerousness issue was greatly exaggerated, but they could not fail to respond to it. Alan Short, a Senator from the Stockton area who had been involved in all the significant legislation with respect to the insane, objected that

> I have prosecuted many a person for murder and not a damn one of them had ever been in a state hospital. Not a one, that I can recall, had been to a psychiatrist before. I have friends, attorneys, judges, etc., that have committed suicide and God only knows that they would do a thing like this. I think that what we are asking the psychiatrists to do is really be God, and they can't do it. And it isn't fair to ask them to do it.[62]

And Andrew Robertson, who runs California's mental

health system, commented that of the many thousands of people who have been released from state mental hospitals under LPS, only a very few had actually committed dangerous acts.[63] But the public wanted the law changed, and the Committee is recommending to the Legislature that the definition of "dangerousness" be broadened. According to Paul O'Rourke, medical consultant to the Committee, they expect a major controversy with civil rights organizations over their recommendations, and O'Rourke acknowledges the difficulty of determining when a person is "dangerous." Nevertheless, the Committee feels it must respond to public demands. They intend to include evidence of delusions and hallucinations in the broadened definition and to give more leeway to psychiatric judgment.[64] The state is also responding to the pressure. On October 9 Andrew Robertson quietly announced that the eleven existing state mental hospitals and hospitals for the retarded would remain open "for the foreseeable future." [65]

What seems saddest about this turn of events is that the California system seemed to be working well, or at least it was beginning to work well. Some areas of the state, Santa Barbara County, for example, had managed to find services for all its mental patients at the local level; Santa Barbara was simply not sending any patients to state mental hospitals. Substantially the same was true in the Sacramento area.[66] Mental health professionals were generally behind the law; with some reservations centering mostly around funding problems, they thought the law was working. But the public was not buying it. The public wanted to be protected from all those dangerous lunatics. Even·in California, where people do yoga in the nude on the mountains of Big Sur, where eccentrics are as populous as in England, where every strange behavioral fad seems to originate, there is no room for crazy people. Paul O'Rourke calls them "the legion of the lost"; no one came forward at the Committee hearings to speak for them, none of the witnesses were mental patients or ex-mental patients.[67] Their legal fate was at stake, yet they were to have no voice in it. No group of people in America may have less power than mental patients.

V
Inside the Funny Farm

          though it is summer, and hot,
she is wearing a heavy terry-cloth robe,
sweating, with a thin metal chain around her neck:

that's all—
          she is assuring me
she wears nothing under the robe,

that to wear anything
would *limit* her, that the doctors tell her
to have an "identity"
          she must wear something—

"But I don't want an identity!

This way I'm *free.* . . . Everybody else
has a medal on their chain, with a picture

or name on it, but I don't—
this way
I'm not bound down. . . ."

With two hands
she begins to work the chain
around and around her neck, she soon gets
frantically excited,
          and finally the attendant leads her away . . .
          Frank Bidart, "The Arc" [1]

I

Most mental hospitals stand on the outskirts of obscure little towns located in the countryside. The original idea was to isolate the insane, remove them from the pressures and stresses of the environment that drove them crazy. The tranquility of rural life, it was believed, would calm them down; manual labor on the hospital farm would help them forget their troubles. The isolation of the hospital was also reassuring to society; it was as if, by putting them as far from view as possible, society could deny both the presence of the insane and the challenge to accepted social reality they represented. And so we have these giant red-brick architectural wonders which vaguely resemble great European chateaux, wing after wing stretching in this direction and that. And if you take a drive some Sunday afternoon into the country you may still come upon them, standing inexplicably in the middle of nowhere, formidable, indestructible, obviously portentous institutions. You drive by—it is beginning to rain, perhaps—and there on the lawn a man stands at attention singing.

The United States contains three hundred and twenty-four state and county, one hundred and ten Veterans Administration and one hundred and fifty-eight private mental hospitals.[2] The large state hospitals generally cover surprising amounts of ground, up to one thousand acres not being uncommon, and have as many as seventy or eighty buildings. Twenty years ago they contained well over half a million people and all those buildings were in use. Now the population nationwide at any one time stands closer to 300,000 and many of the buildings have been abandoned to vandals and the weather and it is an experience to visit these places and see the ruinous old buildings and the ruinous people wandering among them. You think there must have been a war.

If you walk around the grounds on a nice day, you will find yourself among the insane. It will be both difficult and easy to tell who they are: difficult because some of them walk, talk and act just like people you see on the streets every day; easy because you can usually tell them right away by their appearance. Their hair has been not so much cut as chopped. Some of the women wear too much rouge, or they smear their lipstick on with paintbrushes. But the main thing is their clothes. Something about their clothes is generally wrong. Perhaps the shoulders of a jacket stick up in a style that was popular in the 1940's. Or the stockings are rolled down to the ankles, and different colors. Or the shoes have been cut open to expose the toes. Or the old faded housedress doesn't fit. Or an overcoat is missing buttons. Or everything is inexpressibly baggy; the pants and jacket have obviously not been ironed in a long time. A sudden epiphany: of course—the clothing is all second- or third-hand. These are other people's clothes, discarded clothes given to the insane. The insane, you suddenly realize, have no clothes of their own. Their original clothing has worn away and they lack the means to obtain more. Unlike the rest of us they have no charge accounts at Macy's or I. Magnin's, they have no money, they don't shop and may have forgotten how, they are not consumers. So their families or the institutions clothe them with discards. Therefore nothing quite fits, nothing looks good on them. And you realize further that this is all highly appropriate. The insane themselves are discards, the absolute last-ditch losers, the very bottom of the ladder; it makes perfect sense to dress them badly, it tells you who they are.

You walk around the grounds on a nice day and you are surrounded by losers, by discards. It can be a very unsettling experience. If you watch visitors you notice that they seldom do walk around the grounds. They keep to their cars, sitting there impatiently while someone goes in to visit someone's brother, or else they walk straight to the building from the parking lot and they don't look at anyone. They encapsulate themselves. They are clearly not happy visiting. They come back less and less frequently as the years pass, they don't bring the children any more, they decide brother doesn't want visitors, it just upsets him to have visitors, it would be better to stay away. Visiting has become a meaningless ritual, they decide; besides, everyone knows the extended family is dead. The doctor has solemnly promised them that brother will never be well. Brother, who has lost everything else, has now lost his visitors. Once he was someone's brother. Now he is nobody.

All of this is somewhat painful for me to talk about because I know what these people have lost. It is not just their clothes or their visitors, or even their freedom, although these are terrible losses indeed. It is the sum of these things and more. What they have lost is their identity. The mental patient is a Jew in Nazi Germany, an Arab in Jerusalem. He is a nonperson. He has no status whatsoever. He is of absolutely no account. His very humanity is open to question. It seems to be an implicit function of these great impersonal institutions to make sure he has no illusions on that score. A man becomes a mental patient when he finds out he is nobody. If he comes to the hospital retaining some shred of dignity or pride, the hospital will strip him of it. If he tries to assert himself the hospital will drug him into nonentity. If he tries to deny his insanity, that will be taken as evidence of it; if he admits it, that also will be taken as evidence of it. It is a terrible thing to be alone and crazy and poor. It is worse, however, to be nobody. To exist, yet not to exist.

I know it is worse, through personal experience. I committed myself to Hudson River State Hospital in Poughkeepsie, New York, as part of the research for this book. Hudson River is a place such as those I have described. The grounds are extensive; there are fifty or sixty buildings representing the entire history of mental hospital architecture; the place houses nearly three thousand people. No one at Hudson River knew that I was there under false pretenses and I apologize for the deception, but it falls within an ancient and only slightly dishonorable tradition in the literature of the mental health system.[3] In any case, right or wrong, I did it, and in doing it I learned what it means—something of what it means—to lose your identity. I wanted a taste of the mental patient's "moral career," as Goffman calls it, the processing by which he is transformed from somebody into nobody.[4] I got a mouthful.

It took very little time to reduce me to a mental patient. I presented myself to the hospital on the pretense that I was hearing voices. I told them I had been separated from my wife for about a year and that I was hearing her voice over the radio accusing me of being lazy, useless, and incompetent: a failure. A friend I had supposedly been staying with brought me there, he explained to them, because I had smashed one of his radios and he was afraid I might become even more violent.[5] My act was a rough approximation of paranoid schizophrenia. I had no trouble at all gaining admission and it wasn't long before I found myself being led down a corridor by a very businesslike aide dressed in a white starched uniform.

Being led doesn't quite describe it. The aide walked off ahead of me and didn't bother to look back; he assumed, I suppose, that I would automatically follow. When I caught up to him he had opened the locked metal door to one of the wards with a large brass key. Inside was another corridor, this one at least forty yards long. It was about nine in the evening, the light was poor, the corridor dim. I followed the aide, who said nothing at all;

there was no sound except the sound of his footsteps and the jangle of his keys. The doors were all closed and there was nobody in sight. I remember telling myself that I had no choice but to follow the aide. We came to the end of the corridor and turned right and he let me into a locked shower room. Another aide appeared, an Irishman with a brogue, red hair, and a reassuring manner. I must be quiet and cooperative, I kept telling myself. I knew what happens to mental patients who cause trouble. They get beaten up, they get thrown into seclusion, they get juiced down with two or three thousand milligrams of Thorazine. I was quiet and cooperative.

Then the businesslike aide, the one who never smiled or even spoke to me except to give me orders, very professionally searched me. He checked the inside of my shirt collar, the flaps of my pockets, the little spaces where the belt connects to the buckle. He even found a tiny, wadded-up fragment of a Certs wrapper in the watch pocket of my blue jeans. Having searched my clothes, he told me to strip. Obediently, I stripped: I must be quiet and cooperative. Then he searched my body. The other aide stood by with a clipboard, taking notes. He must have been describing me: clipped beard, mole on left buttock. . . . I had still seen no one else on the ward, neither patients nor staff, just these two men. I was beginning to get frightened, very frightened, but I must be quiet and cooperative, there was still safety, perhaps, in being quiet and cooperative; yet nothing was happening to me besides this very thorough search. Then he was done, and the Irish aide told me to take a shower, and I did. I abandoned my privacy and took a shower, and while I showered the businesslike aide searched my belongings as thoroughly as he had searched my body. I cleaned and dried myself and waited for instructions. The Irish aide handed me a pair of hospital pajamas, which fit, and a hospital bathrobe which didn't. The bathrobe had no belt. Then he gave me slippers, half nylon, half canvas, which stretched to fit anybody's foot.

During all this procedure the two aides said very little to me, and later I came to see why. It wasn't because they disliked me or were trying to frighten me, although they did. It was simply that they were working. This was obviously routine procedure, a precaution they were required to take with every incoming patient to make sure he carried no drugs or weapons or other forbidden objects on his person. I was part of their work, the object they were working on, the thing to be processed. You don't normally talk to your work; if the work is routine, you don't even talk about it. You just do it.

The effect on me of what they took for granted, however, was startling. I did not understand it at the time, but the meaning of the process must have been sinking in regardless. I was an object, possibly dangerous, which had to be inspected; it might be concealing something, it could not be trusted and in any case it had to be described. So they searched it. It never occurred to them to explain to the object what they were doing; you don't explain things to objects, you give them orders. By falling in with this process I automatically dehumanized myself. I accepted the status of an object, the justice of the procedure. I was not to be trusted and therefore liable to search and seizure while they, who explained nothing, who routinely concealed their intentions, demanded and received trust *ex officio*. Naked, frightened, highly vulnerable, apparently I had no choice but to trust them. But I was not resentful. On the contrary, I was grateful that they did not hurt me, grateful that they had done their job so well. In fifteen minutes, the time I spent in the shower room, these two efficient, impersonal men had colonized me.

Within another fifteen minutes the process was complete. Clad now in hospital issue, clutching my bathrobe

around me, I was led back to the nurse's station where a
male nurse was waiting. I had still not seen another patient
and the ward was quiet except for the TV set I could
hear going now in another room. The nurse's station was
a small room off the long main corridor and the nurse
must have been on night duty for the whole building; in
any case I never saw him again. They sat me in a chair.
The nurse glanced at me, then gently replaced a strand
of hair which had fallen across my forehead. He turned to
prepare a syringe. The two aides chatted with each other
as if I didn't exist. I sat there wondering what was going
to happen to me next. I could see the package the drug
came from; it was Serentil, a drug I knew nothing about.
A tranquilizer? A sedative? I hoped it was a sedative, because I had little hope of sleep otherwise. On order, I
stood up and bent over. The nurse pulled down my
pajamas and gave me the syringe in the right buttock.
The aides chatted and gossiped, still as if I didn't exist.[6]
Then the Irish aide led me off to bed. It was all done
impersonally, disinterestedly; it was part of their job. To
them, I was simply a routine admission.

I have thought since about my automatic submission
to this dehumanizing procedure and why I did not protest, did not at the very least ask them what they were
doing or why. Any explanation—"This is just a precaution
we have to take with all new admissions"—would have re-
assured me. But I did not ask them for an explanation.
I fell in with their work. I am persuaded that most people
would do the same in that situation. We are trained from
birth to submit to authority, first in the home, then in
school, and only through a difficult unlearning experience
do we come, if we ever do some, to break the habit of
that response. In a stressful situation we relapse, most of
us, into infantilism, we allow others, those in command,
to make decisions for us, we look to them for our safety.
I was glad to cooperate with these men. My mind numbed

by half-acknowledged fantasies of homosexual rape and unprovoked beatings, I was relieved, more than relieved, to discover that I was only an object being processed through a bureaucratic routine. Relieved, I let them take me over.

It was the drug, however, which really took me over. Serentil is a powerful, fast-acting tranquilizer used for the immediate treatment of hallucinatory symptoms. It also has powerful side effects. I could not sleep after the aide put me to bed; the room was hot, the sheet kept sliding out from under me on the plastic-covered mattress, the other five men in the room were snoring and wheezing, and my mouth was drying out from the drug. After about an hour I got up for a drink of water and staggered out to the hall. But why am I staggering? I thought. What is happening to me? I couldn't control my legs. I was weaving back and forth like a drunk reaching for walls. Sweating and scared, I barely made it to the water fountain. I had no strength in my body at all. On the way back to bed I fell down twice.

Serentil: "Because of possible hypotensive reactions, caution in parenteral use is required." [7] Hypotensive refers to low blood pressure. What happened to me, I believe, is that a sudden drop in my blood pressure weakened me drastically, to the point of blacking out; walking to the water fountain brought me close to collapse. I draw no conclusions from this incident. The drug was not designed specifically to transform people into jellyfish. Nevertheless, there was no question of my giving the staff trouble while under its influence. I would have been as effective as the scarecrow in *The Wizard of Oz*.

Then they would not give me my clothes. I asked for them the next morning; they said that they had to be marked for identification purposes before I could have them. In fact they never marked them, it was a way of keeping me on the ward. I could not wander off in my

pajamas in the middle of January. Be quiet and cooperative, I was still telling myself, but I was getting upset. I
realized for the first time that I *needed* my clothes, they
were *essential* to me. Among strangers, dressed anony-
mously in hospital issue, I had lost access to my image.
To have no clothes is to have no front; it is like losing
the ability to smile. We so take our clothes for granted
we forget how important they are. It took two days to get
my clothes back, and I could not be quiet and cooperative
about it. I pestered the head nurse until he gave them to
me just to shut me up.

The staff continued not to explain anything to me. No
one took the trouble to tell me what the ward procedures
were. I was left to puzzle these out on my own. The
first morning, an aide switched on the lights in the bedroom at five-thirty, walked in the door and bellowed, "All
right, everybody up!" The others got up and immediately
made their beds. I did the same. Then the aide wheeled
in a cart piled with identical bedspreads and handed them
out. The bedspreads were put on in the morning and
taken off in the afternoon. When people had dressed they
shuffled out to the dayroom. We sat in the dayroom until
seven o'clock. Then a call to breakfast, served in the ward
dining room. I was still following where the others led.
After breakfast three or four patients mopped the dayroom
floor. The sun had just come up. Then an aide yelled,
"Medications!" and everybody lined up for their drugs.
I lined up, too. The day went on like this, periods of sitting
punctuated by meals and medications, doors locked and
unlocked at certain times, the whole ward clearly waiting
for something or clearly not waiting, I could not make up
my mind, but they were acting in concert, that was certain,
they were all sitting there marching to this routine.

It was Kafkaesque. I was full of questions: What were
the rules? How often did I get drugs and what were they?
Did I have any duties? Did people check in and out when

they left the ward? I was scheduled for drugs three times a day, but no one told me that; I found it out by accident. No one told me anything. I pieced the routine together, bit by bit, but I never found out why things were done one way rather than another. Apparently the whole routine had been ordained by God centuries ago.

These may sound like trivial complaints. No clothes, no orientation: so what? They hadn't thrown me in seclusion or strapped me to a bed for three weeks; they weren't threatening me with involuntary commitment; they weren't drugging me comatose. And yet that sort of violence might have been more acceptable. Violence at least announces its intentions; win or lose, you know who your enemies are. But here we had no enemies; we had keepers. We were animals or objects, certified losers, creatures of no significance to be herded through the day, to be managed and controlled. And we bought it. We were the most manageable group of people I had ever seen, better than any kindergarten class, better than cattle.

It is really very impressive when you think about it. The hospital had found a way to keep the wild crazy people in their care perpetually stunned, and they did it without resorting to violence. Drugs were part of it. The drugs, in fact, were extremely useful management tools; they could be used to punish difficult patients and they controlled the activity levels of all the patients. But drugs were not the whole story. What subdued us even more effectively was this mindless routine and our mindless participation in it. By treating us routinely as if we lacked the ability to make any choices for ourselves at all, little by little they persuaded us it was true. Subjected to a routinized disrespect and indifference, we began to believe something must indeed be wrong with us, something fundamental must be missing. We began to behave like the empty beings we were supposed to be. The routine had very effectively dehumanized us. It was not a dramatic process, but it was not trivial, either; dehumanization is never trivial.

It is important to understand that the aides and nurses who ran the ward were not cruel or violent people. It was never clear that they were our enemies; some of them even had good intentions. They were simply doing a job, which meant running the ward as efficiently as possible, with the least amount of trouble. They may not have known what effect their routines had on us. Functionaries in an enormous bureaucratic organization, they were half robots themselves; rules and regulations, carefully circumscribed powers, a carefully defined place in the hierarchy—these things constituted their lives. It made sense to them, no doubt, that we should live the same life, only lower down in the hierarchy, much lower, at the very bottom, in fact, where we plainly belonged.

I have been talking about the loss of identity. Erikson, who is the high priest of the subject, says that "an optimal sense of identity" entails such things as "a feeling of being at home in one's body, a sense of 'knowing where one is going,' and an inner assuredness of anticipated recognition from those who count." [8] It also entails the successful fulfillment of social roles. At one time the people on my ward had been chiropractors, laborers, salesmen, garage mechanics, sergeants in the Army. They had bought their own clothes. They had thought of themselves as someone's brother or husband or cousin, or all three together. They had been connected to the world. They had been free. They had had a future.

You understand the loss of these things when you realize that the hospital will go on forever just as it goes on now, with the same people or people like them sitting through an infinite retrogression of routine. The institution envisions no other future for the great majority of its patients. The basic attitude of the institution is that the status of mental patients is permanent and that realism

requires us to face that fact. To be sure, the hospital did
establish therapeutic goals for a few patients, a kind of
life plan reserved for those whose identity seemed sufficiently malleable to have their lives reshaped. For the rest
these plans were on the order of Freud's concept of normality, an "ideal fiction" out of their reach. But even the
life plans the hospital did set up constituted only the
most minimal kind of future. I was thought to be a hope-
ful case, for example, so the doctor assigned to it worked
up a life plan for me. She explained it to me in a public
conversation in the nurse's station a few days after I was
admitted. I say public because a nurse and two aides were
also present. I was to stay in the hospital three months or
so to stabilize my life, she said. When I seemed up to it
I would go to work in the hospital's "sheltered workshop"
where I would make boxes for IBM and be paid on a
piecework basis. When I had made enough boxes I would
then be moved to the halfway house in Kingston, across
the Hudson, where they would arrange a job for me in
a special place called Gateway Industries established for
the rehabilitation of mental patients. There I would presumably make more boxes. Eventually I might move out of
the halfway house into my own apartment.

It was no longer possible simply to be quiet and cooperative. She demanded an answer to this plan, and the
answer had to be no. I explained to her that the hospital
was getting me down. I wanted to get out, and as a voluntary patient I could leave on three days' notice. I didn't
like it there, I told her; I was going to contact my wife,
from whom I was supposed to be separated, and see if she
would take me back. I said all this not unpleasantly, but
nevertheless firmly. This was my plan; this was what I
was going to do.

The doctor reacted savagely to this. In front of our
visibly surprised audience she reminded me how anxious
and fearful I had been when I was admitted. Then she

started to wonder whether I wasn't in fact the person my wife had been describing over the radio. What made me think my wife would want me back? Didn't I think she would want a "real man" back, someone who could make it on his own? Was I "mature" enough not to become dependent on her? Didn't "maturity" mean putting off getting out of the hospital until I had regained some control, some direction? She went on in this vein, using against me everything I had told her about my supposed past in our initial interview a day or two before. She was relentless. By refusing "my" life plan I had apparently touched a nerve.

I think I know now what that nerve was. I was the patient, for one thing, and she was the doctor, the authority figure, and I was supposed to follow orders automatically because she knew best. But more than that, I think that in refusing the life plan I was refusing a way of life she identified with. She had her own life plan; she had perfected her identity within the context of a pseudomedical bureaucracy where she enjoyed a high measure of authority and recognition and might aspire to become someday a chief of service, in charge of a whole building, or perhaps even a Director.[9] That is what she *was*, a rising hospital psychiatrist. And something like that was her vision for her patients. We could not become psychiatrists, of course, but we might nevertheless aspire, the very best of us, to become makers of boxes or hospital aides or some other very minor functionary—and thereby gain an identity.[10] To her that was what the concept of identity meant; until you occupy a place in one of America's business or service institutions you have no identity, you *are* nobody. By refusing "my" plan I was not only questioning her authority, in a sense I was attacking her identity, denying, as it were, the ground of her being. So she tried to destroy me.

But what of those who had no future, who did not

merit even the attenuated life plan she established for me? What identity could they aspire to? None, none, none. The most they could hope to become were "good" patients, meek, submissive, anonymous. That was the future the hospital designed for them and it hardly mattered whether they lived it inside the hospital or at home or in some board-and-care facility. They were mental patients, they would always be mental patients. They had lost all rights to their identities, to their humanity.

My ward was full of "good" patients. They seldom spoke to each other, they almost never broke the rules, they sat through the day placidly, dutifully, they gave every sign of emptiness. They had no life plans. For them there was nothing: no plans, no therapy, no hope, only the dulling of consciousness that comes with months and years of tranquilizing drugs and an endless dehumanizing routine. Living that life for the eleven days I could bear it, I learned something about despair. It is not anguished and tormented; it is not defiant; it is not romantic or Faustian. Rather it is voiceless. It quietly watches television all day long. It reads a real estate handbook over and over again. It sleeps a great deal. All its days are the same.

II

The hospital's success in transforming crazy people into "good" patients was, in fact, one of the most disturbing aspects of my experience there. I expected the patients to be rebellious, to defy some of the more absurd rituals, at the very least to complain about them. It never happened. On the contrary, some of the patients seemed to have internalized the routine. I remember one man in a wheelchair who used to tour the ward every morning after we had made our beds and carefully straighten all the bedspreads to make them uniform. Then he would ask an aide to check his work. Although they humored him, the aides were obviously indifferent to this man's sad obsession with the bedspreads. They expected only that the beds be made. Making the beds was part of the routine; straightening the bedspreads was not. The bedspreads were put on in the morning and taken off in the afternoon. *That* was the routine, and it was beyond reason. We were simply to follow it. How well we did a job was immaterial; what mattered was our compliance.

Any spontaneous act of rebellion would have been welcome. But almost without exception the patients remained withdrawn and apathetic. No one protested, few patients even talked to each other. We were the victims of what is known in the psychiatric literature as "institutionalism," a word which almost explains itself. Abandoned in a large impersonal institution which systematically robs him of his identity and forces him into a dehumanizing routine, the mental patient withdraws from other people, loses interest in his environment,[11] eventually even loses his desire to leave the hospital.

For years these effects of prolonged institutionalization were thought to be the end state of chronic schizophrenia. Lack of affect, withdrawal, *la belle indifférence* were symptoms of a "disease," manifestations of a supposed "schizophrenic deficit." Now, however, the consensus is that institutional life itself is responsible for these "symptoms." J. K. Wing and G. W. Brown, who went to great lengths to test the phenomenon scientifically in a comparative study of three British mental hospitals, conclude that

> The various stages of this study point towards a conclusion which is very difficult to resist—that a substantial proportion, though by no means all, of the morbidity shown by long-stay schizophrenic patients in mental hospitals is a product of their environment.[12]

Wing and Brown are only the latest in a long line of

investigators who have studied the obvious connections between the structure of the hospital environment and the behavior of those who live in that environment. Since Stanton and Schwartz published their book, *The Mental Hospital,* in 1954, a great deal of work has been done describing the effects of bureaucratic structure, formal and informal communication networks, patient cultures and staff cultures, patient-staff interaction and avoidance patterns, and so on, on mental patient behavior.[13] Goffman's well-known book *Asylums* is perhaps the most prominent in the line. Almost all of this work has been directed to finding ways to improve the intrahospital situation.

Interest in the subject has faded, however, since the 1960's. The advent of tranquilizing drugs in the mid-1950's made possible a substantial reduction in the number of long-term patients. The average daily census of United States mental hospitals has been dropping steadily for about twenty years, even though admission rates have been rising. This fact, plus the development of the community mental health movement in the early 1960's, made it seem as if the mental hospitals would eventually wither away; drug management of patients in the community and the availability of community mental health centers would obviate the need for them. It was no longer necessary, therefore, to think and write about mental hospital problems.

Unfortunately history has not followed this utopian design. We have more mental hospitals now than we had twenty years ago. The admission rates are still rising. There are indications that the average daily census is bottoming out. Community mental health centers have not been uniformly successful in preventing hospitalization, nor are there enough of them to have had a significant impact on the structure of the mental health system as a whole. Everything points not only to the continued existence of mental hospitals, but to their continued use by society as the favorite dump for those people we decide are crazy. The mental hospitals are not going to disappear.[14]

Mental hospitals are simply too useful to society. Robert Edwalds describes the mental hospital as having two social functions, a "primary" function *"demanded* of the institution by society" and a "secondary" function "characterized by *hope."* [15] Society hopes the institution will carry out the secondary function in addition to the primary, but it insists that it carry out the primary, which Edwalds describes as follows:

> Primary functions demanded of the state mental hospital have included (A) public safety and the removal from society of individuals exhibiting certain kinds of socially disruptive behavior; (B) custodial care for persons who, by reason of mental disorder, cannot care for themselves or be cared for elsewhere. These primary functions have not really changed over the past 100 years; "change" has occurred chiefly with regard to our lack of candor concerning them.[16]

The secondary function, of course, is treatment and rehabilitation of the insane, the function generally called therapeutic. Psychiatric rhetoric has been trying for decades to persuade us that the therapeutic function is in fact primary, "leading," as Edwalds dryly notes, "to a remarkable amount of self-deception and confusion on the part of society and the personnel working in these hospitals." [17] In fact it is plainly not primary. The mental hospital is essentially what we want it to be, and we want an institution which will take disturbing people off our hands. We want someone else to take custody of them. Only a change in attitude on *our* part will eliminate the need for such custodial institutions; and it would be utopian indeed to hope for such a change.

It is their social function which leads to the kind of experience I described in the first section of this chapter, and to the kind I will describe later on. The primary function of the hospital is custodial; the mental hospital confines and maintains people, it locks them up and takes responsibility for all their physical needs. It not only feeds and shelters them, it cleans their clothes and provides clothes if necessary, it provides recreational, dental, medical, and other services, it provides toilet paper, toothbrushes and toothpaste, it takes care of everything. It does so on the assumption that crazy people are incapable of meeting their own needs, an assumption which neatly fits in with the institution's need to operate as efficiently as possible.[18] Thus the typical mental hospital prepares meals in a central kitchen, or a kitchen in the basement of each building, and sends them up on steam trays to the ward dining rooms; the meals arrive and the patients eat at prescribed times every day. This is more efficient (and cheaper) than having a restaurant or restaurants patients might patronize at will and it also ensures that every patient eats, the assumption being that patients will not eat unless the hospital feeds them.

Since most people in the hospital are (or once were) fully capable of deciding for themselves what and when to eat, the hospital has to allow for the possibility that some patients will resist this assumption of incapacity. This is one function of the identity rape new patients experience. The hospital must pacify patients who resist being assumed incompetent. It is more efficient to pacify patients in advance, at the time of admission. Here is where the medical model comes in handy. If crazy people are "sick," it becomes appropriate to assign them to the "sick role" we talked about in Chapter Three; they must become, that is, passive, cooperative recipients of care. They must see themselves as "patients" whose role in the hospital is to "get well." Getting well is defined, however, not in medical but in behavioral terms; a patient gets well or better when he learns to behave himself properly, when he learns to "take some responsibility for himself." But the institution has provided for his every need, so he has no opportunity to take responsibility for himself. Therefore he can never "get well."

course, is designed to
its custodial function.
al. The hierarchy is not
in most bureaucracies,
izations, corresponding
to its primary and sec-
ture is custodial; it ful-
oys primary responsibil-
p with the hospital ad-
e a psychiatrist; usually
al Director as well, i.e.,
ing both line and staff.
descends from him into
s such as food service,
nursing service, which
ce has its own hierarchy,
top, one or two super-
f nurses, and at the very
st contact with patients
ization; it seems to be a
this sort that status in-
ient.[20]
sional and stands in an
he line organization. To
utic function of the hos-
eful distinction between
ng to the distinction be-
tween staff and line functions.[21] Generally, the professional enjoys a certain authority in an organization by virtue of his specialized knowledge, his long and difficult training. But he may not have as much power as someone operating in the organization's administrative line. The

psychiatrist, of course, is the supreme professional in the staff structure, followed by psychologists, social workers, occupational therapists, and other therapeutic specialists. We are used to thinking of psychiatrists as having absolute power in the mental health system, and this is largely the case. In the subsystem of the mental hospital, however, any given psychiatrist may have considerably less power than any given head nurse. He may be granted more prestige, a correlate of his greater authority; but when it comes to controlling the life of his patients, the head nurse usually outranks him.

These distinctions are not always visible, to be sure. Sometimes the line and staff functions merge at certain points in the hierarchy. A chief of service may have full control, at least on paper, over the nursing staff in his building, as well as over the professional staff. Or he may not. His control may be limited entirely to the psychiatrists on the service; the psychologists may have their own hierarchy, answerable only to the Clinical Director, or possibly the administrator. Sometimes psychiatrists are in nominal charge of a ward (or wards) and presumably control the nursing staff on that ward. These practices differ from hospital to hospital; sometimes from Unit to Unit if the hospital has been unitized, or even from ward to ward.[22] At Hudson River psychiatrists were assigned patients at random as they were admitted and might have patients all over a building; they had no control at all over ward life. At Topeka State Hospital psychiatrists were assigned to wards, not to patients. It makes little difference, nevertheless, whether or not the staff, the professionals, are given line control. Even when they do have line power they tend to abdicate it.

This is understandable. Nothing in a psychiatrist's training fits him to run a ward. The psychiatrist has been trained as a therapist, an expert; he sees his function as the "treatment" of "sick" patients, all with their highly

individual psychopathologies, their unique pathogenic histories. Patients live in the hospital, but from the psychiatrist's point of view this is a matter of little moment,
merely a confirmation of their clinical histories. His job
is to intervene in the patient's life in the therapeutic
setting of the group therapy room and to prescribe the
proper drugs, or, if the patient is not suitable for therapy,
as most of them are not, simply to prescribe the drugs.
The average hospital psychiatrist sees no connection between ward life and his therapeutic role.[23] So he avoids
administrative responsibility for the ward even when it
is given to him; indeed, he even avoids the wards physically as much as he can. At Hudson River doctors make
grand rounds on Monday mornings, staying on each ward
for perhaps five minutes. I never saw a doctor on the
ward at any other time.[24]

This leaves ward life in the hands of nurses and aides:
people famously rigid and authoritarian in their attitudes.
These attitudes ought not to be seen as aspects of their
personalities, however; they are role attributes, they come
with the job. Consider the lowly aide. In city mental hospitals he is frequently black; in the country hospitals he
may be the son of a farmer. In any case he tends to come
from the lower or lower-middle class and to have no education beyond high school. The job pays very little, perhaps $8,000 a year on the average, and there is no real op-
portunity for advancement, unless the aide goes to nursing
school. There is, however, great job security. The job is
so unattractive that the aide need not worry about being
fired.

Since the aide has no training and little education,
the hospital does not expect much from him. In fact, the
hospital assumes that he is incapable of operating effectively without very close supervision, and it circumscribes
his sphere of action with detailed rules and regulations.
The aide is not alone in this situation; the nurses too are

governed by rules and regulations. In fact, much of the work of the hospital concerns the carrying out of rules and the minor changes in them which sift down continuously through the administrative hierarchy. The hospital is a bureaucracy, after all, and that is how bureaucracies function.

It is only natural that the aide and the nurses above him should develop attitudes commensurate with their inflexible roles. They become subject to what the literature calls "goal displacement." In time the nursing personnel come to see the rules and regulations and the hospital routine, which were originally means to an end—the efficient operation of the hospital—as ends in themselves. As Robert K. Merton describes the process,

> Adherence to the rules, originally conceived as a means, becomes transformed into an end-in-itself; there occurs the familiar process of *displacement of goals* whereby "an instrumental value becomes a terminal value."
> Discipline, readily interpreted as conformance with regulations, whatever the situation, is seen not as a measure designed for specific purposes but becomes an immediate value in the life-organization of the bureaucrat. This emphasis, resulting from the displacement of the original goals, develops into rigidities and an inability to adjust readily. Formalism, even ritualism, ensues with an unchallenged insistence upon punctilious adherence to formalized procedures.[25]

It is a process familiar to anyone who has worked in a large organization or has had to deal with one. The patients are only patients, but the institution goes on forever:

Indeed, the patient, who is a prisoner of the institution, not a participant in it, must bear the accumulated burden of the entire organization's displacement of goals.[26] All the rules and regulations, intended as bulwarks of efficient operation, serve ultimately to ritualize his life. The nursing personnel, particularly the aides, who have the greatest responsibility for controlling patient behavior, tend to regard this as particularly fitting. The mental patient is a person whose unreliable (rule-free) behavior and lack of discipline are precisely his problem. By definition he cannot manage his own life; it becomes incumbent upon the institution, therefore, to manage it for him, even to the last detail. In this view of things it makes a certain kind of sense to structure hospital life along the most inflexible, rule-bound lines, to treat everyone impersonally, to adhere to a rigid routine. This structure is natural to bureaucracies. In a mental hospital it may come to seem not only natural but necessary, an essential corrective to the dangerous unruliness of the insane.

The consequence of all this is an existence on the wards which forces patients into a pathological relation to time. In normal life, time is submerged in movement, activity, and intentionality. Life is purposive, we have goals, and time assumes importance only in relation to those goals. On the mental hospital ward the ritualization of existence, the displacement of intentionality from ends to means, severs this relation between time and our activity in time. Time becomes a thing apart, heavy, palpable, insupportable. The night aides wake us up at five thirty A.M.; the daytime staff begins to appear by six thirty, so to distribute the work load more evenly the night aides wake us up. It is still dark; there is no hint of the dawn. Hostility runs high, breakfast is not until seven o'clock, there is nothing for thirty-five men to do but get out of bed, move to the dayroom, and wait. A young man called Peter sits in the lotus position and tries to meditate, but someone is complaining about something out loud and he cannot think. "Keep it to yourself!" he shouts at him. That might be the ward motto. An old man, a Russian who speaks no English and shits in his pants and frequently has to be tied into a chair because he goes to sleep in other people's beds, wanders the room restlessly while a man with a face shaped like a hawk's, a former Army sergeant, harasses him. The hawk is always harassing him; the old Russian is the only one left he can tell what to do.

Another young man named Michael steadily shoves cassettes into his tape recorder. It is all hard rock music. Michael never listens to a song all the way through. He has been in and out of mental hospitals twelve times and knows how to get by but he still hates it, he is perpetually angry. Still another young man sits by himself and waits to go to work. He is one of the few with a life plan, he is working now at Gateway Industries, he has bought the garbage, in other words, and even when he is with us he seems not to be with us, as if he were suspended in the ward on wires, a bathysphere, just dropping in. Occasionally he lectures us about getting our heads together. Alcoholic Eddie has been trying to do that, dreaming up life plans of his own; he will train to be a trucker when he gets out, or he will move to Pennsylvania, he will wait on tables or wash dishes, he will do something *but he must get out.* The young men all want to get out. The old men just sit there; nobody knows what they want.

Only a few patients give any sign of being crazy. A man named Carpelli walks around muttering to himself and eats little but bread, great stacks of it. The old Russian is probably senile, but nobody speaks Russian so nobody knows.[27] An Irishman in a semistupor eats pieces of dirt off the floor. The sun rises shortly before seven o'clock. The aides stay away from us; they are busy dressing the man who is paralyzed; they are changing shifts; they are following their routine. It is early morning but the day already seems endless.

At seven thirty, immediately after breakfast, the day's first drugs are given out and the dayroom calms down. There is finally something to do: the floors must be mopped. Three or four patients get mops and buckets, the rest of us move our chairs first to one side of the room, then to the other, and the floors are mopped. The same patients do it every day, directed by the hawk, of course. Later an aide will mop them all over again. The huge color television set which dominates the room goes on about eight A.M. and plays continuously until late at night. Sometimes Michael, who hates the television set, plays his rock music in competition with it and the din becomes unbearable, nearly unbearable. But after eight o'clock or nine o'clock he wanders off if his ground privileges have not been taken away, talks to his friends, meets his lover on the female ward. Half the ward wanders off; only the older men and the zombies stay in the dayroom watching television or just sitting there, one or two still in their pajamas. One man never gets dressed. He is fussy, he does not walk but minces; he may be there because homosexuality was until recently a "mental illness." He is one of those who does nothing all day long, never leaves the ward, never talks to anyone. He neither reads nor watches television. He is a "good" patient.

The day wears away. The day is rock eroding. Time becomes geologic in scope. A large clock stands on the wall above the door. The day accumulates, ice building up on the surface of a lake. There is nothing to do.

There is nothing to do.

A small bookcase stands in a corner but the fifth-hand books in it look unreadable. We have a pool table but no reason to play. Only the television plays. In the afternoon two aides play cards with two old patients who have been there for many years. I look for magazines, I start a jigsaw puzzle, I take notes in my notebook or write a letter to a friend or repair to my bed, the only place I can be alone, and read. I am desperate for distraction. At four o'clock the bedroom doors are locked and we are confined to dayroom and corridor, all of us together again. Michael is

back with his tape recorder, the television is turned up,
the noise level rises and I am going crazy, I pace the corridor, try vainly to read or watch the TV, praying for
dinner, for anything. Day after day repeats itself like this,
each day a mirror to the last. The days become abstrac-
tions.

Many of the quiet older patients seemed almost con-
tented with this life and you could not help wondering
what had brought them to that state. But in fact it is possible to become accustomed to the routine. I interviewed
a man named Sam who spent eight and a half years in
Kings Park State Hospital on Long Island. Sam is a beautiful round man with a great halo of pure white hair and
beard circling his face. Foregoing theories or explanations,
he described matter-of-factly to me the three or four times
he went crazy and started having delusions.

> . . . in the normally accepted sense of the term, I was
> insane. I don't agree with . . . the people who say there
> is no such thing as insanity. . . . I think you can get into
> a state where you are a danger to yourself, not only to
> yourself but you are dangerous to people around you.[28]

The first time he thought he was a superman who was
going to gather other supermen together and lead them to
another planet, leaving women behind, and "surgically
making it possible for men to bear their own children.
. . . That's how fed up I was with civilization, women in
particular." He was violent enough during this period
that the staff at the mental hospital locked him in seclusion "naked with a mattress," as Sam puts it, and he tore
holes in the mattress with his teeth. Sam indeed knows
that people sometimes go crazy.

But Sam's episodes of insanity seldom lasted very
long. He describes himself as being ordinarily a quiet, in-
troverted man who prefers solitude and reading to company and conversation. Until he went crazy he led a

conventional life, working in machine shops, going to school nights for a degree in mechanical engineering, getting married, having a child, buying a house in Brooklyn. That life fell apart, though, when he fell apart. The first episode lasted, he says, about a year, long enough to break up his marriage and his career. After that he went insane twice more and finally wound up at Kings Park. The second and third episodes were brief, however, and at Kings Park he was "fairly back to normal" after three or four months.

Back to normal and anxious to leave. "I tried to get out, I wanted to get out of the hospital, see, I wanted to get out and back in the rat race I'd been in all my life." But his first doctor, who was ready to let him go, was transferred, the second doctor went on a long vacation, and before too long Sam started to get used to the life. He had a pal, they both had grounds privileges, and he and his pal would skip lunch, go to a nearby bar, and spend the day drinking beer behind the bar, having a good time. They took to going on picnics, they even went to the beach on weekends. It was all strictly against the rules, of course, and Sam was a quiet, conventional man at heart, a man who believed in rules. But the rat race must have seemed less and less desirable after a while.

Then Sam and his pal got roaring drunk one day and the police caught them building a huge bonfire in Sunken Meadow Park. That cost Sam his grounds privileges; he was thrown on a locked ward. From there he went to the violent ward when he casually mentioned the possibility of escape within earshot of an aide. He didn't leave the building for two solid years. Two solid years on a ward much like mine at Hudson River, I imagine. Sam adjusted to the life all too well:

> . . . for almost five years I did nothing but sit and look at television morning, noon and night. . . . I stopped

brushing my teeth. All my teeth broke off, one fell out.
I stopped taking showers. . . . I spent all my time
looking at television, reading. I had everything I wanted.

Even after Sam got his grounds privileges back he seldom
used them.

The only time I'd leave the ward was to go to another
building nearby where they had a candy machine to get
candy. I had grounds privileges, I could go anywhere,
but I didn't use them. The funny part, the screwy part of
this whole system is that all of this time, most of this
time, they were still giving me Thorazine. Even after I
had become . . . institutionalized.

After five years they finally stopped the Thorazine. Sam,
after all, was as tranquil as anyone could ever want him
to be. During all those years the staff left Sam alone; they
made no effort to remotivate him:

About once a year the doctor would come around and
he'd say, "Do you want to get out?" and I'd say, "No, I'm
institutionalized, I have no desire to get out." And
he'd just leave it at that.

No longer delusional, no longer agitated, back to his quiet,
normal self, Sam might nevertheless be there still had not
someone thrown a pair of shoes at him. Sam was "institutionalized." He had gotten used to the life.

Fortunately for Sam, however, someone threw a pair
of shoes at him.

Then about two years before I got out a guy came over
to me one day, this guy was an orderly, he threw a pair
of shoes at me. I had been wearing slippers for a whole
year. I hadn't been wearing shoes at all, because the only
time I went out was to go over to the dining hall which
was a hundred feet away and it was a tunnel to go
through when the weather was bad so you didn't have to
wear shoes if you didn't want to. So he said, "You're
going to work in the kitchen." In the kitchen you have

to serve, and afterward you help clean up. You work
maybe four and a half hours a day. You work fairly hard.
And that's what started to snap me out of it.

The pattern was broken. A new doctor noticed that Sam,
perfectly sane, had no business being in the hospital and
he started trying to persuade him to leave. A social worker
noticed how much money he had in his savings account
and told him he could make it outside without much
trouble if he went on welfare. Finally Sam left Kings Park.
He had been out two years when I talked to him. At first
the change excited him and he was delusional for a while,
living alone in a small room, but he has friends now, he
sees people frequently, and as he puts it, "For a year and
a half now I've been pretty fucking normal." Except, perhaps, for that great halo of white hair, which makes him
look like a highly improbable Santa Claus.

Some people grow accustomed to the life. Sam talks
about being "institutionalized," substantiating the claim
of Wing and Brown that most of the "symptoms" of
chronic schizophrenia are in fact the result of living in
the sterile, deprived environment of the mental hospital.
Braginsky and his colleagues look at the matter somewhat
differently; in their view long-term patients are not so
much victims of the mental hospital as users of it. It has
become their home, a place which fills their needs and provides them with a very real sense of security. In order not
to jeopardize their place there mental patients, they say,
manipulate the staff through "impression management,"
matching the signs and symptoms of their "illness" with
staff expectations:

> When the self-interest of patients is at stake, they can
> present themselves convincingly as either "sick" or
> "healthy" depending on which mode of self-presentation
> is believed to increase the probability of desired
> outcomes.[29]

Summing up their research, they state:

> Mental patients, for all their pathology, are in most
> respects, most of the time, just like the rest of us; they
> want to live in a mental hospital in the same way that
> ordinary persons want to live in their own community—
> that is, they can be expected to try to satisfy their needs
> and, to a considerable extent, to be able to do so.[30]

Perhaps both interpretations are correct. Patients become institutionalized, withdraw into impenetrable emotionless shells, lose interest in leaving the hospital, because the hospital induces and reinforces this kind of response, and then this becomes their life, the only life they know or can hope for, and they quite naturally become attached to it. It is at least secure. No one makes demands on the mental patient. He knows what to expect, even if it is nothing. Besides, as Goffman reports at length, the hospital has an underlife, what we might call extracurricular satisfactions.[31] Sam made a life for himself against the rules. Drinking, the trips to the beach, the picnics: patients do similar things in every mental hospital. Sarah managed an active sex life at such a controlling institution as the Menninger Foundation. At Hudson River, Michael, who was handsome and aggressive, acquired several girl friends: he was one of four or five patients on the ward with a private room and he occasionally used it for sex, as he also occasionally used the visitors' room. Patients went out and got drunk; marijuana was available in a pinch, if you had enough money. How extensive this underlife becomes depends, of course, on the hospital's watchfulness in controlling it. At some institutions it may be limited to carrying matches, which patients are not supposed to have. But people always find ways to give themselves a little elbow room, even in the most restricting situations. Mental patients are no less adept at this than prisoners, privates in the Army, high school students, or anyone else subject to rigid institutions.

But the fact that some people make a kind of surreptitious life for themselves in the mental hospital cannot change the fundamental nature of hospital experience. Sam seems to be aware of this. "For sensitive people," he says quietly, "it's a terrific shock to be thrown into a reception ward where you get everything from the highly agitated to the extremely depressed and everything else in between." It is not at all those crazy people, however, which wipes you out. It is the *meaning* of being hospitalized. You have a problem, your family is driving you up the wall or vice versa, it is very bad at home, people are screaming, you are screaming, someone is threatening murder, someone else suicide, you aren't sure who you are or who is speaking to whom, it is bad, all right, but it is life, *your* life, temporarily out of control but still *yours*. Then all at once it is not. Your difficult private situation and your bizarre but still private solution to it has been transformed, you don't know how, into a permanent public humiliation. You have been institutionalized. You are the loser in a race you didn't even know you were running.

What has been transformed, once again, is your identity. You have become the victim of what Harold Garfinkel calls a "successful degradation ceremony." Whereas before you were a confused, irritating, strange, withdrawn *person,* you are now something else entirely. The ground of your being has been put to the test and found wanting. You are not the *person* you appeared to be, but something else. "In the social calculus of reality representations and test, the former identity stands as accidental; the new identity is the 'basic reality.' What he is now is what, 'after all,' he was all along." [32] What you are now is a mental patient, certifiably insane. You have been institutionalized and stripped of your identity, the stripping process confirming and reinforcing the "basic reality" of your new status. Of course, we should have known it all along; it explains everything. You're crazy.

The shock of being thrown among crazy people comes

when you realize that everyone considers you one of them.

I cannot lay claim to this "terrific shock" because I was playing a part. The hospital staff could not rob me of my identity because they did not know who I "really" was. Yet something happened to me at Hudson River, something nearly drove me crazy. Perhaps it was sensitivity after all. My mother used to tell me I was too sensitive by far. I have a great aversion to noise. I am sensitive to places; where I am seems to have a large effect on me. Flat country, for example, irritates and depresses me. The noise level on the ward was high and the hard, concrete walls, the tiled floor bounced noise up and down the corridors like a rubber ball. The buildings were stark, colorless, devoid of imagery. I am fond of baroque music and cannot take television except in very small doses. And though I was not a "real" mental patient I was under the control of the staff, I was living like a patient, I was empathizing with my fellow patients. My situation began to *feel* ambiguous. And I began to panic.

Even though my case was atypical, I was not alone in this reaction. Michael was in the hospital for the thirteenth time, yet he still hated it, he was in a constant state of mute rebellion. A young man named Billy was cracking up under the pressure of confinement. "There must be something wrong with me," he said to a group of us once; "I just can't make it in this place." Another man who was to leave soon toured the bars in Poughkeepsie one day and got drunk; he couldn't wait any longer, his patience was gone. The young man with the life plan always seemed about to cry. I was not alone; other people were experiencing the same inner panic, panic that it might inconceivably be true, it was not accidental or unlucky or just a mistake that we were there, we might really be crazy.

The day I left, Eddie, the alcoholic, came over to where I was cleaning out my bureau drawers. Eddie seemed to be living in the 1950's; he sported a crewcut, his slang was out of date. Was I leaving? he asked me. Yes. Could he have those oranges a friend had brought me? Of course. And then he gave me his advice. Move out of state, he said. That way they won't be able to get you in here again. Eddie was a sensitive person, very easily hurt. He would be talking to you and something you would say, you never knew what, would offend him and he would say, "Excuse me," and abruptly walk away. People avoided him because he summed it all up. The place was destroying him and you could see it happening; besides, he was always bumming cigarettes. After he delivered himself of this advice I should have said, "You're right, Eddie, I'll do that," but instead I stupidly told him it was not a problem for me, I was a voluntary patient signing myself out, they couldn't lay a finger on me; and Eddie, who was not on voluntary status, who had no idea when— whether—he would ever get out, said, "Excuse me," and abruptly walked away. Excuse me. Pardon my insignificant life. The words will be on his tombstone, no doubt. I wanted to cry.

Twenty minutes later my wife, Barbara, walked down the long corridor smiling at me and I did start to cry. All I remember clearly about leaving is choking back tears. I choked them back all the way home, trying not to let go. In an attempt to comfort me, Barbara made the only insensitive remark she made through the whole experience. I was out now, she said. Think of the people who can't get out. That was just it. Wasn't I one of them? I *felt* like one of them. I didn't know who I was. I didn't know whether I wanted to cry for them or for myself. I was trying not to think about them, I wanted to get away from them, get back into my own life as quickly as possible; if I thought about them I would break down. Months or years of that bitter life remained to them. You try to harden yourself, you try not to identify with other people's tragedies.

III

Nothing I have described is not familiar to mental health professionals. The vast literature on the mental hospital has delineated the features of life on the wards thoroughly and precisely. Most professionals agree that this life is antitherapeutic, that it creates passive, dependent people, "chronic schizophrenics" who lose their ability to cope with life outside the institution. Most professionals agree that ward life ought to be organized along more stimulating lines.

In view of all this agreement it would seem that the prospects for changing the mental hospitals would be good. We will have much more to say about these prospects in the next chapter. Right now, as a starter, I want to talk about the fate of one particular model of change introduced in the early 1950's by the English psychiatrist Maxwell Jones. I refer to the "therapeutic community" idea.

Jones developed this idea during World War II in a unit treating men with "effort syndrome." [33] Jones found that, rather than giving the men traditional one-to-one psychotherapy, it made much more sense to teach them where their symptoms originated and to change their attitudes toward them via educational means, in large group lectures. Since the men all suffered from the same symptoms, this was a logical step. As the lecture groups evolved they became discussion groups, and issues apart from the men's psychosomatic condition bubbled to the surface. They started to talk about the problems of living together in a treatment unit. Nurses attended the meetings and "began to recognize characteristic patterns of behaviour in their own patients" in the ways they participated in the discussion.[34] Jones started experimenting with psychodrama, the nurses taking various family roles to bring these patterns of behavior into the open. Eventually patients participated in the psychodramas, too, which became "frankly personal" and frankly therapeutic.

As these experiments continued the idea widened. Little was known at the time about group dynamics, but it was obvious that the discussion group was fostering an unusual sense of community among the patients. And patients were demonstrating the same ineffective methods of coping in this new community as they displayed in their own communities outside the hospital. Jones began to see that the hospital was in fact a temporary small society, a microcosm of the real world engendering its own "real life situations" which "might be expected to give more information about the nature of the patient's problems" than the usual doctor-patient relationship. To observe these "real life situations" more closely

> a reorganization of the hospital society was needed with a greater degree of social penetration between the three main sub-groups, patients, nurses and doctors. Thus the original hospital hierarchy was broken down and free communication between doctors, nurses and patients established. The daily discussion between the entire patient population, nurses and doctors and the continuous growth of meetings between various sub-groups, e.g. nurses' tutorials, all aided this process.[35]

At least to a degree, then, breaking down of the traditional hierarchy democratized the hospital. The locus of power shifted from the old formal authority structure to the informal structure of the group.

Jones found that the total effect of all these changes was highly therapeutic. He was inspired to try his idea again on repatriated prisoners of war, and yet again on an "industrial neurosis" unit in a mental hospital. Since that time the concept has spread widely both in England and the United States.

But while the *concept* has spread, the phenomenon has not. The psychiatric literature is replete with discussions of so-called "therapeutic communities," yet there are very few such communities in existence. Numerous mental hospitals claim to run their wards on therapeutic community lines, but generally these claims mean only that they have ward meetings once a week, or group therapy instead of individual therapy. The therapeutic community as Jones conceived it requires much more patient participation than that. In a genuine therapeutic community power over ward life is given to those who live on the ward, to patients, aides, and nurses together. Power is shared. All members of the community have one vote, and the members decide collectively all the issues pertaining to community life. These include issues of who gets what privileges, of what the privileges themselves shall be, and so on. Doctors have no more authority than anyone else when it comes to making decisions; they must particpate in the community as equals. Theoretically the patients have the power to take over the ward.

Despite all the literature, there may be no more than a dozen such communities in United States mental hospitals. I found none in any of the hospitals I visited researching this book. A few places appear to account for the large literature on the subject. According to an article in *The New York Times,* one ward of Yale-New Haven Hospital, Tompkins 1, run since the early 1960's as a therapeutic community as Jones describes it, has been the subject of more than fifty published investigations.[36] The establishment of genuine therapeutic communities seems to be limited primarily to small, highly prestigious hospitals such as Yale, the Austen Riggs Center in the Berkshires, or the Langley Porter Institute in San Francisco. In other words, the therapeutic community is an elitist phenomenon. They simply do not exist in state mental hospitals.[37]

It should not surprise us that genuine therapeutic communities are rare. The fact is that the complex hierarchical structure of the mental hospital is extraordinarily resistant to change. In this way it very much resembles other large public bureaucracies. Everyone has a place, and while mobility is limited everyone knows who he is and may rest assured that his place is secure. The hospital structure reduces uncertainty, and thereby anxiety, to a minimum. Irving M. Berlin, writing about the unwilling-ness of most mental health professionals to change, notes that "For most of us, uncertainty is anxiety-provoking, questioning of our basic premises is threatening, and evalu-ating our work so we can continue to learn and grow is frightening." [38] Why, after all, should a psychiatrist give up his hard-earned authority? He has spent years in train-ing to become an authority on the problems of other people. He may or may not be good at what he does, but it hardly matters; as long as he fills his slot in the structure of the hospital, he retains his authority. But consider what democratization does to him. Democratization opens him up to inspection; now he cannot claim authority but must demonstrate it in open meetings where it will quickly be-come apparent whether or not he knows his stuff. "I also suspect . . . that one major obstacle to change and use of new methods is a fear of discovery that one is not as competent or effective as one had hoped." [39] How many psychiatrists are willing to take the risk?

It should not surprise us, furthermore, that even where therapeutic communities do exist the reality of the power-sharing is open to question. Rubenstein and Lass-well, in their book on the effort to implement the thera-peutic community concept at Yale, print transcripts of the ward meetings in which patient and staff all partici-pated on a supposedly equal footing.[40] The patients used these meetings to complain about rules, to attack the staff, and to discuss issues that arose in life on the ward. The staff listened attentively to what they had to say. But it was an obvious game. The nurses and aides generally held their tongues while the psychiatrists responded to patients' statements by relating what patients said to their individual problems. They ignored the substance of what patients had to say and constantly interpreted their remarks in the light of their putative psychopathology. Patients were encouraged to join the game and respond to each other in the same way. Thus everything a patient did or said was evidence of something else: his "illness." Patients were still not to be taken at face value. They were still not persons.

This type of experience seems to be characteristic of therapeutic communities. Marvin I. Herz, in a critique of the concept, notes:

> Jones believes that if individuals, both staff and patients, participate in the decision-making process, they will be more motivated to carry out the decisions. However, even if the decision-making is apparently democratic, do not those higher up in the hierarchy often carry an undue weight in the process? [41]

The question is rhetorical. John Bickford, writing in *Hospital & Community Psychiatry*, similarly asks whether reality approaches the therapeutic community ideal and answers in the negative: "Although the medical status system is nominally democratized, the medical staff retain the decisive vote." [42] Others have noted the same discrepancy between ideology and actuality. Rubenstein and Lasswell, summing up the situation at Yale, state:

> Decisions about fundamental and pressing issues in the lives of patients were decided by others than the individuals most concerned. Despite the modifications introduced, the basically authoritarian character of the hospital was substantially unchanged. The staff, particularly the director, retained the decisive voice. [43]

At no time, however, did anyone acknowledge that this was in fact the case.

> The burden imposed on the community by the fact

that effective power was retained by the senior doctors was compounded by the new, largely implicit, demand that all now pretend that the hospital was democratic. Any acknowledgement of the limited character of power sharing constituted a violation of the ideology.[44]

The hypocrisy is self-evident.

This hypocritical game may be as capable of driving someone crazy as the routines of a typical custodial mental hospital. The staff pretend to give up power to the patients but in truth the patients remain patients and their behavior is still subject to manipulation and control "for their own good." The patients are exhorted to speak up in meetings and express their point of view, but anything they say may be held against them. It is the familiar situation of the "double bind." The democratic ideology of the therapeutic community masks an *unacknowledged* power structure. Responding to the ideology, patients encounter the power structure, which quickly puts them in their place. If they attempt to expose the power structure, however, they encounter the ideology. The paradox is never resolved and never admitted: a maddening situation.[45]

What are the prospects for change? If the fate of the therapeutic community is any indication, they are not good at all. In spite of its apparent popularity, the innovation called the therapeutic community has had a very slender impact indeed on the actual environment of the mental hospital. The wards are still full of people dully following mindless, dehumanizing routines. There has been no real change for at least one hundred years. The custodial mental hospital with its uniformed staff, its inflexible structure, its authoritarian attitudes endures, and it looks as if it will endure forever.

To put the responsibility where it belongs, it endures because we want it to endure. Let me return to Robert Edwalds' article:

For the majority of state hospitals, a genuine shift in philosophy must precede a change from a primarily custodial care institution to a hospital. If our society is content to *demand* security and custodial care but merely *hope* for effective treatment, the state mental hospital is likely to remain primarily a custodial care institution.[46]

We are the ones who insist upon the primacy of the custodial function.

VI
Administrative Dreams, Psychiatric Nightmares

Curing a sickness is a crime.
It's to squash the head of a kid who is much less nasty than life.

Artaud

I

What are the prospects for change? They are simply not good. Not only critics outside the mental health system but people at all levels within the system have been working for change for years. But the state mental hospital is a remarkably stable institution; and this institution anchors the entire system. Even very vigorous leaders whose primary goal is change have been unable to make a lasting impact on the mental hospital. An outstanding example is David J. Vail, whose book, *Dehumanization and the Institutional Career,* attempted to specify in detail those mental hospital practices which reduce mental patients to a nonperson status, so that in detail they could be corrected.[1] At the time he published his book Vail was in a highly favorable position to implement his reforms. He was running the state mental health system in Minnesota.[2]

Vail did have a definite impact on the system while he lived. He developed humane treatment guidelines for hospital staff; to make sure they were following them, he would walk onto hospital wards unannounced.³ He instituted annual surveys of ward atmosphere, recruited men like Russell Barton, a British expert on the effects of institutionalization, as consultants, and made a concerted effort to interest the legislature and the public in reform. Thanks to this work the Medical Services Division of the Minnesota Department of Public Welfare received a Bronze Award from the American Psychiatric Association in 1967.⁴

But mental hospitals in Minnesota are no better now than they ever were. Vail remained in a kind of adversary relationship with his own bureaucracy, prodding it from the top, and after his early death in 1971 (he was forty-five) the hospitals rapidly abandoned his reforms. Understaffed and overcrowded now, they are known for their heavy reliance on shock treatment, which most state hospitals have given up. Budgets are low, drug dosages are high; ward routines have returned to the rigid mindlessness typical of custodial institutions.⁵ Hastings State Hospital, according to one ex-patient, is an "absolute hell hole." At Rochester State Hospital, which is associated with the Mayo Clinic, they do psychosurgery.⁶ Anoka State Hospital has named a building after David Vail, but his work in Minnesota has been undone.

What happened in Minnesota is typical of what happens whenever someone takes over a large, complex bureaucracy and tries to change it. The situation, he finds, is not entirely under his control. The system is a kind of sponge which absorbs and dissipates energy no matter what its source. The larger the bureaucracy, the less effect dynamic leadership (or any kind of leadership) will have on it.⁷ For all their fierce drive, men like Vail inevitably discover that they are working in a vacuum, in what Ray Birdwhistell calls "the isolation of the administrator."⁸ People start hiding from them in the nooks and crannies of the huge bureaucratic monstrosities they have to run; their lines of communication rigidify, they no longer know what is happening on the ward level, they become trapped in "a world of words and the use of words on memo, communiqué, and balance sheets." [9] Most of the words are lies; no one tells them the truth any more.

The largest mental health bureaucracy in the United States is unquestionably the Department of Mental Hygiene in the State of New York. The Department operates twenty-eight mental hospitals (not counting institutions for the retarded); these hospitals house thirty-nine thousand mental patients.[10] Four of them—South Beach in Staten Island; Elmira; Capital District in Albany; and Central New York in Syracuse—are brand new. Its annual budget for 1972–73 was $680 million; [11] for 1973–74, $819 million; [12] now it is over $900 million. It employs nearly forty thousand people in its mental hospitals alone, and another thousand or so in its headquarters in Albany, a big, bright new office building near Nelson Rockefeller's famous Albany Mall.[13] The Department is so complicated that its organization chart looks like a map of the New York City subway system.

The Department is a fascinating object of study. Much that happens within it is beyond any one person's control; history takes over and nobody can stop it. Take the case of the four new hospitals. At first glance there would appear to be no need whatsoever for new mental hospitals. The daily patient load in New York mental hospitals has dropped from ninety-three thousand in 1955 to thirty-nine thousand today, and it is still falling at the rate of approximately 10 percent a year. Alan D. Miller, the present Commissioner, expects it to stabilize at about twenty- to twenty-five thousand sometime in the future.[14] Already the state's existing mental hospitals have closed down some of their buildings; eventually a few of the hospitals themselves will close, as has happened in Cali-

fornia, Massachusetts, and other states. Yet New York is
building four new hospitals. Why?

One reason the Department gives is that some of the
old hospitals were located away from the main population
centers; until recently, for example, 60 percent of New
York City's mental patients were sent to hospitals out of
the city, some as far as sixty or seventy miles away.[15] The
new hospitals such as South Beach in Staten Island would
enable the state to keep these people close to home. But
this argument is no longer valid. With the drop in hospital
population, the state hospitals which serve New York City
such as Creedmoor, Brooklyn State, the three branches of
Manhattan State, all within the city limits, are no longer
filled to capacity. That particular problem has vanished.
Another reason the Department gives is that the old hospital buildings are obsolete and unusable. Brooklyn State,
some of the catchment area of which South Beach has
taken over, is run down and "not good," in Miller's words.
But Miller is not abandoning Brooklyn State. On the contrary, he wants to tear down the older buildings and re-
build the whole institution.[16] He plans to stay with it, in
other words; South Beach is not meant to replace it. That
argument doesn't work, either.

Actually it looks as if the Department is simply trying to make the best of an inherited situation. New York
is building new mental hospitals because in 1965, when
it started planning for the future of its mental health
system, the state badly miscalculated the trends in this
field. The State Planning Committee on Mental Disorders,
established to fill the planning requirements of the Federal Community Mental Health and Retardation Act of
1963, projected in 1965 a need for nearly eighty thousand
mental hospital beds in 1975. The actual need stands at
about half that figure. According to the plan, "The physical reorganization of the State hospital system should be
effected through new construction, relocation to popula-

tion centers and abandonment of obsolete and inappropriately located hospitals." [17] Miller, who had nothing to
do with conceptualizing the plan, has little choice now
but to implement it. The plan set in motion a bureaucratic and political process he would have had difficulty
stopping even if he had wanted to. The economy was
strong then and Nelson Rockefeller loved to build buildings. The Department was committed to growth, growth
conceivable apparently only in terms of more: more hospitals, an ever bigger budget. And it all made good sense
at the time. Everyone knows that things become obsolete:
programs lose their effectiveness; new ideas replace failed
ones; and buildings—most of all buildings—become dis-
functional. It was obvious finally that there would always
be plenty of mental patients to occupy these new hospitals
—eighty thousand in 1975.

There is more to it than this blatant error in numbers, of course. Each new hospital has its own complex
reasons for being born in the mazes of pork-barrel politics.[18] But now the Department has to figure out what to do
with these new hospitals in the context of a different historical situation. New York is building new mental hospitals,
and it doesn't need them. It seems self-evident that the
whole thing has been an absurd waste, smaller than but
just as silly as the Albany Mall. But Dr. Miller, for his
part, won't commit himself one way or the other to this
point of view. When I asked him about the new hospitals
he answered with a daring non sequitur to the effect that
a state with so many mental hospitals *should* build more.[19]
It was such a bold formulation of unreason that I let it
stand.

Miller is what you would have to call a gradualist,
as opposed, say, to a crusader like David Vail who tries to
change everything at once. Miller works slowly and carefully with what he has. Stuck with new hospitals he may
not particularly want, he does the best he can to justify

them and make them useful. He knows that he must
accommodate to historical circumstances and to the limitations of his power. Miller is like Vail, however, in that
he wants to generate change in the system. He wants the
hospitals to become effective treatment and rehabilitative
institutions. The same kinds of things which nearly drove
me crazy at Hudson River make him, he says, angry. But
he believes that the hospitals will not change unless the
entire system changes. One reason the hospitals are the
way they are, he says, is because the second basic element
of the mental health system, the fragmented local network
of clinics, mental health centers, and general hospitals with
psychiatric wards, use the state hospitals as dumping
grounds for their unwanted, "difficult" patients. Miller
sees the system as having three basic elements—the state
hospitals, the local system, and his headquarters in Albany
—all viewing each other as adversaries, all isolated, all in
competition with one another. This has to change, he says,
before any one of the three elements can change. Everyone
must be brought "to see that they all [have] to become
stronger together." [20]

It is no simple thing Miller is talking about; it sounds
a little, in fact, like some sort of utopian fantasy in which
people who have been at odds with each other for generations suddenly grow "stronger together." Can state
hospital psychiatrists sit down with the directors of a psychoanalytic clinic? They don't live in the same world, they
don't even speak the same language, some of them won't
even sit down with members of their own clinical persuasion. Competition and ideological rivalry are endemic to
the mental health system. Miller knows that he is not going
to accomplish anything by fiat.

> I mean, it's one thing to say to a group, "You must do
> something." But unless there's a fighting chance that they
> can do it, I think it's just a posture. So we try to move
> it as fast as possible without it falling apart.[21]

Miller, that is, feels he must bring about change quietly, almost surreptitiously. He must try to find some administrative device that will rationalize the system without unduly upsetting any particular group. He must bring the system together, making sure there is something in it for everybody, maybe even for the patients, and do it all without anybody understanding the change well enough to become alarmed about it.

The device Miller has invented is called "unified services," and it is sufficiently complicated that no one I have spoken to about it fully comprehends it.[22] As Miller explains it, unified services is a logical extension of the decentralization of the state hospitals which is known as "unitization." We will have more to say about unitization later; right now a brief description will have to do. Under unitization, which has been adopted almost countrywide, each hospital in a state is assigned a specific geographic catchment area. That area is then broken down into smaller geographical areas such as a county, and a particular treatment unit in the hospital—a ward, a group of wards, a whole building—becomes responsible for the residents living in that county who might come to the hospital. The unit also takes responsibility for patients already in the hospital who were originally admitted from that county. Unitization thus automatically redistributes a hospital's patient population. The old-style mental hospital was divided into acute and chronic services. Acute wards held people who had been in the hospital less than two years, chronic wards those who had been there longer. Unitization, by reassigning people to wards on a geographical basis, mixed the chronic and acute cases together.

Miller calls unitization a "crude" device, but it has certain obvious advantages. One of these is that it provides an opportunity for a particular hospital unit to reach out and make contact with the people and agencies who service the county or area the unit is responsible for.

It does not mandate such contact, and not many hospital units in New York or elsewhere have taken advantage of it. But the opportunity is there.

Unified services, however, in effect mandates such contact. The central element of unified services is joint planning between the county and the state facility or facilities which serve it. The county government and the state hospital unit serving the county *must* get together and develop an elaborate joint treatment and facility utilization plan for mental health services in their area. The plan *must* include a joint statement of goals, a joint inventory of present services, a joint proposal for filling gaps in those services, a joint description of program responsibilities among agencies "with particular emphasis on geographic districting of responsibility," and a joint budget. The county government and the directors of services in the state hospital serving that county *must* agree on the plan.[23]

Miller has sweetened the package to make it as attractive as possible. First of all, the whole arrangement is voluntary. The state now reimburses counties for the net operating cost of local mental health services at the rate of 50 percent. Counties can continue operating on that basis if they wish. Under the new funding pattern, however, unified services will return even more money to most (but not all) counties. The state will grant each county a "local population credit" of ten dollars a head up to one hundred thousand residents, and five dollars a head for all additional residents. If the joint state-county costs add up to more than would be covered by this per capita credit, the state will pay 80 percent of the excess, up to thirteen dollars per head. If the excess works out to greater than thirteen dollars a head, the state will pay 65 percent of the additional excess. It sounds (and is) very complicated, but the Department calculates that forty-three counties plus New York City will pay less under unified services than they are now paying for mental health services, while fourteen will pay more. And if the cost is higher, a six-year phase-in program will soften the blow. These calculations are based on the assumption, however, that there will be no change in the present level of services.[24]

This roughly describes what unified services is, but it doesn't answer the question of what it is all about. Miller talks persuasively about building flexibility into the mental health system and designing services at the local level, where the need for services presents itself. Alvin Mesnikoff, the Director of the new hospital at South Beach, writes:

> Now, unified services by requiring joint state and county responsibility introduces a constructive tension between the two levels of government. . . . This innovation may well serve to counter the tendency toward a bureaucratic and institutional focus and shift greater energy and attention to the pressing needs of the community.[25]

Fascinating. But can it really be that the Department wants to dismantle its own bureaucracy? Does the Department, involved in building four new mental institutions, really intend to shift the focus away from the institutional approach? And whose flexibility are we talking about, the Department's or the counties'? Local providers of service have traditionally seen the Department as a kind of adversary, as we talked about above, and it is only natural that they should continue to look for the hook hidden in the worm. Their question has to be, what is the Department fishing for? Is unified services really a fancy way of consolidating the Department's power relative to them, of abridging their independence? What happens to them in a joint planning arrangement?

What will happen to them remains to be seen. No

New York county has yet seriously attempted to plan an entire range of mental health services for its citizens, so they have little planning experience. Under unified services, furthermore, the Department of Mental Hygiene will retain a veto power over local planning on the vague basis of whether or not the plan establishes "the most effective and economical provision of services." [26] Does this mean that the Department intends to force expensive long-range responsibilities on the counties in the name of "effectiveness?" Or will they cut the heart out of the plan in the name of "economy?" It is all up in the air. In the meantime everyone is full of uncertainty and local providers of services are beginning to run scared.

Fear may indeed be justified, but perhaps not at the local level. I think the primary aim of unified services is not the taking over of local services but the transformation of the state hospitals. Through the administrative device of unified services Alan Miller is trying, I believe, to accomplish what he has been unable to accomplish through unitization or judicious appointment to key positions or by any other means. He is trying to get control of the hospitals and force them to change.

This may seem to be contradictory. Under unified services the Department is *giving up* the power to plan services to the state hospitals and the counties they serve. It is not taking that power from them. What Miller has discovered, however, is that the Department by itself never had the power to control the operation of the hospitals. Analyzing the situation once more, he says,

> . . . three sorts of groups each saw two enemies. The local government people thought that the hospital people, or the institution people, and the headquarters people both had all the power and were controlling them. The headquarters people thought that the other two had all the power and the institution people thought the other two had all the power, and it's really an

> interesting phenomenon, because none of them had
> any power.[27]

None of them had any power, Miller perhaps least of all.
One reason Hudson River State Hospital is the kind of
place it is is because Miller has lacked the power to change
the institution's mode of operation. He could and did
force it to unitize, but Hudson River is controlled by an
old-line psychiatric staff strongly oriented to a disease
model of insanity and a Director so deeply entrenched
that Miller simply does not have the power to replace him;
and unitization, which theoretically decentralizes the hospital, enhancing the power of the unit chiefs, has had no
effect on Hudson River at all. The unit chiefs are of a
type with the Director. There has been little "outreach"
to the communities being served. The doctors still identify
themselves with white lab coats. The staff is apathetic,
imprisoned in their rigidly defined roles.[28] The whole
place is like a small medieval fief, and as well defended.

This is what Miller means when he calls unitization
a "crude" device. Unitization doesn't *necessarily* accomplish anything. It doesn't require the Director of a state
hospital or his unit chiefs to come to terms with the community or area they serve. Everything can go on as before,
each element in the system ignoring the other, with the
third party, the Department of Mental Hygiene in Albany,
frustratedly trying to grasp the whole. Unified services,
on the other hand, *requires* joint planning. The two elements have to sit down with each other and develop a
mutually agreeable plan, they have to negotiate common
goals, a common philosophy.

> The providers are required to come together to define
> their respective roles in this system, which emphasizes
> responsibility and accountability. To operate, unified
> services will require peer negotiation, planning,
> implementation and monitoring. The providers, in

serving the same population, will perforce monitor each other's activities as patients move through the system. Funding will be an open book, with the role of each component and the resources for the task spelled out.[29]

Suddenly everybody is accountable to everybody else. The responsibility for change is thrown directly onto the shoulders of the service providers. They can no longer blame Albany, or each other, for their manifold failures.

The impact this may have on the hospitals is obvious. Unified services makes decentralization a reality; and genuine decentralization always effects a diffusion of power. Thus a man such as the Director at Hudson River will no longer be able to slough off attempts at reform. He and his unit chiefs will have to deal separately with professionals from each of the several counties the hospital serves. Each county may demand something different in the way of service style or involvement from the hospital and none of them may settle for the custodial situation which currently prevails there. The Director will be relatively powerless to resist these demands, within reasonable funding limits; the survival of his institution as an institution will depend on his willingness to cooperate with county authorities. For funding now goes to the planners jointly, not to the hospital separately. Funds are allocated from the Department, that is, through the planning mechanism; he has no choice but to become involved in that mechanism. With one clever administrative stroke Miller has cut off his Directors' heads and delivered their power into the hands of their enemies. If it works.

As I say, nobody knows whether it will work. Miller is a gradualist and he will move slowly, you can count on it. Some counties will stay out of unified services in order to observe what happens to those who adopt it. Others will adopt it for the economic benefits but hold back on joint planning, just go through the motions, and Miller will probably not force the issue, at least not yet. Forcing the issue, he believes, accomplishes little, it just makes people angry. He wants to give people time to get used to it. "I don't really think that a lot of people who are for it understand how revolutionary it is," he says.[30] He thinks some morning the dawn will break and people in the mental health system will suddenly realize that their whole way of doing business has been transformed. It will have been a *fait accompli,* a piece of magic done right before their uncomprehending eyes. Such are the dreams of administrators.[30a]

Unified services is one way of forcing change upon the mental health system (particularly the state mental hospitals) from the top down. Other administrators in other states are trying other ways of reaching much the same goal. In California, for example, where state hospital programs are still wholly under the control of headquarters in Sacramento, William C. Keating, Jr., has found a way of avoiding some of the pitfalls of that control, or the lack of it. Keating's idea was to divide the large state hospital into little hospitals:

> Let's take this state hospital, of, say, 3,000 patients, and divide it up into a bunch of little autonomous programs, little hospitals, and take the so-called medical director and just make him a clinical coordinator. And take the business manager and make him a hospital administrator. Make him the hotel man, make this other guy the clinical coordinator to keep his children from fighting. . . .[31]

Each separate, autonomous program would serve a minimum of sixty people, a maximum of two hundred and seventy, and it would have an administrative hierarchy of just two people: a Program Director and an assistant. To avoid the pathologies of professionalism, the Program Director could be a psychologist, a social worker, a psychiatrist, he could be anybody, in fact, as long as he was a clinician. A few programs have aides as Program Directors.[32]

Program Directors report to the hospital's clinical director for coordination, but they make their yearly contract, which stipulates what services they will provide, what their goals are, how they expect to reach those goals and how much it will cost, directly with Keating himself. And Keating insists that all program goals be, as he puts it, divisible by two:

> I insisted that people not talk in terms of any kind of objective that wasn't divisible by two. I don't care about goodness and happiness and things that nobody can put a handle on and which I can't judge you on afterwards. They are factors and I admit they're real factors. But you explain them to me in terms so I can divide by two, then I'm willing to accept them as a good objective, but otherwise I don't know what you're talking about.[33]

Keating publishes the programs and they are available to patients. So he wants program objectives to be formulated in such a way that patients can understand them. Consequently treatment goals are formulated almost exclusively on behavioral terms. "To return the patient as soon as possible to a level of functioning appropriate for community living" is typical. Making objectives direct and understandable on behavioral terms also builds accountability into the system. Keating has made sure, furthermore, that accountability leads directly to him, not to a hospital director who may or may not tell him what is going on. When I visited hospitals in California, therefore, Keating advised me not to bother talking to the medical directors at the "top" except as a matter of courtesy, but to deal with the program directors, who were the key people. Presumably that is what Keating himself does.

Keating's system has flattened the traditional state hierarchy and given him some control over the operation of the hospitals; but control at Keating's administrative level is only possible in a state such as California where the numbers are small. California has fewer than five thousand people classified as "mentally ill" in state hospitals, whereas New York has thirty-nine thousand: one obvious reason why Alan Miller hit upon the more ponderous approach of unified services. It would be difficult to say, given the circumstances, which approach is "better." Who is to say, besides, what "better" is in the first place? Is it "better" if patients are happy, whatever that means, or if something is being done with them or to them that is divisible by two? Maybe it is "better" just to note that each approach has been adapted to a particular historical situation. In California the goal was to eliminate the state hospitals altogether by a certain date. New York, on the contrary, is committed to the continued existence of its hospitals. Keating's system with its direct line to programs has allowed him to disregard the hospitals as entities in their own right, and this has facilitated the process of closing some of them down. Keating's system is also much more flexible than unified services will ever be. But the state hierarchy in California is much more subject to political control than the Department of Mental Hygiene in New York, which has always had a reputation for being apolitical, so flexibility was a must for California. In short, it may be that the historical situation each system operates in is too different to make useful comparisons between them. In fact, we might generalize this and say that perhaps no state system can serve as a touchstone for other states. Mental health systems everywhere suffer the same kinds of maladies, yet each state may have to find its own cure.

It is interesting in this connection that Massachusetts recently announced that it was planning, like California, to close its state hospitals within five years.[34] This decision came after an eighteen-month investigation of the mental health system in Massachusetts by the Mental Hospital Planning Project, a group jointly formed from the Massachusetts Department of Mental Health and United Community Services of Metropolitan Boston.[35] The Project's final report proposes that the state hospitals be phased out over a period of five years and be replaced with community mental health programs of various sorts.

It would be no great loss. The population in Massachusetts mental hospitals has dropped from a high of twenty-three thousand in the mid-1950's to about seven thousand now. One hospital has been closed already and many buildings in the remaining ten hospitals have been abandoned: literally abandoned. Roofs have collapsed, vandals have broken the windows, thieves have torn out the plumbing and all other movable goods. And even buildings still in use seem uninhabitable. I will never forget the ward I visited at Boston State Hospital. Paint was peeling off the walls, the lighting in the halls was totally inadequate, the heat was turned up far too high, the toilet stalls had no doors. But it was the smell that overwhelmed me, the smell of shit and urine, so powerful I almost threw up. The place was clean, the staff explained; it was just that over the years the smell had gotten into the woodwork and the walls and no amount of scrubbing or disinfectant would ever eliminate it.

The Project's report is only a proposal, of course, and there isn't much point in talking about it until something concrete happens. It is based on the assumption that present levels of funding in mental health have reached a ceiling, and as long as the state siphons off so much money —$80 million a year currently—for the maintenance and operation of mental hospitals, community and area programs and facilities will never be able to grow to the point where they can take full responsibility for their respective populations. The Project concluded that the only way out would be to close the hospitals down. As in New York, it remains to be seen what will happen. Massachusetts has traditionally (and by law) held mental health to be a state responsibility; the state has no precedent for parceling its responsibility out to regions or communities. One dissenting member of the Project takes note of its "overly simplified view that we need only go from point A to point B; that we need only close up the hospitals and start up community-based programs." [36] And there has been no time at this writing for public feedback to develop. It is the public, after all, which ultimately decides these matters, as the California experience exemplifies. As in California, the public may simply not allow Massachusetts to close its state hospitals.

It is interesting nevertheless that Massachusetts should decide to move in this direction. The Massachusetts mental health budget has stagnated for years now and the state's Department of Mental Health may be desperate. Even discounting this, however, it is becoming obvious that at least some of the people at the top of the system are no longer willing to preside over these derelict institutions, these stinking beached whales. In their eyes the mental hospital as it now exists no longer seems viable. Either the hospitals must change or they must go. It is surprising indeed to find this attitude at the top, but there it is. Of course, this is not true in every state, not by any means. In Kansas, in Minnesota, in New Jersey,[37] and in many other states there is no commitment to change anywhere in the system. Nevertheless you can feel a certain uneasiness even in these states, a sense that the pot they are perched on is beginning to boil. Nearly everyone, and that includes the administrators who have to run them, knows how badly the mental hospitals do their job. Nearly everyone sees the necessity for some sort of radical shift in their *modus operandi*. These hospitals are sour, pathogenic places. It is hard even for administrators not to know this.

II

Yet the prospects for change remain poor. The administrator may want to change the system but the system defeats him; the system is an out-of-tune piano that not even the greatest administrative virtuoso can play well. Proponents of change, however powerful the positions they occupy, face equally powerful opposition not only from the public but from titular subordinates entrenched in and committed to the status quo. As every administrator discovers, his subordinates lie to him, they hide from him, they build little empires he finds he has no choice but to support. Over the years they achieve a kind of impregnable independence; and these are the people who, to protect that independence, sabotage all administrative efforts to redirect the system.

I am talking, of course, about professionals. No matter how he tries to manipulate the system from the top, the administrator faces a situation which in its basic elements is extremely difficult to change. In order to run the system, he has to attract professionals to it—psychiatrists, psychologists, social workers, occupational therapists, and so on. These are the people with the presumed expertise, the people who know, supposedly, how to treat the insane. Unfortunately, however, the administrator hasn't the money to pay these people what they might earn on the outside. State mental health systems are traditionally beggars at budget hearings; legislators would much prefer to build roads. In order to attract professionals to the system, therefore, the administrator has to sweeten the deal by giving them a great deal of freedom. He must give them "professional license" to pursue their ideas and follow their interests; he must unleash them into the system. And in doing so he gives up his power over them. He cannot make them accountable for what they do. The problem of change thus becomes linked with the issue of professional accountability, and on this rock administrators founder.

The situation exists in all of medicine, to be sure, but it is especially striking in psychiatry, where no one agrees on what the best treatment modality, the best professional practice, is. In psychiatry everything is in dispute; therefore anything goes. Psychiatrists can pursue whatever semirespectable notion they may have about the treatment of the insane and no administrator will dare to say nay because first, who knows, the notion might work, and second, he might lose that psychiatrist to another hospital, another state, if he does.

Let me illustrate with a chilling example from Kansas.

The children's and adolescent unit at Topeka State Hospital is run by a psychiatrist named Donald B. Rinsley. It boasts, Rinsley told me in an interview conducted in June, 1973, thirty beds for children aged five to twelve and fifty beds for adolescents up to the age of seventeen. It is a kind of small independent psychiatric hospital within the larger Topeka State setting. Rinsley has been in charge of the adolescent section since 1968 and the children's section since 1970, and he had been the assistant chief since 1960. Before that he worked in a Federal prison.

Donald Rinsley is in many ways a very impressive man. He speaks rapidly in highly technical psychiatric terms, so rapidly it is hard to follow him, much less question what he is saying. At the same time he has a knack for personalizing a formal encounter, for getting under the skin quickly. As a psychiatrist he makes the very large claim that his unit "cures" schizophrenic children. But the unit is quite expensive, with costs averaging two thousand dollars a month per child and the average length of stay standing somewhere between twenty-nine to thirty-six months. The cost of "curing" a single child might then run as high as seventy-two thousand dollars or even more. When I asked him how he justified this to the powers that

be, he smiled and said that he has been able to establish a
special relationship with the Kansas legislature, a relationship he attributes partly to his own charisma and partly to
the fact that his unit is one of three children's psychiatric
units affiliated with state hospitals in the United States
which has been fully accredited by the American Association of Psychiatric Services for Children.[38] Rinsley is clearly
proud of his unit and he sticks with it even though the
pay for psychiatrists in Kansas state hospitals is low.

He sticks with it, perhaps, because he has a remarkably free hand. His position is secure, and it is a position
from which he has been able to build up a national reputation as an expert on the residential treatment of children. He is widely published; he serves on the editorial
board of *Psychiatric Quarterly;* he reviews books for the
American Journal of Psychiatry.[39] No administrator in the
Kansas state system to my knowledge has interfered with
his method of operation or intends to. The administrators
have left well enough alone. It is hard not to suspect that
it is this freedom which keeps Rinsley in his low-paying
position.

It is men like Rinsley, secure, powerful, unchallenged,
accountable, in effect, to no one, who represent the real
barrier to reform. For Rinsley is definitely an enemy of
change. Here he comments on California's aborted decision to close its state hospitals:

> American society is presently in a state of flux. When
> the flux subsides, the public mental hospital will be
> rediscovered, the community mental health fad will have
> been exposed for the hoax that it is, and the extremists
> who deny the fact of mental illness and view physicans as
> agents of a monstrous conspiracy to deny the mentally
> sick their civil rights will assume their proper places in
> the pantheon of paranoid personalities. Meanwhile, the
> task of most of us remains the treatment and cure of
> mental disorder and we shall doubtless stay at it
> uninterruptedly while the demagogues have their say.[40]

It is a strong statement. Community mental health is a
hoax, those who question the reality of "mental illness"
are extremists, paranoid personalities, demagogues, the
public mental hospital will endure. There can be little
question about Rinsley's point of view.

Rinsley is equally definite in his psychiatric opinions.
On adolescent psychiatry, for example, he disputes the
views of such well-known people as Erik Erikson, Anna
Freud, K. R. Eissler, Nathan W. Ackermann, and Kenneth
Keniston, the whole group of those, in other words, who
view adolescence as basically "a psychologically disturbed
state or period, or as a time when the individual under-
goes some sort of 'normative crisis.' " [41] Rinsley calls this
the "turmoil school" and characterizes its position as
asuming "that all adolescents are in various degrees psychologically disturbed or ill," that it is therefore difficult
if not impossible to diagnose illness in them and it is also
extremely difficult to treat them because of their tendency
to "act out," their "low frustration tolerance," proneness
to regression, and so forth, that even quiet adolescents
are really quite sick, and that, as a result of all the pre-
ceding, adolescents become a "muddled, kaleidoscopic
transitional phenomenon" forced to create their own sub-
culture.[42]

None of this, says Rinsley, is true of adolescents *in
general*. On the contrary, it is true only of a small group
of adolescents. According to Rinsley, most adolescents "do
not experience significant parent-child dislocations, claim
relatively few feelings of alienation and isolation, and tend
to accept the sociocultural values of their parents." [43] The
turmoil school is mistaking the elephant's trunk for the
whole body. The majority of adolescents in Rinsley's view
are just normal, healthy kids.

There are, however, adolescents who do fit the pattern
described by the turmoil school. These adolescents, indeed, are "seriously psychiatrically ill"; they have failed
to achieve "age-appropriate degrees of separation-individ-

uation, hence emancipation." [44] The trouble with the
turmoil school is that it doesn't take evidence of adolescent turmoil seriously enough; since the turmoil school sees
turmoil everywhere in adolescence, turmoil becomes normal. As Rinsley says, if we accept the position of the turmoil school,

> . . . there is really no good reason for alarm should the
> adolescent be found to reason autistically, at least at
> times, or otherwise display the tangential, associatively
> loosened, overinclusive-overexclusive, syncretic and
> concretistic thinking pathognomonic of schizophrenia
> among adults! [45]

Rinsley, obviously, does view these "symptoms" with
alarm. The "turmoil-ridden adolescent" *is* "ill." "His
problems are not expressive of some sort of temporally
circumscribed, phase-specific 'adjustment reaction,' and he
will not 'grow out of' them." On the contrary, they are
evidence of permanent psychopathology. Therefore he
needs "intensive and often prolonged psychiatric treatment." [46]

This is not the place to attempt an evaluation of
Rinsley's psychiatric theories. We need only note, as Rinsley himself notes, his opposition to Erikson, Anna Freud,
and others who are known internationally for their work
with children and adolescents. My interest is not so much
in Rinsley's theories as in what they lead up to, what they
allow. [47] I am interested in the "therefore"; therefore the
"sick" adolescent as Rinsley describes him needs "intensive
and often prolonged psychiatric treatment." What Rinsley
means by this is *residential* treatment. As he himself sums
it up,

> Exposure, analysis and resolution of the adolescent's
> "psychotic transference," expressive of failure of
> inception of the primal symbiosis (in presymbiotic cases),
> or of separation-individuation (in symbiotic cases), are
> best carried out within the intensive residental context.[48]

It is best carried out, that is, in a mental hospital. In a unit, I asume, much like his.

"Intensive residential treatment": he means treatment lasting between two and a half to three years on the average in which children from the ages of five to seventeen are separated from their parents and live in a mental hospital. It seems safe to say that most children and most parents would object to this separation, and Rinsley confirms it:

> The opening or (as the author chooses to call it) the *resistance phase,* dates from admission through the end of the first six months to one year of residence. During this period, the child's and the parents' verbal and nonverbal behavior on the ward and in casework, respectively, centers upon their anger and anguish over separation, and when carefully studied, is found to resemble the responses of separated infants during Bowlby's "stage of protest." [49]

Both parties, that is, protest the enforced separation; they resist it mightily with a "rich complexity" of maneuvering:

> For both kinds of [parent-child] dyad, resistances to treatment are often kaleidoscopic and herculean, oriented toward preventing the treatment staff's perceived efforts to dissolve the fusions, hence to destroy the partners to them, or else, for the autistic-pre-symbiotic adolescent, to take away the dereistic, magic-hallucinatory constructions that serve the child as substitutes for objects. Thus, the therapeutic resistances are life-and-death matters, and the staff members are deeply perceived as plunderers and murderers. [50]

Resistance is generally so strong, in fact, that the staff must go to great lengths to control the situation. There must be "consistent recognition and appropriate interpretation of resistance behaviors." That means that staff members must constantly remind the child that he is resisting treatment. Then,

> Liberal use of long- and short-term restrictions, including isolation (seclusion), early inhibits access of raw instinctual drives to motility, limits the patient's use of ward peers as a refuge from the staff members, and promotes the unlayering of over-determined defenses by engendering regression through limitation of sensory stimuli.[51]

That means that the child must be put in seclusion, a room with a mattress, just like Sarah's, long enough for him to begin to regress; or until his eyes glaze over from "limitation of sensory stimuli," long enough to persuade him, at any rate, that there can be no refuge from staff members. The child's parents similarly must not be allowed to become a refuge: "Strict limitation of contacts with family members, whether vis-a-vis or via letters, similarly inhibits the child's defensive use of such figures." [52] That means that parent-child visits are normally restricted to half an hour a week. Staff members sit in on these short visits to prevent hugging, kissing, or other displays of affection between parent and child, displays which might encourage the child's "defensive use" of his parents.[53]

I assume that in many cases this is successful, that Rinsley is able to break the children's resistance to treatment within six months to a year. In at least one case that I know of, however, his methods appear to have failed. The case involves a little girl whom I shall call Melissa. According to her parents, this particular child was born with a mild case of cerebral palsy, one of the symptoms of which was something called "tongue thrust." Her tongue pushed the food out of her mouth when she tried to swallow. It is a fairly common symptom in CP and it sometimes makes for difficult feeding problems.

Melissa's case was mild, however, mild enough, in fact, that over a period of years different doctors made different diagnoses; some decided she suffered from allergies, others from brain damage suffered at birth, and so on. Meanwhile Melissa, who was a bright child, learned to walk, albeit clumsily, and talk, though with a speech defect, and development seemed to be proceeding almost normally.[54]

Then at about the age of six or seven Melissa stopped eating and began to lose weight. She compained that she could not swallow her food, she pushed the food back out of her mouth, and her parents finally sent her to the Kansas University Medical Center for tests. Although she had a disability card which officially designated her as a crippled child, the doctors at the Medical Center decided that Melissa's real trouble was not cerebral palsy or any other physical condition. Melissa, they decided, was emotionally disturbed. She could not swallow because she *would* not swallow. Operating, apparently, on Rinsley's principles, they started controlling visits between parents and child. Only when Melissa was a "good girl," only, presumably, when she succeeded in swallowing her food, was she allowed to see her parents.

Her parents were not at all satisfied with this treatment and after three months they took Melissa out of the hospital and went back to treating her at home. She was then eight years old, and it was late October. The doctors at the Medical Center were so persuaded of their diagnosis, however, that they kept after the family, telling them they didn't know what they were doing, they were killing their daughter, and periodically sending a social worker to the house to check up on them. The day after Christmas the doctors finally went to court, charged the parents with medical neglect, and took Melissa back to the Medical Center. One of psychiatry's typical *pro forma* hearings was held and Melissa's parents lost legal custody of their child.

Under psychiatric care Melissa did not eat any better than she had under her parents' care. In fact, she lost still more weight, going, her parents say, from thirty-six pounds to perhaps twenty-eight at the Medical Center. The doctors had to resort to tube feeding. In the meantime visits between Melissa and her parents were again strictly controlled. They were never allowed to see her alone during the eighteen months the Center kept her. The doctors had the idea that by depriving the child of affection and other comforts they could *make* her swallow. As her father explained,

> It was like a battle that they said, "You can swallow, Melissa," and Melissa says, "I can't swallow." They said, "We're going to *prove* to you you can swallow." [55]

But the trouble was, apparently, that Melissa really could not swallow.

After eighteen months the Medical Center gave up on Melissa and sent her to Rinsley's unit at Topeka State, where the battle intensified. Lacking legal control, her parents were able to do nothing about this move. Rinsley followed the same treatment principles as the staff at the Medical Center, of course, only more so. As we have already seen, Rinsley fully expects a "resistance phase" with all of his patients, and there was no reason why Melissa should prove an exception. And so, in her father's words,

> It was just a fight. It was a hospital versus a child, in just total, every day—just like, just like you would, what I would hear about they would do in a communist concentration camp, you know, just, "You're wrong, Melissa. You're lying. Why don't you swallow?" And it was just a fight. She resisted them. They resisted her with, with all kinds of punishments, of not being able to see us, not doing this, not doing that, locked in her room. [56]

It was a fight, but a fight, oddly, that Rinsley's unit was not winning. They could not make Melissa swallow. She weighed twenty-eight pounds and she was only nine, then ten, then eleven years old, a little girl probably suffering from cerebral palsy—she almost died several times from other diseases—weak, skin and bones, but still "resisting," still, that is, not swallowing.

Rinsley's unit kept Melissa for three years and in all that time they never broke her "resistance." Yet they did manage to change her in other ways, to transform her from a smiling child who "would hug people, she never met a stranger, she had a very outgoing personality," to a child who hated the staff so much she would do nothing, nothing at all they wanted her to do:

> It got so bad that she would not walk. She would not talk. She would not sit in a chair. . . . She just gave up her life. She just said, "There's no sense in going on, ever." She just gave up.[57]

She just gave up. Except that she still would not—or is it could not?—swallow.

Sometime during the third year on Rinsley's unit, when Melissa was eleven, she choked to death during a tube feeding. No one was with her at the time. According to her father,

> She died in restraints. And when she was dead—she died in restraints, and she couldn't get up for herself. She choked to death. And then—she was kicking and hollering, what we understand it. But they were so fed up with her. They said they were short . . . on staff that night, and when they were short on staff, they said they, as sometimes they did, they just let her holler and kick. And what she was doing this time, she was hollering and kicking for help and she choked to death.[58]

She choked to death, it would seem, because the tube

backed up somehow and Melissa really could not swallow her food.

It takes a certain dedication to pursue a course of action for years on end when it is clearly not working. Some people might call this dedication fanaticism. On the other hand, some people have called Melissa's parents fanatics; they are fundamentalist Christians and when they took her out of the Medical Center the first time they made the mistake of saying that they were going to pray for her. That seems to have triggered something in the minds of the psychiatrists there who apparently thought they were going to give up medicine and try for a faith cure. But Melissa's parents had no such intention, they say; they intended to pray *and* to continue following medical instructions—with the love and care parents frequently manifest. There is no doubt in my mind that Melissa's parents loved her, no matter how many problems, how much anguish she created for them. It is not so clear that the psychiatrists loved Melissa. With amazing restraint her parents characterize the psychiatrists as

> . . . a bunch of people that really walk around like computers and zombies. It seems like they wouldn't show any emotion, emotion was out, parenthood was out, God. . . . There's no way for doctors and psychiatrists to take the place of parents.[59]

God, parenthood, love were out; they had all been replaced by psychiatric theory. A theory to which they were willing to sacrifice a child's life.

I have tried to allow for the possibility that I am merely being sentimental about Melissa or about children in general. Crazy children can indeed be difficult to deal with; they can be relentlessly violent, they can destroy families, drive parents mad, they can even resist treatment. But it is highly doubtful that Melissa was ever in any sense crazy, unless Rinsley's staff drove her crazy. Furthermore, I have consistently understated the case against Rinsley's methods. I have quoted nothing I could not produce or verify in a court of law. The observation that staff members come to be seen as "plunderers and murderers" by both parents and children is Rinsley's, not mine. Melissa's story is taken directly from a tape-recorded interview with her parents and the tape is clear and easy to hear. I have not said that Rinsley is responsible for Melissa's death, and I do not mean to imply it. Melissa's parents instituted a suit against Rinsley and others involved in the case, but that does not mean that negligence can be presumed.[60]

Yet I have reached a point where I can no longer contain myself. I must express my overwhelming anger and rage at the unbelievable arrogance of this man's methods. On the basis of a half-baked, highly speculative theory about what is going on in children's heads, a theory no one will ever be able to confirm or deny, he justifies forcible legal separation between parent and child,[61] highly controlled visitation rights, long periods of seclusion for the child, the use of physical restraints, and God knows what other cruelties he calls treatment. Has he done any follow-up studies to evaluate the long-term effectiveness of his methods? I have scanned his writings and found none.[62] Does it ever occur to him that he might be *wrong?* That his whole theoretical analysis and its treatment implications might be one big fat mistake? I have found no evidence of self-doubt.

What does it take to put a stop to such a man? How many more children must die?

What it takes to stop such people is a reliable system of accountability, a system conspicuously absent in Kansas and in most other states. I doubt very much whether Dr. Walter Menninger, clinical Director at Topeka State, has ever called Dr. Donald Rinsley into his office and said, "Look here, you can't do that." Rinsley is a *professional.* Almost by definition that means that no one holds him

accountable. And so we have this total picture, a picture
that could be reproduced in countless other places with
different details but the same general outline. A psychiatrist gains some kind of tenure in a mental hospital, a
relatively unassailable position which frees him to pursue
his notions about treatment without interference from
anybody. He defends that position, both for himself and
for the profession, against efforts to dislodge him or his
kind or to make them accountable for their methods to
some higher authority. The administrator who may want
to make him accountable or to bring change into the system finds himself in a bind. Both professional courtesy
and the reality of his need to attract staff by giving them a
free hand prevents him from taking effective action. So
the status quo is preserved. Every reform, every new administrative manipulation of the system comes to nothing.

Mental hospitals are full of men like Rinsley. And
mental hospitals are the same kinds of places now that they
have always been.

III

Mental hospitals, however, also contain people dedicated to rapid, indeed revolutionary change. It would be
a mistake to think of all mental hospitals as essentially
horrific places dominated by conservatives determined to
protect their positions and points of view against all attack.
Some hospitals have more of these people than others; a
lucky few don't have any at all. Even at Topeka State there
are innovators. Right next door to Rinsley's unit a young
woman runs an attractive nursery school where mothers
in outpatient treatment bring their little children, watch
them play and are taught by the staff how to interact with
their children in a healthy manner. Only a few miles from
Hudson River State Hospital in Poughkeepsie there is a
unit at another hospital, Harlem Valley, which has
achieved a remarkable record in only one year of opera-

tion; fewer than 4 percent of the patients it has discharged have returned to any institution for residential treatment.[63] That contrasts with a statewide recidivism rate of well over 20 percent.[64]

This unit is an excellent example of what can be done with a custodial institution when enough enthusiasm and intelligence are brought to bear upon it. Harlem Valley State Hospital is located in Wingdale, New York, deep in the backwoods of Dutchess County, miles from anywhere. Originally designed to be a prison, it has been known for many years for the quality of its custodial care; in fact, veteran mental patients used to aspire to be sent there. The experienced, relatively stable staff was dedicated to providing a clean environment and the best possible food and clothing. The place was so well run that many doctors who worked for the state, like the old-time mental patients, tried to get transferred there when they neared retirement age because the work load was so light. This is not to say, of course, that Harlem Valley was a nice place. We are still talking about a mental hospital. And while the hospital kept patients clean and well fed, it did not pretend to treat them.

Then in 1973 a new Director, Anthony Primelo, whose mission it was to unitize the hospital, came to Harlem Valley. Traditionally the hospital had served New York City; then New York City was taken out of its provenance and Putnam and portions of Westchester County became the hospital's catchment areas. When Primelo arrived the hospital had been serving these areas for about four years; but it still contained a large number of patients who were originally from New York City. All of these patients had been at the hospital at least four years; most of them had been there much longer. The average length of stay for the New York patients, in fact, was over twenty years. When Primelo unitized the hospital, therefore, he placed all the New York City patients in one unit, the

Metro Unit, and assigned a young psychologist named
Martin Von Holden to run it. Von Holden's mandate was
to return his eight hundred or so patients, all of them, as
I say, long-term, some of them resident in the hospital
forty years or more, to the community.[65]

By any standards Von Holden's job was a difficult
one. He was faced with returning more than eight hundred thoroughly institutionalized patients to communities
they had long ago forgotten, with which they had no real
ties of any kind; and his staff was committed to the rigid
hierarchical roles common to custodial institutions and the
paternalistic attitudes those roles engender.[66] Most of the
staff thought of the patients as children who would always
be in their care and most of the patients thought of the
hospital as home. Theoretically Von Holden could simply have discharged his patients *en masse,* but even if
he had wanted to Primelo forbade this tactic. The
Department of Mental Hygiene in New York has been
widely accused of dumping thousands of patients on un-
prepared communities. Some New York mental hospitals
have dumped patients, discharging them indiscriminately
without any provision for follow-up care. But not Primelo;
Primelo insisted that patients be carefully screened before
being placed in the community, he insisted on follow-up,
and he insisted that the community facilities they were
placed in be not only suitable in general, but suitable for
each particular patient sent to it. Primelo is a conscientious administrator who had no wish to be attacked for
dumping his patients.

Von Holden is also conscientious; more than that, he
seems to be someone born to the task of administration.
Faced with a difficult challenge, he carried the additional
burdens of being young—barely thirty—and of not being a
psychiatrist. It is quite unusual, though becoming less so,
for unit chiefs not to be psychiatrists.[67] In spite of these

drawbacks, however, Von Holden has been successful. Here is how he did it.

Administratively Von Holden established the Metro Unit in a single chain of command.[68] He divided the Unit into four teams, subdividing each team into area teams and each area team into small groups. The small groups consisted of eight to ten patients and an aide, the group leader. Teams were led not by psychiatrists, although psychiatrists were attached to them, but by a nurse in one case, social workers and a psychologist in the others. Team leaders reported directly to Von Holden. He himself had a staff of two, a clinical deputy chief who had to be a psychiatrist for legal reasons, to formalize discharge decisions, and an administrative deputy chief who had once been a nursing supervisor. There was no separate nursing hierarchy and no separate clinical or psychiatric hierarchy. The psychiatrists worked on the teams as team members. Von Holden was proceeding on the theory that if psychiatrists had plenty of opportunity to do good clinical work they would stop fretting about their status and lose interest in administrative roles for which they were not suited. To a limited extent this has been true, although the Unit now has fewer psychiatrists than it started out with. But then it has fewer patients. Other clinical personnel, such as psychologists, have been content to work as team members without special status.

Von Holden established this administrative structure in one day, the day the Unit came into being. There was no period of transition, no negotiation about roles and responsibilities, no discussion and no argument. Von Holden decreed it: that was the way it was going to be. He called a meeting, presented everyone with a document describing the Unit's organization, and told the staff that he expected each team to have a full, scheduled program going by the end of the week. He gave the impression that there was no time to experiment, that the organizational structure was simply an accomplished fact, and that he was definitely in charge of it.

During this time Von Holden says he played roles furiously. On one of his first days on the job one of the teams lost a patient. It came time late in the afternoon to count noses, and this man was nowhere to be found. After some desultory looking someone informed Von Holden that the man was lost and asked whether he should call the hospital security force, which was standard operating procedure for the rest of the hospital when someone was lost.

Von Holden erupted: "We do not lose people on the Metro Unit!" He went to the patient's ward and personally started searching for him, looking under every bed, opening closets, checking stairwells and basements and tunnels, every possible place the patient might be hiding. If he found a locked door and an aide told him the patient couldn't possibly be behind it, it had been locked all day, Von Holden insisted nevertheless that it be unlocked and checked. Soon his whole staff was running around the hospital looking for the man. Someone finally found him in a locked basement room the hospital painters used to store their equipment.

It is clear enough what Von Holden was up to. The message was not just that the Metro Unit didn't lose patients. The message was a more general one about accountability. Staff responsibility was not compartmentalized according to whether you were an aide or a security policeman. Staff were responsible for people, and you cannot compartmentalize a person. Staff did not get one piece of him, the "therapeutic" or the "custodial" or the "security" piece; he was *all* theirs, he was a human being, not to be divided up, and they were accountable for his welfare. Accountable to Von Holden. To underline the message Von Holden moved to the hospital grounds and put himself on call twenty-four hours a day.

This kind of commitment cuts across both hierarchical and professional lines and demolishes the job description. But commitment, Von Holden believed, was essential, particularly commitment from the aides. These were the people in continuous contact with the patients, the people who dealt with them the most and could be most effective in preparing them to leave the hospital. These were the people, in fact, best suited to *treat* the patients. Under the hospital's old system, of course, the aides had had no treatment responsibilities; they were considered incapable of "treating" patients in any meaningful fashion. As a result the aides took little interest in any but custodial work, accepted the limitations of their role without question, and were reluctant to take on greater responsibilities. The job was low in status but very secure. The picture is a familiar one. Von Holden erased it in one stroke. Aides, he said, would now have primary responsibility for patients, not just in custodial matters but in treatment as well. The small groups led by aides were to meet at least three times a week.

> At this meeting the small group leader may discuss with the patient such things as medication (side effects, responses to medication, etc.), plans for discharge, responsibility of the patient in and outside the hospital and any individual problems that the patient may bring up.[69]

To emphasize the aides' new responsibilities he discounted the role of the professionals:

> The group leader is completely responsible for the total care of the patient members in his/her group. He is responsible for care of the group members while in the hospital through aftercare treatment and crisis

intervention if necessary. The small group leader is responsible for making sure that a treatment plan is formed with the help of other staff members and that its goals are met.[70]

Von Holden did not expect the aides to do in-depth psychotherapy with patients, of course. Treatment was to consist of something akin to William Glasser's "reality therapy," or, more descriptively, attitude therapy.[71] At small group meetings the group would discuss "real" events and "real" issues, such as hospital routines, practical arrangements for leaving the hospital, what would be expected of patients outside, practical problems and fears the patient might have, and so on. In daily contacts with patients, aides would adopt attitudes appropriate to a patient's behavior pattern. If a patient was withdrawn, an aide was "actively friendly," tried to get the patient involved in ward activities, initiated contact with the patient, suggested things for him to do, and made every effort to show his interest in him. If a patient was "suspicious," aides were "passively friendly," did not seek the patient out, let him initiate contact, were helpful on demand, and tried not to frighten him. The aides made no effort, in other words, to penetrate the psychodynamics of the patient's "illness." They simply responded to patients in a manner consistently adapted to the patient's dominant behavioral mode.

To encourage aides to take the responsibility he gave them, Von Holden did a number of unusual things. For one, he gave the aides access to the records of their patients. Not only did he give them access, he had the aides present their patients at clinical team meetings, giving a full history from the records, describing the patients' present behavior, family situation, and so on, and their opinion of the patients' suitability for discharge. In short, they presented the case. To everyone's horror he even had aides present cases before psychiatrists and administrators at hospital-wide meetings, without telling anyone that the person doing the presentation was an aide. He also gave aides full responsibility for family contact; it was up to them to write the families, meet them when they came to visit, answer their questions and talk to them about the patients' discharge. Von Holden trained aides to make site visits outside the hospital and report on the suitability of family care and adult home facilities. As patients began to be discharged the aides were expected to visit them as often as once or twice a week and make sure they were doing all right. Von Holden wanted them to learn that their job was not with an institution but with people and that their responsibility followed the people wherever they were sent.

None of this was easy, none of it happened smoothly. Some aides resisted this abrupt change in their roles, some left the Unit. Others were hesitant or uncertain, all were concerned about losing their jobs. Psychologists, psychiatrists and social workers spent a large part of their time initially with the aides, reassuring them about their capabilities, helping them with problems and training them informally to do this kind of work. The aides are still adapting after a year; some of them still think of the patients as children, they are slow sometimes to contribute their point of view at meetings. These are people, after all, who used to stand up automatically when a doctor entered the room. Nevertheless there has been fundamental change. Aides discovered in small group meetings that many of the problems patients talked about were similar to their own. Aides and patients became friends; when patients were discharged aides would visit them on their own time, correspond with them, and act as their advocate with welfare and other governmental and service agencies. The commitment is real and the system is working.

As of this writing the Metro Unit has placed more

than three hundred patients in various types of homes in New York City and on Long Island. Only nine of those discharged have returned to mental hospitals anywhere for any reason. Part of this unusual success, to be sure, is fortuitous. Many of the patients on the Metro Unit were to all intents and purposes sane. If they had ever been crazy they had long since gotten over it. These patients were easy to place and there was little chance they would have to return to a hospital. But this cannot by itself account for the Unit's success. The great majority of discharged patients displayed the extremely limited repertoire of behaviors which characterizes the chronic mental patient. If it were not for the Unit's commitment to its patients and its intense follow-up work, most of those patients would probably be back in Creedmoor or Brooklyn State Hospital or wherever.

It is worth noting that the Unit's success did not depend on an enlarged budget or additional staff. The Unit has, in fact, taken on an additional responsibility, a "live" catchment area in a portion of Westchester County, and is setting up a day-care treatment program, a mobile treatment team, possibly a halfway house as well, all in the community, all with hospital staff. While some staff were added with the new catchment area, the Unit has no more staff to fulfill its responsibilities than similar units elsewhere; it sends workers into the community for follow-up and maintains ward activities with the same staffing ratios it started with. Much can be done with little, says Von Holden, if people put their minds to it. This is only a homily, but it is hard to explain things more precisely. What matters is commitment. Von Holden has learned the secret of motivating his people, and when people are motivated, like master chefs, they will find ways to do much with little.

Much of the Unit's success, it should be noted, stems from Von Holden's dynamism. Other units at Harlem

Valley, organized along similar lines, have not done nearly as well. Administratively, nevertheless, there are lessons to be learned from the Metro Unit. First, it is clear that flattening the administrative hierarchy and distributing treatment power to the aides mobilizes the aides' personal resources, their capacity to do more meaningful work. Aides have always had a great deal of custodial power over patients, of course, but they have never been given the kinds of responsibility for patient treatment we have seen here. Those functions were always reserved for professionals. The Metro Unit's organization, however, gave them that responsibility, and the Unit's experience has shown that aides can be effective "therapists"; they can, that is, relate to patients as people, become friendly with them and committed to their welfare, in the context of an administrative structure which supports that kind of relationship.

The second point to be made about this structure is that it does not try to spare the feelings of the professionals. Psychiatrists, psychologists, and social workers stand in the single chain of command like everyone else and they are made accountable for their work like everyone else. As we have seen, professionals expect a free hand; they consider themselves accountable to nothing but the standards of their profession. Here is Von Holden, however, monitoring their professional practice, telling them what kind of treatment they will undertake and what the goals of treatment shall be, and holding them accountable for what they do.

As a result he has lost some of his psychiatrists. And those who stayed on, as far as I can gather, made no serious attempt to fit into the system.[72] They did not come to team meetings regularly, they did not cooperate with the structure, they did not visibly subordinate themselves to it. But it didn't matter. The Metro Unit functioned without them. It did not need them, it did not take them into account. As we learned in the third chapter and relearn here, professional roles are not sacrosanct. Other people, even psychiatric aides, can perform genuine therapeutic work. The professionals vanished, and the world went on without them.

The way Von Holden is operating is not, needless to say, the way things are normally done. Normally a hospital or unit administrator believes that professionals, particularly psychiatrists, are essential to a therapeutic system and he makes heroic efforts to attract them. Normally he is unsuccessful. Who wants to work in a mental hospital when he can make twice as much in the comfort of his own office, with a portrait of Freud on the wall? The hospital jobs thus fall to foreign medical graduates who have little understanding of American culture and are notoriously ineffective in their work.[73] Occasionally, however, an administrator does manage to attract a large professional staff. His hospital or unit is then taken as a paradigm for others to follow.

Under Israel Zwerling, Bronx State Hospital in New York City was such a place, and other hospitals have taken this route at one time or another: Boston State, for example, under Milton Greenblatt.[74] The trouble with such a policy is that often a basic antagonism exists between the interests of professionals, which lie in experiment, in innovation, and in ideas, and the service needs of a population.

Take the story of the psychiatric residents at Bronx State. One of the main professional emphases there is on community psychiatry. A unit of Bronx State known as the Tremont Crisis Center serves a community of about one hundred thousand in the mid-Bronx with a mixture of black, Puerto Rican, and white ethnic neighborhoods. It is run by a psychoanalyst-turned-community-psychiatrist named Edward Hornick, who wears loud clothes, swears a lot, and the last time I saw him was sweeping the floor at one of the Center's buildings. Hornick is devoted to the principles of community psychiatry. He maintains a ward at the hospital for his patients but his goal is not to have to use it. He wants to keep all his patients functioning in the community, and if he has to shoot them in the ass with prolixin once a month he damn well doesn't care.[75] Israel Zwerling, until recently Director of Bronx State, is also devoted to the principles of community psychiatry. Zwerling believes, furthermore, that it is or ought to be the psychiatry of the future, the direction psychiatry should follow. So Zwerling decided to put all his marbles in this one basket. On July 1, 1973, the hospital was getting twenty-seven new psychiatric residents to be trained. Zwerling put every single one of them in the Tremont Crisis Center.

Now consider another arm of Bronx State Hospital, a facility oriented, like the Tremont Crisis Center, to keeping patients out of the hospital, interested in community psychiatry, trying to establish contact with other community agencies. I refer to the Bronx Aftercare Clinic. In the spring of 1973 the Bronx Aftercare Clinic was serving a population of nearly five hundred thousand people, five times that served by the Tremont Crisis Center. It had the time of one and three-fifths psychiatrists. It had no psychiatric residents and would get none.

Obviously the service needs of the Bronx called for a more equitable distribution of psychiatrists throughout the population. Professional interests, on the other hand, seemed to call for the intensive training of community psychiatrists in what amounted to a community laboratory setting. The professionals won.

Bronx State, like other "progressive" mental hospitals, is an instructive place, and it has a high reputation among professionals. Their opportunities at Bronx State are remarkable: they can watch family therapy sessions from behind one-way mirrors; they can do behavior mod with a token economy system; they can live with Hungarian or Puerto Rican or black families and get to know those subcultures and their pathologies. They can collect statistics and publish articles. The place is a big psychiatric university. Which is precisely the basis, interestingly, on which Alan Miller criticizes it:

> I think there have been times when . . . the Bronx tends to be elitist. I think that as the equivalent of the university . . . some of the bias of university life has infected [it], not always benignly, and some of them, you know,—when I hear any of the hospitals . . . some of the people in the hospitals misreading, but understandably misreading, something that's said on the administration level, "So and so is too sick for us," then I know something's wrong.[76]

The point Miller is rather hesitantly trying to make here is clear enough. Bronx State Hospital thinks of itself as a professional institution first, a state hospital second. And it is clear enough that that reverses the recognized priorities of state mental hospitals. As Commissioner, however, Miller appears to have done nothing about his criticisms; he merely voiced them. It is just one more example of professional courtesy. In psychiatry one professional leaves another alone.

I know of no specific abuses associated with this hospital. Bronx State Hospital is not the same kind of place as Topeka State at all. The doors are open, patients come and go (except on certain wards) as they please. There could be no abuse of children because, until recently, there was no children's unit. The quality of the professionals at Bronx State is high. At Bronx State it is not so much a question of making individual psychiatrists accountable as of making the whole professional system accountable to the public it supposedly serves. In the words of one set of critics, ". . . professional autonomy results in extremely limited social accountability." [77] At Bronx State the professionals have all the autonomy they could possibly want. The result is that professional interests override service needs. And the professionals all persuade themselves that this is a huge success. It is—for them.

IV

A development which raises the question of professional accountability in a particularly acute way is the battle over the "right to treatment" currently being waged in the Federal courts. A lawyer and physician named Morton Birnbaum originated the "right to treatment" concept in 1960. In an article in the *American Bar Association Journal,* Birnbaum suggested that if people were committed to mental hospitals against their will on the basis of their "need for care and treatment," it became incumbent upon the committing agency, the state, to provide treatment commensurate with the need.[78] To deprive people of their liberty on that basis and not provide treatment for them was a violation of due process, and therefore unconstitutional. The logic of Birnbaum's principle seems self-evident, but not until 1966 did it become operative in a court decision, and in that particular case *(Rouse v. Cameron)* only in reference to criminal law. The first application of the "right to treatment" principle to involuntarily committed mental patients did not come until 1971, with *Wyatt v. Stickney,* which is still in the courts on appeal.

Wyatt v. Stickney was brought in the state of Alabama when Dr. Stonewall B. Stickney, Commissioner of the Alabama Department of Mental Health, fired fifty employees of Bryce State Hospital for reasons of economy.[79] The employees sued on the basis that the patients' "right to treatment" was being abridged by this action. Organizations representing mental patients joined the case, as well as various professional groups, including the American Orthopsychiatric Association, the American Psychological Association, and the American Civil Liberties Union, among others, all of which quickly recognized the case's potential importance. Experts from all over the United States appeared as witnesses and others submitted depositions. The deposition taken from Israel Zwerling runs to some one hundred pages. The professionals understood very well what was happening in this case. The courts were entering virgin legal territory, and the professionals were clamoring to be guides.

Federal Judge Frank Johnson handed down his initial decision in March, 1971, and continued to develop law in the case through the spring of 1972. In his decisions Judge Johnson not only affirmed the "right to treatment" principle, he established a set of "minimum constitutional standards" of treatment which the state *must* meet in order to comply with the law. These standards include "(1) a humane psychological and physical environment, (2) qualified staff in numbers sufficient to administer adequate treatment and (3) individualized treatment plans." [80] In an appendix to his order the Judge defined these standards more precisely. A humane psychological and physical environment included a right to privacy and dignity, rights to visitation, reasonable access to a telephone and uncensored written communication, the maintenance of ordinary civil rights such as the right to marry and the right to vote, a right to wear your own clothes, a right to be free from physical restraint and isolation unless ordered and justified in writing by a "Qualified Mental Health Professional," and so on.[81] The order contains twenty separate rights under this provision alone; it details minimum square footage per patient, the number of toilets and showers per patient; it is, in short, comprehensive.

It is no less comprehensive in the other two areas: the provisions for adequate staff and for individualized treatment plans. The order enshrined the idea of continuity of care, that one "Qualified Mental Health Professional" shall have overall responsibility throughout a patient's hospital career for implementing his treatment plan; it set standards for patient records; it delved into the area of the treatment of children. And it allowed no excuses: ". . . the unavailability of neither funds, nor staff and facilities, will justify a default by defendants in the provision of suitable treatment for the mentally ill." [82] If the state of Alabama could not for practical reasons comply with this sweeping order, it would nevertheless have to comply—or else turn its mental patients loose.[83]

This is one way to change the state mental hospitals, and it may work where nothing else has. Few mental hospitals anywhere in the country meet the standards mandated by Judge Johnson; if these standards become a constitutional requirement under due process, most of the states will have to upgrade their mental health systems markedly. Since the case is still at issue, however, it would be premature to make predictions. Alabama is bearing the brunt of things right now. That state's mental health system is unquestionably poor; to bring it up to the standards set in Judge Johnson's ruling would cost $110 million, according to George Wallace, Governor, money the state claims it does not have.[84] Nevertheless Alabama mental hospitals are trying bravely to make some improvements. The patient population at Bryce State Hospital dropped from 5,617 in 1971 to 3,332 at the beginning of 1974.[85] Bryce State Hospital has been advertising (unsuccessfully) for five psychiatrists in an attempt to meet the Judge's requirements.

Wyatt v. Stickney was only the beginning of what has become a flood of litigation. Shortly after Judge Johnson's decision, Bruce Ennis of the Mental Health Law Project, collaborating with the New York State Association for Retarded Children, filed a right-to-treatment suit in New York against the state on behalf of mentally retarded patients at the notorious Willowbrook State School on Staten Island. A court in Minnesota accepted the right-to-treatment principle in a suit against Minnesota mental hospitals and the judge suggested in his decision that the use of seclusion and the excessive use of drugs may constitute cruel and unusual punishment.[86] There have been cases in Tennessee and Michigan and an important case in Florida in which an ex-mental patient collected damages from two state hospital psychiatrists on the grounds that they had confined him against his will and failed to treat him.[87] Recently the Federal Government, acting through the Justice Department, sued the state of Maryland, charging that mentally retarded patients at Rosewood State Hospital were being denied treatment.[88] In February, 1974, suit was filed against St. Elizabeth's Hospital in Washington, D. C., which is a Federal facility; this suit is an attempt, among other goals, to "extend the legal principle of right to treatment beyond institutional walls, by attempting to compel placement of more than 1,500 St. Elizabeth's patients outside the hospital." [89] Suits of this kind will no doubt continue to appear as the trend toward legal intervention in the mental health system grows.

These suits have originated for the most part with young socially-minded lawyers, but the psychiatric establishment has become increasingly interested in them. The American Psychiatric Association, for example, stayed out of *Wyatt v. Stickney* at first; when the case went to the Fifth District Court of Appeals, however, the APA joined the plaintiffs as *amicus curiae*. Since then the APA has joined other suits, including a suit against a local ordinance discriminating against ex-mental patients and the suit against St. Elizabeth's Hospital. In the last named suit, APA joined not just as an *amicus curiae* but as a plaintiff. This suit names various St. Elizabeth's staff members (as well as Bertram Brown, Director of the National Institute of Mental Health, which operates St. Elizabeth's) as defendants; thus the APA finds itself in the curious position of suing its own members. Comments Brown: "One finally finds the answer to schizophrenia. My professional self has sued my political self. And I will find myself testifying sincerely on both sides." [90]

Brown's dilemma is psychiatry's. Psychiatrists must take both sides in these right-to-treatment cases. Psychiatrists working for the state must defend it against judiciary encroachment. At the same time their professional ethic requires them to promote the cause of treatment against a state government which is not particularly interested in treatment. Their professional ethic requires it, and their self-interest. As one psychiatrist observes,

> First, litigation is a powerful if blunt weapon that can affect our goals for the better or the worse. Second, if APA does not provide guidance and leadership in litigation, change will more likely be destructive, and psychiatrists may be held *personally* accountable for money damages. Thus, APA must be involved both for professional reasons and for reasons of self-interest.[91]

Personal accountability is the killer. Already, as we noted above, two state hospital psychiatrists have been found liable in Florida; the damages came to more than $38,000. From the point of view of the psychiatric establishment, the central issue in right-to-treatment has become, who will set the treatment standards? To whom, that is, will psychiatrists be accountable? They clearly do not want to be accountable to lawyers or even to judges. Basically they want to be accountable only to themselves. What we are seeing, I believe, is a growing realization on the part of psychiatrists that if they want to prevent wholesale encroachment on their professional preserve they are going to have to join the lawyers and try to direct their efforts. As one young psychiatrist puts it,

> As this suit represents a possible trend, we may see the class action suit used more often in the medical field in

the future. We must be prepared for this and through interdisciplinary discussions join with lawyers in attaining the goals which we desire.[92]

Or as another says more plainly,

> Psychiatrists at this time must deal with the problem of the camel whose snout is in our tent. We can recognize that there is a right to treatment. We can also insist that courts use simple yardsticks—which psychiatry will have to develop quickly—to keep the legal determination of treatment adequacy from usurping psychiatric authority and determining hospital policy.[93]

Psychiatrists are in favor of the right-to-treatment as long as they determine what "treatment" shall be.

And that is the flaw in the right-to-treatment movement. The movement threatens to become a movement to strengthen professional control over the operation of mental health facilities, a movement which, in the end, will actually increase the freedom of mental health professionals to put into practice, in the name of "treatment," whatever insane idea may occur to them. If I had to predict an outcome in the *Wyatt v. Stickney* case, for example, I would guess that the courts will affirm the right-to-treatment principle but will leave the setting of treatment standards to some sort of independent board of mental health professionals. The right-to-treatment principle unmistakably implies standards of treatment, so if the court does grant the right it will have to do something about setting standards. But it will probably give the problem of standards back to the psychiatrists rather than involve the courts in the endless controversies surrounding psychiatric treatment. In the long run that can only strengthen psychiatric control.

In all the discussion about the right-to-treament, however, only one group sees this danger:

> The right to treatment issue, now on appeal with

Wyatt v. Stickney and *Burnham v. State of Georgia* in the Fifth Circuit Court in New Orleans, was discussed vigorously in the conference, with several former mental patients insisting that the right *not* to be treated was the tantamount [sic] issue.[94]

The right *not* to be treated—that is what the mental patients want. But who listens to former mental patients? Certainly not psychiatrists, perhaps not even lawyers. For they are obviously crazy irresponsible radicals. Nothing they say can be taken at face value. Their protests must be seen as a manifestation of "negative transference," not as raising real issues.

The true irony is that former mental patients are the people mostly like to *know* what mental health professionals will perpetrate in the name of "treatment." Through personal experience they *know* that continued use of phenothiazine derivatives (Thorazine, Stelazine, and so on) and other neuroleptic drugs leads to an irreversible syndrome of the central nervous system known as tardive dyskinesia which is characterized by uncontrollable protrusion of the tongue, uncontrollable facial distortion, and "other bizarre muscular activity." [95] In mental hospitals everywhere neuroleptic drugs are the treatment of choice, indeed the only treatment available in most cases. They *know* that in the name of "treatment" in the 1940's and 1950's neurosurgeons performed lobotomies indiscriminately upon tens of thousands of people, that they are performing them today, and that the concept of "informed consent" to psychosurgery in a mental hospital setting is laughable.[96] They *know* that a high staffing ratio such as exists at Topeka State Hospital may lead not to a higher level of treatment but to closer observation and control of behavior. They *know* that it is a common technique in behavior modification programs to take all "privileges" away from a patient, including such "privileges" as food, a place to sleep, freedom of movement, clothing, cigarettes, you name it, to be returned to him only on evidence of compliance to norms of behavior dictated by the staff.[97] They *know* that shock "treatment" may lead to permanent memory loss. They *know* that patients diagnosed as depressed may be forced in the name of "treatment" to scrub a floor with a toothbrush. I could go on and on, but we have had enough horrors in this chapter already. The point is that psychiatrists, to put it as kindly as possible, make mistakes. Frequently they cannot admit to them and insist on making them again and again. They insist, furthermore, on their *freedom* to make mistakes, on being accountable, that is, only to themselves. We cannot have it that way any more. We must find means to make the professionals accountable to the people they serve, who may at any moment turn out to be ourselves.

VII
Getting Out of the System

Libertas est potestas faciendi id quod jure liceat.

I

Being a mental patient is not a sometime thing. We have followed very roughly in this book the same path a mental patient follows into and through the mental health system. We have noted the importance of the initial decision that someone is crazy and needs treatment, traced the pattern of abandonment within the referral system that leads him inevitably to the mental hospital, and talked about his experience in the mental hospital itself. Now he discovers that the process cannot be reversed. He will always be a mental patient. Once affixed, the mental patient designation becomes a permanent social identity. In a very real sense, nobody gets out of the system.

People do, on the other hand, get out of mental hospitals. Indeed, there has been a countrywide push to get patients out of the hospitals and back "into the community." The new psychiatric ideology is to discharge patients within thirty or sixty or ninety days of admission in order to prevent the onset of institutionalization. Most psychiatrists know now that long-term hospitalization is pathogenic, that it creates chronic schizophrenics. The national hospitalization figures therefore show a dramatic decline in average patient census over the last twenty years, from more than 500,000 in 1953 to 248,562 in 1973.[1] At the same time, the admission rate has climbed from well under 200,000 per year to 377,020 over the same period.[2] More people are being admitted to mental hospitals, but they are staying a shorter length of time. Twenty years ago a mental patient might expect to stay in the hospital a year or more. Now the median length of stay runs slightly over forty days.[3]

A shift in psychiatric ideology accounts for only part of the story, however. Money accounts for the other part. Increasingly the patients being pushed out of the hospital and back "into the community" are not new admissions but the long-term chronic patients who have been in the hospital ten, twenty, or thirty years, patients such as those in the Metro Unit at Harlem Valley State Hospital. The state has discovered how much cheaper it is to maintain these people outside the mental hospitals. In New York, for example, during the fiscal year ending March 31, 1973, it cost the state approximately $24 a day, or $750 a month, to maintain a patient in a state hospital.[4] With inflation those figures have been rising rapidly. The cost of maintaining the same patient in what is known as an "adult home" is only $375 a month, and since this is a welfare cost the Federal Government pays a percentage of that figure. All across the United States, therefore, we are seeing the wholesale transfer of chronic, long-term mental patients from state hospitals to the "community." This move has little to do with psychiatry or its ideologies. It is an administrative maneuver to save money.[5]

Even though people are getting out of mental hospitals in droves, nonetheless, they are not getting out of the system. Adult homes and family care homes, where many of the chronic patients wind up, are as much a part of the mental health system as a mental hospital. Everyone who leaves the hospital, furthermore, is on record as having been a mental patient, and in most states his records are surprisingly available to official agencies of nearly any persuasion; everyone but the patient himself seems to have access to them. Some states—Missouri is an example where this has become an issue—are computerizing their records to make access even easier.

Thus the shameful news follows the ex-mental patient wherever he goes. If he applies for a job, normally he must conceal his past, fill up the gap or gaps in his resumé when he was in the hospital, and resort to other prevarications, because most employers do not knowingly hire ex-mental patients. In many states the application for a driver's license includes a question about whether the applicant has ever been institutionalized for a mental disorder. To obtain a license the ex-patient must once again lie, or else submit to the humiliation of having a psychiatrist attest to his stability. The idea is to keep tabs on the mental patient, to make sure he is "known." The day I left Hudson River State Hospital I was fingerprinted and photographed. Ex-mental patients are always on file.

Yet as always the system is full of contradictions. The public are woefully afraid of people known to be crazy so the mental health system maintains an extensive record bank on its patients. Meanwhile it typically makes no effort whatsover to follow the patients "into the community" and help them adjust to it. Their records follow patients, but the interest of caring mental health workers doesn't. Aftercare, as it is called, is one of the system's many mythological entities. Practically speaking, there is none.

My own experience is typical. As a voluntary patient under New York law, I could leave Hudson River upon three days' written notice, time enough for the hospital to institute involuntary commitment proceedings if it were so inclined. I gave the head nurse my notice and two days later, after the fingerprinting and the photographing, the

ward social worker took me down for an interview with
the unit chief. This man was a friendly, elderly psychiatrist
who asked me a few questions about my plans, chatted
about this and that, and signed some papers. Then I went
back to the ward, gathered up my possessions, and signed
for them. When my wife came for me the charge aide gave
her my two weeks' supply of Thorazine, Stelazine, and
Artane and instructed her about dosage.[6] With that we
left the hospital.

Then nothing. In most cases mental hospitals send
referral notices to a public health agency and/or, if the
patient has no family or other source of support, to the
welfare department, and theoretically that brings a public
health nurse or a social worker or both to see him. But
nobody called and nobody came. There was no follow-up,
no attempt at aftercare.[7]

This is the pattern nationwide. Upon release patients
are either not followed up at all, or else follow-up is so
long delayed that it loses whatever effect timeliness might
have had. A study conducted in Pennsylvania found that
after discharge "a mean of 60.9 days elapsed before the
first follow-up visits were made." [8] In another study conducted in Maryland, the median lapse was fifty-three days.[9]
In still another study, this one of aftercare in Kansas, social
workers to whom patients were referred upon discharge
actually made contact with them in only one third of the
cases. Some comments quoted in this last study summarize
the situation:

> "Aftercare is the greatest weakness in our treatment
> program."
> "Aftercare is one of the last frontiers to be crossed."
> "We would like to know what really goes on 'out there'.
> We don't know." [10]

Nothing goes on "out there." Aftercare is a bottle of tranquilizers.

It may be, however, a slight overstatement to say that there is *no* aftercare. In the last chapter I talked about the Metro Unit at Harlem Valley State Hospital. That unit conducts an extremely active aftercare program which has been largely responsible for preventing the rehospitalization of all but nine of its discharged patients. In isolated places elsewhere in the country similar efforts have produced similar results,[11] and some research attempts have been made as well to identify the variables which help ex-mental patients to make it in the community (or with their families), or at least keep them from returning to the mental hospital.[12] Most of the research concludes, not too surprisingly, that patients to whom an active aftercare program is available and who participate in it do better in the community than those who receive no aftercare at all. Usually, however, communities do not have aftercare programs, or these programs are not equipped or do not want to deal with chronic patients, or else there is no liaison between the hospital discharging the patient and the community receiving him and he gets lost. It is very unusual for a hospital unit to take on aftercare responsibilities itself, as the Metro Unit has done.

The absence of aftercare has become a major problem in states such as New York and California which have been discharging chronic mental patients in unprecedented numbers. Some hospitals have simply dumped their patients on communities without any advance notice or planning at all. One New York City welfare worker I talked to tells stories about busloads of ex-patients pulling up to welfare offices in Manhattan with their pink referral papers, unannounced, unattended, with instructions to apply for welfare.[13] The welfare people have had little choice but to place these patients on emergency home relief, which means, since the patients have no homes, placement in a welfare hotel, where they become the immediate targets of the drug addicts who inhabit them and the people who run them. No one is easier to rob, intimidate, brutalize or exploit than a confused, elderly ex-mental patient who has been living in the relatively sheltered environment of a mental hospital for the last twenty-five years. People who live near these hotels speak fearfully of hearing screams all through the night, empty liquor bottles being thrown out windows, the shouting that accompanies fistfights, wild laughter. Not all the noise, it should be noted, originates with ex-patients. Nevertheless these welfare hotels have become our new madhouses, modern ships of fools moored permanently in the cities. But at least, the ex-mental patients who live in them are back "in the community."

The community wants no part of them, naturally. Residents of neighborhoods in Manhattan actively campaign against the conversion of hotels or apartment buildings in their areas to the use of ex-patients.[14] New York City's Commissioner of Mental Health and Retardation, Dr. June Jackson Christmas, has proposed that the state convert empty buildings in the mental hospitals to "halfway houses for the chronically mentally ill"; she means, of course, that the state should take them back and fill the hospitals up again.[15] In the city of Long Beach on Long Island, which seems to have suffered an especially large influx of ex-mental patients from surrounding hospitals, the city fathers went so far as to pass a law against them. People under "continuous" psychiatric, medical, or nursing care would be barred from living in hotels or boarding homes in Long Beach.[16] A suit by civil liberties groups immediately challenged the ordinance, which appears to be blatantly unconstitutional. These examples are enough to taste the sentiments at work here. Even so savvy a person as June Jackson Christmas wants to ship all the crazies back to the mental hospital. It is obviously fine in principle to deaccession mental patients, to give them back their liberties, as long as you don't house them in *my* neighborhood.

The irony is that the ex-patient is no more "in the

community" than a passenger changing planes is "in" St. Louis. Both are transients; the ex-mental patient may spend ten or fifteen years in a proprietry home in Brooklyn but he is still at bottom someone who has been put there to die, he is on his way to the cemetery. No matter where the ex-patient lives, he lives in isolation from the community. He does not attend church. He does not spend money in local stores. He does not join organizations or participate in meetings. He does not write letters to the local newspaper. What he does is the same thing he did in the mental hospital. He watches television. He sits and stares. He sleeps.

I recently visited some adult homes in Queens. As the hospitals become increasingly sophisticated in their discharge methods they are using adult homes more and more as the preferred repositories, rather than dumping patients into welfare hotels. The adult homes are by far the best of the post-hospital facilities available to mental patients. They look very much like motels. Originally they were intended to serve as homes for what is known as the well geriatric, an older person, that is, who has no major health problems. In New York the State Board of Social Welfare licenses them on the basis of a code designed for a well-geriatric clientele. They provide maid service, three meals a day in the house dining room, a recreation worker to run bingo games and the like, and a few other marginal services. These are profit-making homes. Living in one would be something like spending your life in a crowded Holiday Inn where you shared a room with someone else, there was only one television set for everybody, and the food was often not very good.

The first home I visited was called Queens Manor and I knew right away that I was back in a mental hospital. It used to be a motel—Eddie Arcaro, the jockey, owned it—but now it is a mental hospital. Inside the front door there is a small lobby full of chairs lined up one next to the other, and all the chairs are full, ex-patients sitting there staring. Downstairs in a darkened room other patients watch television while still others sleep in their beds or roam the halls or pace about in the dining room. Three recreation workers from a private contractor come in in shifts and try to keep some of the patients active, but there is no real program and aftercare consists of setting each patient's medication by his plate at mealtimes. It might as well have been Hudson River State Hospital.

The patients who live in these homes are "free." They may come and go as they please, miss meals, refuse medications, move out. But freedom is a relative term. Sartre observes, following Marx, that a person cannot be free without the economic means to be free. The checks with which the government supports most ex-patients come made out in the patients' names, but it is the universal practice in adult homes for patients to sign their checks over to the proprietor. He then gives them a cash allowance of, normally, $17.50 a month. The rest is his. Actually it is all his; the law does not obligate him to give patients anything. If you smoke, $17.50 is almost cigarette money; but it is not freedom.

The adult homes are the best places available to ex-patients. They have no provision for aftercare, no rehabilitative programs of any kind, no contact with the community. They are small, isolated mental patient ghettoes. But they are still the best, better by far than any welfare hotel, better than most family care arrangements. So little does the State Board of Social Welfare fulfill its obligation to regulate them, however, that abuse of patients is common. The proprietor of one home in Queens bought a slum-type dwelling down the street from the home as quarters for his live-in dining room staff, all of whom, by the way, were illegal aliens from Colombia. The dwelling had no telephone, only one working toilet, no working sinks. The electricity on the ground floor was out of order. He took three ex-mental patients from the home and put them in the slum dwelling on the ground floor. His practice was to pick these people up in the morning, give them breakfast at the main building and let them spend the day there, then take them back at night. The same proprietor also had an ex-patient housed in a large linen closet (no windows and no ventilation), others in the recreation room on cots, and so on to a total of twelve ex-patients over his licensed capacity. These extra people added little if anything to his costs, so that at $375 a month per patient he was skimming at least three thousand dollars per month, or thirty-six thousand dollars a year, from the state. The patients, of course, were helpless to do anything about it. When the social worker came to visit, they might complain that they didn't really live here in the home, they lived down the street in that slum dwelling, but the proprietor was right there to point out how crazy the patients were, they didn't even know where they lived. It is such a simple matter to exploit an ex-mental patient.[17]

The adult homes are the best, yet abuses like these are not uncommon. There have been cases of forged signatures on checks, cases of outright fraud, other cases where doctors working for the proprietors abused the Medicare system. No community facility takes an interest in the inhabitants of the adult homes, so there is no one to look out for them. The State Board of Social Welfare, like most governmental regulative bodies, does nothing to correct abuses; besides, the code by which it operates was never designed to protect people who are as poorly equipped to deal with the world as chronic ex-mental patients are. Almost automatically, therefore, they become victims.

This system of care has proved to be very profitable for the proprietors of these homes. Adult home bed capacity in New York City has doubled in the past couple of years, a sure sign of a growth industry. If New York continues to discharge its long-term chronic patients—the hospitals still hold thirty thousand of them—the adult home system will grow even larger. But nobody should fool themselves about what is happening. Essentially, patients are being transferred from one custodial institution to another. The function of the transfer is to save the state money. The patients are not "in the community" and they are not receiving any mental health services. They are in limbo: not in hell, but then not really out of it.

Family care is the other major modality of housing ex-mental patients, but it is harder to get a line on what happens in family care homes; they are private homes and therefore even less subject to inspection than the adult homes.[18] Indeed, it is hard to get a line on the whole family care system, since different states have different systems and different types of control over them. In Kansas, for example, the hospitals frequently use a "convalescent leave" procedure wherein a patient may live in some sort of group home or family care setup for a year, during which time he can be readmitted to the hospital at any time. He has not, in other words, been discharged. In New York's family care system patients are sometimes discharged, sometimes not. Many mental hospital staff members prefer a family care system where the patient is not discharged because they retain control over the patient, and can thereby observe and regulate conditions in the family care home. Family care also costs the state less money; $270 a month is the going top rate in New York.

Partly for this reason, however, it is difficult to find suitable family care homes, especially in New York City. Few middle-class families living in New York are willing to take an ex-mental patient into their homes for a mere $270 a month or sometimes less. Ghetto residents will, but then most of these chronic, long-term patients are white, and it would be an obvious cruelty to place them in a black community. It is a situation, once more, ripe for exploitation. Many hospital employees or former employees have jumped into the gap to run family care homes. They are in an excellent position to get patients discharged to their homes, indeed to bootleg more patients into them than the law allows.[19] Some of these employees are honest, responsible people but others house patients in cellars and attics, feed them inadequately, confiscate their welfare checks. The Attorney General of the State of New York has introduced legislation to restrict the right of state employees to operate these homes, which Alan Miller, the Commissioner, has opposed.[20] The abuses, it should be noted, are not by any means the work only of state hospital employees.

I have only sketched in the outline, yet the picture is already bleak. The situation of the ex-mental patient invites exploitation. What is happening in New York is happening elsewhere in the United States, merely on a smaller numerical scale.[21] A Canadian study calls foster homes the "new back wards." [22] It is not just the rampant abuse of patients that is so bad, it is the quality of their lives. I remember walking past an adult home out in the country one summer day. The owner had built a separate building for the patients, eight bedrooms, each with two beds, and a concrete terrace with a roof over it for shade and park benches to sit and there they were, all sixteen patients, sitting on the benches and staring. They might have been a diorama in the Museum of Natural History for all the life they displayed. One of the authors of the Canadian study said that

> . . . the commonest reaction for foster parents was to regard the boarders as incompetent children who were messy or irresponsible and who needed everything done for them. In one home, all the boarders wore floor-length bibs at the table, had special pads placed under their plates, had their food cut into bite sizes, and were made to eat without a fork or knife.[23]

Clearly nothing has changed for these people. They are out of the mental hospital, but they might as well go back for all the difference getting out has made in their lives.

Many of them do go back, creating what is known as the "revolving door" syndrome. They go back for a variety of reasons; they neglect or refuse to take their drugs and start behaving strangely, or they utterly fail to make any adjustment outside the hospital, or they have returned to their families and the same things which drove them crazy in the first place drive them crazy again. And sometimes they go back because, in any rational comparison of the hospital and their new environment "in the community," the hospital comes out ahead. An aide in one hospital told me about a patient who stayed one night in the adult home he was sent to, walked out the door the next morning and spent the next three days trying to get back to the hospital. He had friends at the hospital, a job in which he was of real use, even though he didn't get paid for his work, a sheltered environment, a country atmosphere. Many studies have been made to determine which factors seem to keep patients out of the hospital and which lead to their return, but few of them mention the patients' ties to the place which has been their home.[24] The patient in question had been in the hospital for nearly forty years, his entire adult life. Much of the success of Harlem Valley's Metro Unit in keeping discharged patients out of the hospital must be attributed to staff persistence in maintaining ties with patients, maintaining a connection with their place, their past. If the ties are broken and the patients are set adrift "in the community," they are more than likely to find some way to go back to the hospital, even if this means going crazy again to do it.

It may seem odd to be talking about patients wanting to return to such a place as a mental hospital. And the situation is not all one way or the other. I know of another patient who runs to her room and locks the door whenever hospital staff members come to visit her; the woman is terrified they will take her back. Others, nevertheless, are anxious to return. When someone has spent twenty or thirty years in one spot. however depressing it may be, that spot becomes home. These are people, after all, whom the hospital has systematically reduced over the years to a childlike dependency. They cannot get jobs, they are incompetent to deal with any but the most sheltered environment, they are socially inadequate and don't know how to greet people, how to carry on a conversation or have someone in for tea. In the hospital they were adjusted, "good" patients, people created, as it were, by their environment. Thrown "into the community," they all too often drown.

It is indeed a bleak picture. Right now the action is in New York. If Massachusetts carries through its plan to close its mental hospitals, it will no doubt move there next. Even in New York, however, things are far from over. New York has thirty thousand more chronic patients to go. Some of them will die, but many more will be sent back "into the community," there to survive as best they can.

Everywhere, eventually, we may find ourselves in the position California has been in for several years, where all but a few hundred long-term patients have been discharged. The result in California, as we saw in Chapter Four, was an hysterical public and heavy political pressure to change the state's discharge policy and its liberal commitment laws. There is no need to go into this again at any length. We have spoken already of the large mental patient ghetto the closing of Agnews State Hospital created in San Jose, the reports in the press of murders and brutalities committed by ex-mental patients, the hearings of the California Senate Select Committee that resulted from all this. Aftercare in California is no better than it is elsewhere in the country. California's board and care facilities, as tney are called, are about the same as adult home or family care homes in New York. The only thing different about California is the amount of public pressure that has been brought to bear on the issue. In California, the public is terrified. They seem to be persuaded that a homicidal ex-mental patient lurks in every orange grove.

> . . . when you have a board and care home with
> disturbed patients in it—I had a family call me to
> Fontana about a month ago. I went out there and they
> had a whole room full of people to talk to me. This was
> an older couple. They had planned their retirement so
> that they wouldn't have to be on welfare or anything.
> They had this home two doors down from them, and they
> had sex disturbed there; they had a stabbing there; they
> had a patient who rung [sic] cats' necks, and did other
> things with cats; and they would urinate out in front of
> little kids—just all kinds of things like that. These people
> were just living in terror of these patients.[25]

The speaker is a California hospital employee. She accurately describes the public atmosphere in that state and potentially everywhere. People do not want ex-mental patients in their neighborhood. People would greatly prefer, in fact, to see them kept in the hospitals, but if that can't be they do not want them where they live and wherever they live they will insist on some system of controlling them.

It is perfectly all right with the public if that system of control is called aftercare.

And here, of course, is the danger. At present we have no aftercare system, no outreach from hospital into community and no community facilities interested in plugging the dike. *Because* we have no such system, patients who have been discharged enjoy a certain measure of freedom. They can leave the state, they can refuse further treatment, they can exercise their constitutional right to behave in bizarre ways. It will pay us all to watch the situation in California closely. The Senate Select Committee, dominated by highly effective liberals like Alan Short, has so far translated the public demand for a system of control into terms of a more or less conventional aftercare system which would train the operators of board and care facilities to deal with ex-patients, establish more stringent licensing regulations for these facilities, and provide more help to community programs. So far so good. But it is all too easy to see such a system developing under public pressure into a much more controlling ex-patient management system which would return patients to the hospital for even the slightest aberration.

The danger may seem remote. Yet some people are alive to it, namely the people with the most experience with the mental health system and its inherent coerciveness.

> We have said we want a good mental health service, but we've got to have it within the constitutional limits of the United States of America, and we have to train people and educate them to understand that these individuals, once mentally ill, and still perhaps disturbed in some way, have all of the rights of the rest of us who do not proclaim to have had that sufferance.[26]

The speaker this time is Andrew Robertson, a high official in the California Department of Health. He has been echoed by Alan Miller, who according to *The New York Times* told a legislative committee in Albany that "there was no need for 'some coercive net that keeps track of people forever.'"[27] It is officials in State Departments of Mental Hygiene who are turning out to be the civil libertarians. What Miller in New York and Robertson in California both understand well is that any large-scale state system will inevitably become authoritarian and controlling and it will destroy people. That is what happened to the mental hospitals, and the mistake must not be repeated.

We are left with a dilemma. We have a definite need

for an aftercare system: a system, that is, which would re-
educate chronic patients in particular to the exigencies of
life outside the hospital, rehabilitate them socially, offer
them meaningful work experience in a sheltered environment, and connect them in some way to the communities
they are being returned to. Any genuine aftercare system
would have to include these elements as a minimum. But
this is not what the public wants in an aftercare system.
The public's interest lies first and foremost in control,
whether in the hospital or outside it.[28] Any aftercare system, therefore, if it is not carefully hedged with legal safeguards, threatens to become one more system which
functions not to assist people who need assistance but to
control them.

The danger is not remote, it is real. *The New York
Times* wants to keep ex-patients in "open halfway communities" located in rural areas, where some of them can
work at farming or handicrafts and the crazier "can have
at least security and where medical care is always at
hand." [29] Whose security is the *Times* talking about? Elsewhere in the country we find the same fears, the same
pressures to keep mental patients out of the community.
It is the same old story. Get them off the streets. Put them
out in the country. Let them pick cotton.

The issue is the freedom of individuals. Freedom may
indeed be a relative concept for people who have no skills,
no money, no friends, who are withdrawn and alone and
apathetic, wholly defeated in their lives. It is indeed questionable whether such people, given their freedom, would
be able to use it in any way we would think constructive.
There is an old Latin sentence which originates, I believe,
with one of the church Fathers: *Libertas est potestas faciendi id quod jure liceat.* Liberty is the power to do what
the law allows. Much can be said in support of this point
of view. The trouble is that our liberties are not written
that way. The constitution does not establish tests of what

people may or may not be capable of before it grants them liberty. Quite the opposite. In principle the grant is absolute. Set a mental patient loose who has been in the hospital for thirty-seven years and still thinks he was a doctor when he was three and a half and he very well may urinate in front of little children to teach them anatomy or wander about frightening old ladies, but that is how it has to be. That is one of the many risks involved in granting liberty to everyone to do with what he will.

II

We have returned then to the basic issue which everywhere underlies the operation of the mental health system. The issue is liberty versus control. The community demands that a certain class of people called mental patients be subjected to a set of controls not applicable to other classes. The community denies this class of people membership status; it drives them off the streets, isolates them in custodial institutions, and does its best to keep them there. The community says, in effect, that these people are not human beings; it strips them of their human identity. They are now and forever hereafter mental patients, crazies, creatures of disorder.

Too few mental patients protest this state of affairs. The vast majority do not commemorate themselves. They sing no songs, they unfurl no banners. Quietly, hesitating briefly in the light, they file out of Creedmoor or Hudson River or wherever and into Queens Manor and it is all the same. Of Joyce's triumvirate they have silence and exile but no cunning. They are not "in the community" nor do they have a community of protest of their own. It is a dismaying, terrible thing to meditate on these people.

I turn with relief to those who do protest. However strident in voice or action, protest is infinitely more bearable than the defeated silence of the chronic patient.

It is also greatly overdue. We have had people protesting against abuses in the mental health system since the time of Dorothea Dix in the 1850's, but most protestors have been outsiders, liberal reformers looking for a cause. They have not been mental patients, with few exceptions. Now, however, for the first time, we are beginning to see ex-mental patients organize in opposition to the mental health system.

The first such group to form, and still perhaps the most prestigious, is the Mental Patients Liberation Project in New York, which dates from 1971. Only ex-mental patients may belong to MPLP, a fact which is one of the sources of its prestige. In many similar groups which have been founded since, sympathetic professionals are either welcome, or the professionals themselves have founded the group. MPLP in New York, however, has remained "pure." Another source of its prestige has been its effectiveness. Members have appeared on TV talk shows, staged guerrilla theater demonstrations at psychiatric conventions and confrontations with administrators at Bellevue Hospital in New York City, and given courses, lectures, and talks whenever the opportunity arose. It is, in other words, a political organization. While the members do support each other emotionally and have helped a great many people get out of mental hospitals, therapeutic self-help has not been MPLP's principal goal. The thrust of its activity has been directed at changing the mental health system.[30]

MPLP was the inspiration for other groups which have sprung up since 1971 in Baltimore, Boston, Philadelphia, Oregon, Michigan, Kansas, and other areas under such names as Mental Patients Liberation Front, Mental Patients Resistance, Insane Liberation Front, Mental Patients Association, and so on.[31] In addition legal aid and research groups have formed in California, St. Louis, and Pennsylvania, and in Minot, South Dakota, in 1970, a publication known as *The Radical Therapist* appeared which has since become the principal voice of the mental patients liberation movement, its newspaper of record.

Like most radical movements, this one has followed a rather twisted path, reflected best, perhaps, by the career of its newspapers. *The Radical Therapist*, or *Rough Times*, as it now calls itself, was not founded by ex-patients but by professionals, including at least one psychiatrist. For a while it maintained a kind of radical-professional point of view, carrying numerous theoretical articles with lots of footnotes which exposed the denigration of homosexuals and women built into psychiatric theory and inveighed against the abuse of mental patients, but which retained, at the same time, a therapeutic orientation. In the beginning you could not have called this a revolutionary journal. Then the editors, or enough of them to count, decided that they were only talking to themselves, that they were not reaching or serving the ex-patient and other minority groups whose struggle they were trying to identify with. So in 1972, as well as changing the name of the publication to *Rough Times*, the editors also decided to make it "more readable, with briefer articles, news stories, non-technical language," and, more important, to develop "a socialist editorial policy." [32] They decided, in other words, to abandon their middle-class origins and become genuine revolutionaries. To become Marxists.

This was obviously a crucial decision, and it appears to have split not just the staff of *Rough Times*, but the whole "radical therapy" movement, in two. Shortly after the shift, a group of people (most notably Joy Marcus and Claude Steiner) associated with the Radical Psychiatry Center in Berkeley, California, started their own publication, *Issues in Radical Therapy*.[33] Steiner went to school to Eric Berne and he is at bottom a practitioner of transactional analysis, and *Issues in Radical Therapy* has followed a TA line, printing long articles dealing with such matters as fat liberation, masturbating without guilt, and bioenergetics; the magazine, while it does make ceremonial bows to political matters from time to time, is very definitely an outlet for therapists. Meanwhile still another publication, *Madness Network News*, based in San Francisco, has stepped in to represent the civil-libertarian, politically practical side of the movement. *Madness Network News* includes at least one ex-mental patient on its staff and it has turned out to be the publication most closely allied with the interests and politics of ex-patients.

I write about these differences and divisions not to cast aspersions on this movement but to highlight the problem which plagues it: the absence of a theory which would account for the presence of insanity amongst us. The movement by and large angrily rejects the prevailing theories of the psychiatric establishment, theories the movement sums up in the person of Freud, but it has not been successful at replacing them with a theory of its own. In all these publications you find numerous articles attacking Freud for his insistence on intrapsychic factors in the causation of crazy behavior, his refusal to question the givens of society, his biased views on women and their place in the scheme of things. But you do not find a revolutionary psychology capable of explaining in detail the insanity persons sometimes manifest. You do, however, find that psychology in Freud. Freud's explanations may be wrong, but they do explain. That is very important. People cannot survive without explanations.

The people who write for these publications are fully aware of the problem; indeed, they could not fail to be—it is· the sword that divides them. Those with a Marxist orientation point to those with a transactional analytic orientation and characterize them as bourgeois, accuse them of failing, by their emphasis on personal growth and individual change, to focus on the capitalist "false consciousness" which enslaves us all, sane and crazy alike. The TA people accuse the Marxists of ignoring "the immediacy of people's psychiatric needs." [34] Others have tried to effect some kind of theoretic rapprochement, digging usable insights out of Freud or other psychologists and reburying them in Marxist terminology.[35] None of this has been very satisfactory. The movement lacks a philosopher even approaching Freud's stature, and it suffers in consequence. Movement writers criticize Laing for his interest in Eastern mysticism and his disinterest in politics. Szasz, for all the obvious usefulness of his attack on psychiatric explanation, is a political embarrassment; Szasz is conservative politically, he is a one-time Nixon supporter, and he is also still very much committed to the private practice of his own idiosyncratic professionalism. Thus the movement has no spiritual leader and no alternate ideology. It is a very serious problem, one which confronts anyone, including myself, who wants to change the mental health system. For all his faults, Freud remains an extraordinarily compelling figure.

The only figure who can match him, in fact, is Marx, and it may be partly for this reason that so many theorists of this young movement have turned to his works. But a turn to Marxism was inevitable, perhaps, as soon as movement theorists started to view crazy behavior as not crazy at all, but a sane, or at least functional, response to the larger craziness of society as a whole.[36] If insanity could be seen as one more "symptom" of a "sick" society, a product not of individual psychopathology but of the oppression of the working class, the whole question of an alternate revolutionary psychology might be translated into Marxist terms. The concept of psychological "illness" or disturbance might then be subsumed under the Marxist concept of "alienation"; "paranoid schizophrenia" might become an only slightly exaggerated consciousness of real oppression by capitalist oppressors. The entire issue of what causes crazy behavior might thereby be set loose from its individualistic, intrapsychic cage.

The Marxists have a point. A strong case can be made —it has been made throughout this book, and by many others as well—that mental patients constitute an oppressed class; and it has become self-evident that the mental health system, virtually by definition, serves the established order. It *is* a system of social control. Another case can be made that the predominant values of society, acting through such institutions as the family and the schools, oppress and alienate people from their "natural" or "true" selves and that the capitalist system maintains this alienation and grows fat upon it. This seems undeniable. (It would be true, however, of *any* society, including a Marxist one; and it is this truth which has driven R. D. Laing away from politics.[37] But that is neither here nor there.)

The problem is that Marx nowhere specified how or even whether alienation explains insanity. The problem is generally recognized. For all Marx's brilliance, he never developed a psychology of any sort, and Marxists since his time interested in psychology have been hard put to create one.[38] In the absence of such a psychology it becomes extremely difficult to explain an individual case of insanity— indeed, to explain an individual—in Marxist terms. More to the point, there is no evidence that even if it were possible to make such an explanation it would help the individual involved: help him become less crazy. It might clear his mind about the reality of his position in society, but it would not necessarily stop him from hearing the voice of God.

Strict Marxists, aware of the difficulty, transcend it. Individual problems such as someone's repeated and overwhelming auditory hallucinations—he is hearing the voice of God—are an aspect of "individualism," which in a Marxist frame of reference is a bourgeois value that has to be destroyed. The Marxist is interested in the masses, not in individuals; he wants to educate the workers to their oppression, not "cure" them of their insanity. For a grocery clerk who is *suffering*, who keeps hearing the gigantic voice of God booming in his ear telling him that the horses are pounding up behind him, the big brown horses with acid frothing out of their mouths and fire snorting from their nostrils, there can be very little consolation in learning how the capitalist pig boss who owns the store oppresses him. The strict Marxist says that "Individualist notions of bourgeois therapy combat healthy collective efforts, try to undercut struggle, and deny the righteous anger of the masses." [39] But the grocery clerk does not want to join a collective farm and sing angry songs about the capitalists. He wants help. He wants to stop hearing that voice, which is driving him absolutely bananas, and he will do just about anything to silence it. And here Marxism becomes irrelevant. Marxist thought offers this individual neither theory nor therapy; indeed, it denies the value of providing the kind of help an individual might want simply because he *is* an individual, someone interested primarily in solving his own problems, not the problems of the working class.

It would be a shame if the ex-patient groups now in existence lost sight of their actual political goals and adopted the line which strict Marxists like Michael Glenn, quoted above, are pushing on them. Glenn was one of the original members of the group which started *The Radical Therapist*. He is an apostate physician who has been converted to the Marxist line, and no one is more religious than a convert. Glenn criticizes

> mental patients liberation groups which fail to challenge the ruling-class as an enemy but instead identify attendants (working-class people), individual doctors and-or nurses, and family members as The Enemy—a

tactic which divides the proletariat and its allies by
failing to identify the real enemy.[40]

Mental patients who see the real oppressor as being the
mental health system and its practitioners, in other words,
are misdirecting their fire. They should be *joining* these
people in a battle against the common enemy, the ruling
class. This is openly absurd. It is not the ruling class which
is the enemy of mental patients. It is the community. The
people who hate and fear mental patients the most are the
people who insist on a system of strict controls for them,
the very "masses" Glenn would have them ally with. If
Glenn or someone who thinks like Glenn captures the
minds of these groups they will not survive.

The best hope these ex-patient groups do have for
survival, I believe, is to become involved in establishing
alternate systems of care for people who are going crazy
and aftercare for people who have been there. Most ex-
patient groups are founded on anger. They are a special
kind of what Sartre calls "serial groups"; their orientation
is external to themselves, it points toward the mental
health system and is an angry response to it.[41] They are
issue-oriented, in other words, and they tend to collapse
when their anger has dissipated or the issue has been resolved. These groups have a continuous reason for being,
of course; the mental health system is a compost heap
which breeds anger without let. But people's anger does
dissolve with time. No one wants to be angry all his life.
No matter what has been done to you, a time comes when
you just want to forget about it and move to the country,
or read a book about Patagonia. For ex-mental patient
groups to survive and grow, then, they must move beyond
their justifiable anger and do work that is constructive as
well as critical.

The Mental Patients Liberation Project in New York
is trying to take this step now.[42] Other groups, one hopes,

will follow this example. From the office of their unique experience, ex-patient groups can supply other patients and ex-patients what they cannot obtain in society: communality. By organizing and building upon their experience, providing help in nonpsychiatric, nonjudgmental, nonlabeling settings, they create the makings of a community. Which is the basis of a powerful and meaningful politics.

Unfortunately there is little chance that such a politics might arise. Ex-patient groups have yet to attract a large following among the hundreds of thousands of ex-patients available for membership, and it is questionable whether an attempt to organize these hundreds of thousands would be successful. I must stress again the effectiveness of the mental health system as a mechanism of social control. The people abandoned in adult homes and welfare hotels have been *silenced.* They are people to whom it simply never occurs to speak up for themselves or their rights. The psychiatric evidence demonstrates beyond a reasonable doubt that this is not the natural conclusion of a pathological development. It is rather the result of the extraordinary destructiveness of long-term dehumanization in custodial institutions, a process in which the adult home is only the final step.

Nevertheless these abandoned individuals represent the real constituency of ex-patient groups and the best hope they have for establishing a power based not on rhetoric but on numbers. Perhaps it is sheer fantasy to imagine that anyone could organize the residents of Queens Manor or your typical welfare hotel into a power bloc. But the ex-patient groups are new. The first one was not formed until 1971; they did not hold their first national convention until 1973.[43] Once they have achieved some stability it might indeed be possible to think about mental patient liberation on a larger scale. If anyone can reach these hopeless individuals, it would only be other ex-patients, people who understand something of the experience they have endured.

But the community also has a responsibility to these people, a responsibility of which genuine aftercare would be only a beginning. The community has condemned generations of mental patients to the living death of chronicity in state mental hospitals. It has been a kind of genocide. Too many of those who failed to make it in American society have wound up in these places, and we continue to ignore the situation. Once more, it is the patients themselves who best understand this:

> While citizens of every race, creed and economic class have suffered in the hands of Institutional Psychiatry, the ethnic minorities and economic underclass are its foremost victims. The aged, poor and alienated—all of the victims of exploitation, social changes and dislocation, unaided by adequate provisions for the general welfare of the people—find their way into the hands of psychiatric custodial care. It is a social disgrace that Institutional Psychiatry has elected, and been permitted, to be the custodian of the superfluous and unwanted Americans.
>
> To the degree that psychiatry serves to encompass those suffering from social and economic deprivation, to that degree the community is relieved of its responsibility. When an aged woman, struggling to survive on a meager VA pension and welfare supplement, is relegated to a mental hospital, over-medicated until in a state of coma, and left to rot in her own feces—that woman has been disposed of as a community responsibility. Social intervention is obviated when people are shoveled out of sight and mind and piled upon the dung hill of psychiatric victims. Indeed, Institutional Psychiatry has provided the "final solution" for hundreds of thousands of "unproductive" (and thus burdensome) citizens.[44]

Psychiatry is only an instrument in this process, a way the community has of passing its responsibility on. The community itself makes the fundamental decision.

But to talk of community responsibility presupposes the existence of a community, and this is what trips up every attempt at social reform in this country. For one of the criteria of whether or not a group of people living in a certain geographic or spiritual area constitute a community must surely be their willingness to take care of their own. Where do we find that in America? The idea of community in this country has degenerated to the idea of a "catchment area"; it is a geographical fiction, an account of city and agency boundaries, bureaucratic entities dividing populations against themselves. The spirit is fled, the flocks sicken and die. The American community abandons its old to Florida, its crazy to mental hospitals, its useless to welfare. The Marxists are right about one thing. We are indeed an alienated people. We are alienated from ourselves.

VIII
Alternatives

Joy: The urge to write is enormously strong.
Reason: One hears of innumerable kinds of
melancholy. Some throw stones, others write books. For
one, writing is the beginning of madness; for another,
it is the end.

Petrarch

I

In 1963 Congress passed the Community Mental
Health Act which empowered the National Institute of
Mental Health to establish "community mental health
centers" around the country. This Act was the first substantial intervention by the Federal Government into the
mental health system, traditionally under state control. It
was aimed specifically at creating a large-scale alternative
system which would bypass the state governments with
their state hospitals and find its base in local communities.
The reasoning behind it was that the mental health system
as it existed was too rigid, too bureaucratized ever to become responsive to people's needs, and that the only hope
was to set up a whole new system outside the old, an alternative system which in time would replace the state
hospitals, rationalize the referral system, and humanize the
treatment of the insane.

The Act is now more than a decade old. Approximately four hundred community mental health centers are in operation or have been funded by NIMH. Medical schools and psychiatric residency programs are training more and more students in community psychiatry. The psychiatric literature is bursting with books and articles on the unfamiliar problems of community practice. Many mental health professionals believe that the community mental health movement has been a great success; some have tagged it as still another psychiatric revolution. A few, indeed, might even claim that this entire book has been irrelevant because, as the centers replace it, the system I have been writing about is fading away like the Cheshire Cat and soon nothing will be left of it but its evil grin.

Soon, soon. The operative word is not *soon* but *now*. Right now implementation of the 1963 Act is stalled dead center and has been for two years, the Federal Government's continuing commitment to it is a matter of unresolved dispute, many of the centers are running out of money and curtailing their services, and in some states proponents of change consider the whole movement a dead issue and are looking to other sources for ideas. Besides, even where community mental health centers have been established they are not necessarily an improvement on the old system. To create a real alternative means more than just to create new institutions. Only if the new system abolishes the mass dehumanization of the old and makes a genuine effort to meet the expressed needs of its clients can it be said to replace it; otherwise it represents merely a duplication of the old system on a smaller scale. Whether the centers now in existence have, in fact, systematically incorporated fundamental, humanizing changes remains seriously open to question.

We must situate ourselves historically before we can discuss this question in more detail. The 1963 Community Mental Health Centers Act, passed in John F. Kennedy's

Administration, was the legislative outcome of the input provided by the Joint Commission on Mental Illness and Health, established by Congress in 1955.[1] The Joint Commission was charged with the responsibility of making a study of the mental health system and recommending improvements. The Commission's work was deep and lengthy; it cost well over $1 million and the final report was not submitted to the Surgeon General until December 31, 1960. It was published in 1961 under the title *Action for Mental Health*.[2] The report was broadly critical of the state hospitals, but it did not propose abolishing them. Instead, it recommended transforming the smaller ones into intensive residential treatment centers for acute cases and the larger ones into institutions for the long-term care of all kinds of chronic diseases, including physical diseases such as tuberculosis. At the same time it recommended the establishment of "community mental health clinics" for each fifty-thousand segment of the country's population, and it also recommended a sharp increase in the psychiatric services available in general hospitals. More significant than any of these specific recommendations, however, was the recommendation that the Federal Government "should *share in the costs* of services to the mentally ill," and that its money grants for services "should be awarded according to *criteria of merit and incentive*." [3] That meant that the Federal Government should establish standards: an accountability system.

In November, 1961, President Kennedy created a high-level committee to report on the report, so to speak, and in February, 1963, the work of this committee culminated in Kennedy's famous message to Congress calling for a "bold new approach" to the problems of mental illness and mental retardation. The bold new approach went considerably beyond the Joint Commission's report. It emphasized the importance of prevention in mental health, an idea to which *Action for Mental Health* gave little attention, and it broadened the idea of the community mental health clinic to that of a "comprehensive community mental health center." These new emphases originated in NIMH, which was considerably more liberal than the mental health establishment as a whole.

Naturally these proposals aroused opposition, but it was unorganized and focused less on the basic proposals themselves than on specific features. One of these was staffing grants; the American Medical Association seemed to accept a Federal role in the construction of buildings but it objected to Federal staffing money, which smacked of socialized medicine. The AMA did not want the Federal Government paying the salaries of doctors. Accordingly staffing grants were eliminated from the original Act and had to be added in 1965. Other political problems surrounded the bill, but we cannot go into them here. In October, 1963, the bill passed both houses and was sent to the President for his signature. The bold new approach had become law.

It is surprising that the Act did not arouse more opposition than it did. As it had come through Congress, it was clearly and explicitly intended as an impetus to the establishment of an alternative to the traditional state mental health systems. The House Report on the bill stated,

> Either we must develop the quantity and quality of community services which will ultimately replace these institutions or we will have to undertake a massive program to strengthen the State mental hospitals. The Committee believes that the development of new methods of treatment, the impressive evidence of the possibilities for rehabilitating the mentally ill, and a lessening of our disposition to reject and isolate sufferers, all argue strongly for the treatment of mental illness in the community.[4]

And Dr. Robert Felix, head of NIMH at the time, said,

"I wish to God I could live and be active for 25 more years, because I believe if I could, I would see the day when the State mental hospitals as we know them today would no longer exist." [5] This sweeping reform was not what the Joint Commission had had in mind, but there was no question that replacement of the state mental hospitals was the intent of Congress in passing this legislation.

In line with this intent, the new mental health centers were not to be simple clinics along the usual lines, dealing weekly psychotherapy to the usual "neurotic" outpatients. To qualify for a Federal construction grant, a mental health center had to agree to provide "five essential services": (1) inpatient care, (2) outpatient care, (3) partial hospitalization, especially day care, (4) emergency services, and (5) consultation and educational services to other community organizations.[6] To ensure that the centers did not become typical referring agencies selecting their clients according to their own needs, they were required to provide services to *all* residents of their catchment area, "regardless of age, sex, race, creed, color, national origin, diagnostic category, voluntary or involuntary status, or ability to pay." [7] That seemed to be everybody.

In fact it was not. In 1968 Congress amended the Act to include grants for services to alcoholics and drug addicts, and in 1970 programs for child mental health services were added. The latter year also saw changes in the staffing grant provision which had been added in 1965. The original staffing grants allowed for Federal support at a declining rate over a fifty-one-month period. The 1970 amendment extended staffing grant support at a higher rate for a longer time; now funds for staff would be available for eight years, not four and a fraction. This amendment also set priorities for grants; "poverty areas" would have their applications approved first, and they would get more money: 90 percent of staffing costs for the first two years, down to 70 percent for the last two. This compared with 75 percent for the first two years, down to 30 percent the last two, for non-poverty areas. About 25 percent of the catchment areas in the country qualify as poverty areas.

Very generally, that sums up the legislative history of the Community Mental Health Centers Act. What is important about this history is the evidence it presents of continued Federal involvement in the provision of mental health services and of increasingly specific Congressional intervention in the way services are to be provided. Congress has not left these matters to the mental health professionals to work out on their own; on the contrary, Congress is sold on the idea of community mental health centers and has taken on a paternalistic supervisory role over the development of their services. The Congressional idea has plainly been continuously to enlarge the centers' area of service, thereby to enforce the meaning of the catchment area concept, that a center will be responsible for *all* the residents of a given geographic region. Implicit in this concept, furthermore, is the need for basing services in the communities involved. The original NIMH regulations called for "community coordination," meaning that centers must coordinate their services with other caregivers in the community, and the original Act recommends "citizen participation" in the planning and operation of the centers.

The fact that Congress has had to be so paternally involved with the implementation of the original Act can be looked at from another angle, too, as a sign that implementation has been slow. And this is definitely the case. In the beginning the mental health professions viewed the Act largely as an instrument for applying traditional psychiatric services to traditional middle-class populations. The community mental health center would be not a real alternative to the system but just one more element in it, one more agency caring for its selected clientele. Even the necessity of providing inpatient services did not force changes in this perception. Many general hospitals saw this provision as an opportunity to add a new wing with fifty or one hundred beds, or as a way of expanding their psychiatric ward. Some state hospitals spruced up an empty building or two, called it a community mental health center, and got staffing money for outpatient services. There was no effort within the mental health system to fulfill the intent of Congress.

This was partly the fault of Congress itself. The law had been passed so quickly, with so little chance for extended debate, that the mental health system had not had time to adjust to the new ideas, or even to understand them. But it was also the fault of a great deal of vagueness and imprecision at NIMH, which was administering the law. The NIMH guidelines for center development and operation left so much unsaid that opportunists could read into them more or less what they wanted. And NIMH, while it had regulatory responsibility, had very little regulatory authority. Its only real sanction against violators of the guidelines was total withdrawal of funds. NIMH was generally unwilling to take this drastic step. No matter how flagrant the violation, NIMH preferred at least a semblance of a center to no center at all. Some of the centers, therefore, got away with murder. One used ninety-thousand dollars of NIMH money to finance the cost of a hospital business office which had nothing to do with the center.[8] The original plan drawn up by Columbia University in New York for its mental health center included 407 private offices for psychiatrists.[9]

If the vagueness of the NIMH guidelines has opened the way to corrupt practices, however, it has also allowed an amazing diversity to develop in what are called community mental health centers. They range from centers which are self-contained psychiatric worlds at one extreme, an entire mental health system in miniature, to those which are not really centers at all at the other, but ad-

ministrative arrangements connecting preexisting mental
health services and dividing responsibilities among them.

An example of the former type is the Harry C. Solomon Mental Heath Center in Lowell, Massachusetts. This
center is housed entirely in a brand new building built
with Federal funds. It contains a small mental hospital of
thirty beds, offices for staff, rooms for occupational therapy,
group therapy and the like, and long corridors: all the in-
gredients necessary to a mental health system. The staff is
headed by J. Sanbourne Bockoven, M.D., who is an ardent
advocate of community psychiatry, and it is divided into
professional roles along traditional lines. It is, in fact, a
very traditional place. It has a backup state mental hospital, Worcester State Hospital, which takes patients the
center feels it cannot handle.[10] The outpatient service
does mostly individual psychotherapy, and in fiscal year
1972 only two blacks and one Spanish-speaking person
were in outpatient treatment.[11] The "Emergency Team"
works nine to five, Mondays through Fridays. In spite of
Bockoven's leanings, the center has done very little preventive work in the community and calls its community programs "endeavors" "since they have neither formal structure nor assigned administrative heads."[12] This has become
a source of anxiety to the staff, who feel locked into their
beautiful new building.

> The principal determinant of our state of flux and the
> paramount source of unrest in the Center is the desire
> on the part of many staff to make the community mental
> health mandate a reality and to establish a multiplicity
> of Neighborhood Centers that would bring mental health
> services to the several communities. The desire, indeed,
> if not the anxiety, to achieve this objective is a powerful
> motive force toward change and innovation.[13]

But change and innovation have yet to come.

The Solomon Center, then, is an alternative to the

present mental health system only in the sense that a crazy person has a choice of going to a private psychiatrist and drifting through the referral system, winding up eventually at Worcester State Hospital, or going to the Center and having the same thing happen. The Center has succeeded only in concentrating the system into one building; it has not actually changed the system. Patients are still seen to be either too "sick" for psychotherapy, in which case they become inpatients in a thirty-bed mental hospital, or else they are white and "neurotic" and suitable for psychotherapy and perhaps able to pay for it, in which case they become outpatients and talk to the psychiatrist once a week. Thus the Center perpetuates the dual system of care we talked about in Chapter Three; it makes no substantial effort to work in the community; and it maintains the same professional hierarchy in which the system has always stagnated. Nothing has changed. To be sure, the Center has succeeded in reducing the number of admissions to Worcester State Hospital from its catchment area. But that does not make it an alternative. It makes it a substitute.[14]

At the opposite organizational extreme from the Solomon Center are those centers which have been created administratively from existing agencies and facilities, which were created, that is, to take advantage of the chance to obtain Federal funds. This has become a popular tactic in areas with a high concentration of mental health services already, and there are well-known examples in West Philadelphia and San Francisco. The West Philadelphia Mental Health Consortium consists of the psychiatric services of no less than six separate hospitals with the staff of the Department of Psychiatry of the University of Pennsylvania Medical School as the binding element.[15] Another example is the Shawnee Community Mental Health Corporation in Topeka, an administrative entity which contracts with Topeka State Hospital for partial hospitalization and child development services, Stormont-Vail Hospital for emergency and inpatient services, the Family Service and Guidance Center and the Menninger Foundation for outpatient services, the local Mental Health Association for educational and consultation and more emergency services (a hotline), and St. Francis Hospital for still more emergency and inpatient services. Even the Veterans Administration Hospital in Topeka is an informal affiliate of the Corporation. Patients do not "go," therefore, to the Shawnee Community Mental Health Center, because it is not "there." The Corporation is the Center, and although it has an administrator the Corporation is little more than a legal fiction.

There is considerable evidence indicating that this type of arrangement subverts the intentions of the Community Mental Health Centers Act. One of the difficult problems the Act was intended to solve was the problem of continuity of care. The idea is that one professional or one agency should follow a person from the beginning to the end of his "illness"; he should not get lost in the referral system or have to tell his story over and over again to different professionals working in different places. Robert L. Leopold, however, writing about the development of the West Philadelphia Consortium, noted "a tendency for the system to fragment" as it became "increasingly bureaucratized." [16] He means, I take it, that the close coordination among agencies upon which continuity of care depends broke down over a period of time. According to Robert Blake, the social worker who runs the Shawnee Corporation in Topeka, one of the principal reasons for setting it up, aside from taking advantage of the availability of Federal money, was to coordinate the many diverse mental health services in that town. But that is precisely what has not happened, he says. These agencies remain highly competitive and suspicious of each other, and the patient gets lost in the shuffle. And once again, these administrative "centers" or consortiums are plainly offering nothing new in the way of services; they are re-arrangements of the old services, the Federal money paying mostly for extra staff. Robert Blake confirmed this, saying that the Shawnee Corporation was trying not to duplicate services already in existence.[17] It is hard to see genuine alternatives to the present mental health system arising from these sophisticated administrative entanglements.

The Shawnee Corporation and the Solomon Center stand at two organizational extremes, but they are generally typical, nevertheless, of what has happened to the community mental health movement. We are seeing little more than old wine being poured into fancy new bottles.[18] It was inevitable, perhaps, that implementation of the Community Mental Health Centers Act should follow these well-worn paths without vigorous leadership or at least a strong system of accountability pointing in new directions. Accountability, however, was left to the National Institute of Mental Health, which did not begin to evaluate any of the center programs it was funding until late 1969, six years after passage of the original Act, and then only after Congressional prodding. Evaluation is still not a high priority at NIMH. In 1972 a Ralph Nader study group stepped in to fill the accountability gap with a report on the community mental health center programs at NIMH. The report was widely critical of NIMH and therefore not very well received there. Nor has the psychiatric establishment generally been very receptive to it.[19] Which is what we would expect. The Nader people were outsiders, and nonprofessionals at that. As we know very well, psychiatrists do not like to be held accountable to anyone but other psychiatrists.

But certainly an accountability system that does not employ outsiders can have little effect. To expect NIMH (or psychiatry generally) to evaluate its own programs is, in the words of one Congressman, like putting a rabbit in charge of the lettuce patch.[20] In the final analysis it is precisely "outsiders" to whom the system is accountable. And we are those outsiders. It is the public that supports and uses the mental health system, and ultimately it is the public that must demand accountability. One of the principal lessons to be drawn from the Nader report is that the public need not be afraid to make that demand on the basis of its lack of expertise. As one of the authors puts it,

> From our point of view the real value of the report lies in two other areas. First, it provides a model for consumer action in a field where it has long been dormant. By consumer action . . . we mean those efforts by citizens to take a critical look at the effectiveness, relevancy, and value of their own mental health services. We hope our report has shown that the common sense and knowledge available to all educated men and women enable citizens to conduct a useful study of mental health services. M.D.s and Ph.D.s hold no monopoly as spokesmen on issues relevant to us all.[21]

The issue is an important one. In certain areas of the country, especially in the cities, consumers have indeed been conducting "useful studies" of the community mental health center programs serving them—conducting "studies" of them, and taking them over.

This development seems to have been a rude surprise to psychiatry. The original Act envisioned nothing so drastic as a community take-over of community mental health services. The Act talked only about "citizen participation" in the centers. Unfortunately the authors of the Act neglected to define the term. Center administrators interpreted it, therefore, in predictably traditional ways. To them "citizen participation" meant, first, having elite "advisory boards" composed of representatives from local power groups. These boards would have no power over center programs but would function merely as a bridge to the local power structure. Second, it meant hiring local people to work as "paraprofessionals." This idea fit in with the new careers movement of the 1960's, which was an attempt to create meaningful jobs, jobs with a future, for the inner-city poor. The psychiatrists working in city mental health centers saw these people as a bridge to their clientèle.

Most of this was standard practice in the mental health systems. The whole system has an "advisory board" of sorts in the National Association for Mental Health, which is a kind of giant psychiatric rubber stamp; and "advisory boards" are common in the subsystems as well. Even state hospitals in some states have visiting committees of "concerned citizens" who are carefully selected, of course, for their ability not to take their job seriously. The paraprofessionals, to be sure, appeared to be a new idea, and in some centers they quickly became indispensable. We have talked about them before. Middle-class psychiatrists don't know how to relate to lower-class or black or ethnic crazy people and frequently cannot distinguish between what is crazy and what is normal in those populations anyhow. The paraprofessionals, who are generally given a smattering of psychiatric training, sometimes on the job, translate the complaints of their friends and neighbors into terms psychiatrists can understand. Then they translate what the psychiatrists say back into the language of their friends and neighbors. In some centers, paraprofessionals have become so adept at working with their friends and neighbors that the psychiatrists have simply unloaded many or all of their patients onto them, especially the difficult ones. This aspect of the use of paraprofessionals is not new; it is close cousin to the practice of sending difficult people to mental hospitals where aides—a kind of paraprofessional —care for them. Nevertheless, the advent of paraprofessionals, indigenous mental health workers, or whatever they are called has generally been a blessing; they are able to develop closer relationships with clients than is possible for a psychiatrist unfamiliar with what it means to be poor, and those relationships often prove to be helpful.

This was the pattern of "citizen participation," but in a number of cities it just hasn't worked. Two instances in New York stand out. In the first, Columbia University's College of Physicians and Surgeons tried to colonize the West Harlem-Washington Heights-Inwood area of Manhattan with a community mental health center established along very traditional lines. The Department of Psychiatry at P & S, which is located at Columbia-Presbyterian Hospital near the George Washington Bridge and runs the nearby New York State Psychiatric Institute, is a training ground for psychoanalysts and an enormously conservative organization psychiatrically. It is not immediately apparent why the Department would want to become involved in community psychiatry at all, unless it simply saw a chance to acquire a new building. At any rate the Department submitted plans for its community mental health center to New York City's Community Mental Health Board in 1966. These plans included the aforementioned 407 offices for private psychiatrists, a two hundred-bed inpatient unit, and a "community organizing proposal," a plan, that is, "to organize the community to become the recipients of mental health services." [22]

This plan assumed, of course, that the community was disorganized, and so it must have appeared to the Department of Psychiatry. Probably few Department members actually lived in that particular community, which was 40 percent black, and even fewer understood how ghettoes organize themselves. They must have been quite surprised, therefore, when a whole set of small service agencies emerged from this "disorganized" community and demanded a voice in the planning of the proposed center. There was a confrontation between community representatives and Department planners at a storefront meeting, and the Department and its sponsoring organization, the Community Mental Health Board, were forced to admit that they had made a mistake. The community was indeed organized and perhaps it did deserve a voice in planning the center. Accordingly an Ad Hoc Advisory Committee was formed—standard operating procedure—and community representatives were appointed to it.

This time, however, standard operating procedure failed to do the trick. The Department ignored the Advisory Committee, which was also standard operating procedure, and the community only became more vehement in its demands. The Department responded by creating two new committees, one composed of representatives from local "health, education and welfare agencies," the other composed "of representatives of every social, political, paternal, business, parents, religious, labor and other people's organizations in the catchment area." [23] The idea was to separate the local professionals and service providers from the consumers: to divide and conquer. Unfortunately, the community refused to be divided. The first meeting of the consumers group was packed with agency representatives as well, and it was a stormy disaster. When the Department tried to set up a permanent Area Mental Health Advisory Council at a subsequent meeting, cries of community control began to replace the earlier demands for community participation. Community representatives took the meeting over and chose one of their own, a black man named William Hatcher, to run it. Subsequently the community formed its own group, the Washington Heights-West Harlem-Inwood Community Mental Health Council, which demanded that the Department withdraw from the proposed center entirely and turn over all its plans to the Council. Finally the Department did withdraw.

There is now a Washington Heights-West Harlem-Inwood Community Mental Health Center. The types of service the Center offers are determined not by the professionals who work in it, at least not exclusively, but by the community which controls it, as represented by the Council. The Center operates not out of an elaborate new building with 407 offices but out of already existing buildings in the community. The Chairman of the Council is still William Hatcher, who is not a psychiatrist but a merchant, and the Council has pointed the Center in directions which are often far afield from traditional mental health services but which the Council believes affect the mental health of community residents. The Center sponsors block parties, forces the landlords of welfare hotels to give them space to provide services to the tenants and to correct violations of the housing code, and is trying to develop new ways to organize disorganized elements of the community, such as finding ways for poor people to buy the buildings they are living in and establish co-ops. Says Hatcher, ". . . the professional community in general was not in approval of us. Many times, people thought we did not know what we were doing. . . ." [24] Sometimes that was probably true. But the Center is alive, it is working, it has even achieved a certain fame within psychiatry, both for its successful attack on the establishment way of doing things, and for its innovative approaches to mental health problems. And the community is proud of its efforts:

> Well, the end result is that we now have the only, so far as we know at least, the only mental health center, and we can call it that now even though it is not officially named, that has a program developed by the community and a staff that has been hired by the community and is responsible to the community, I think, in the country, possibly in the world.[25]

The other instance in New York, however, is even more famous, probably because it was so dramatic. On March 4, 1969, a group of 150 or so paraprofessionals took control of the Lincoln Hospital Mental Health Services in the South Bronx. For two weeks these workers occupied offices, booted administrators and professionals out and did their jobs, and demanded redress of grievances and community control of LHMHS, which until that time had been considered a model for delivering mental health services to the ghetto. This story has been told so often it seems unnecessary to repeat it here.[26] The importance of the revolt lies not in its outcome—community control was not achieved in this instance—but in its symbolic value. The revolt served notice that the paraprofessionals were no more willing to be co-opted into the present system than was the community as a whole. It was an announcement to the professionals that token "citizen participation" was no longer enough. Now only complete control would satisfy the community.

Since 1969, then, community control has become one of the hottest issues in the community mental health movement. The issue has not been confined to New York City. The West Philadelphia Consortium was forced to double the size of its governing board, adding an equal number of community members to it, in order to achieve parity between the community and the professionals.[27] At the Westside Community Mental Health Center in San Francisco in 1970, a full-scale community revolt was averted only by the speed with which the Community Advisory Board and the Westside Board of Directors acted in concert to cool out the feelings of those concerned. Subsequently community-sponsored, community-staffed drug programs were added to Westside's spectrum of services and that Center has made a serious effort to respond to community demands. More and more psychiatrists are getting the message. Fewer and fewer communities are willing to settle for less than "effective consumer control." It is a question of power. If power is not shared with the community, the community may very well seize it.

The movement for community control has opened up the possibility of a gradual shift away from traditional service models. At the moment this possibility remains just that: a possibility. The Solomon Center in Lowell and the Shawnee Corporation in Topeka are typical of mental health centers as they exist now. Only in some of the larger cities has the possibility of change become anything like a reality.

Even this limited change, however, can be exciting. An example from Denver comes to mind. A team consisting of a psychiatrist, two psychologists, two social workers, a psychiatric nurse, and five paraprofessionals operating out of a neighborhood health center and "prohibited from developing a waiting list by administrative decree" decided to accept all comers and adapt their services totally to meeting the needs of clients.[28] They call this the "uninsulated caseload" and apparently the demand for services has been nearly overwhelming. The team is located in a poverty area, people come in with multitudinous problems only vaguely connected sometimes with anything called "mental illness," and there are no referrals: the problems are dealt with there and then. Most professionals would walk out on such an impossible situation. Yet this particular team accepted the challenge and learned how to cope.

I could cite other examples as well. The point is that when mental health professionals make a genuine effort to fill the expressed needs of a given population they sometimes discover or invent new and highly effective ways of doing so. Only in rare cases, however, is such responsiveness to a community spontaneous, as it appears to have been in Denver. On the contrary, it has to be demanded. That demand is what the issue of community control is all about. To ensure the accountability of the system to the people, the people must control the system. It is that simple.

What happens next? At this writing the future of both the community mental health movement and community control of that movement is in doubt. If the movement is ultimately to succeed in developing a meaningful alternative to the present mental health system, the psychiatric profession must wholeheartedly commit itself to it. And psychiatrists are profoundly divided, as usual, not only on the basic desirability of the community mental health concept but on the form implementation of it should take. One source of division is the frequent community insistence that psychiatrists become involved in what they call "primary prevention." Gerald Caplan coined this term in his influential book, *Principles of Preventive Psychiatry:*

> Primary prevention is a community concept. It involves lowering the rate of new cases of mental disorder in a population over a certain period by counteracting harmful circumstances before they have had a chance to produce illness. It does not seek to prevent a specific person from becoming sick. Instead, it seeks to reduce the risk for a whole population, so that, although some may become ill, their number will be reduced.[29]

What Caplan is talking about, as he later makes clear, is *social action*. The "harmful circumstances" he refers to are such things as rats in the baby's bedroom, the absence of employment opportunities, not enough money, kids shooting up and stealing to feed the habit, high VD rates, hopelessness, and all the other ills the social flesh is heir to. The assumption is—and it is an assumption shared by the residents of inner-city ghettoes—that these "harmful circumstances" cause or contribute to the prevalence of "mental illness" in a given community. To reduce the prevalence, you must eliminate the harmful social conditions.

Psychiatrists find this very hard to accept. Freud is the source of psychiatric wisdom and he places the source of "mental illness" in the mind, not in the community. Furthermore there is not much money to be made in community action, and psychiatrists are not trained for it anyhow. Community action is politics; if a psychiatrist wants to become involved in it, on behalf of his clientele or for his own reasons, he must abandon his status and expertise and become just another citizen. An M.D. degree cuts no ice in this field. Not many psychiatrists, therefore, have committed themselves to community action.[30] Nor is it clear that this is a proper role for psychiatry in the first place. What use is a white middle-class professional in a confrontation with a Norway rat? Isn't politics the natural preserve of people called citizens, especially those citizens whose lives are encompassed by community issues? If a psychiatrist wants to do "primary prevention" he *must* shed his professional role; he can *only* do so as a member equal to other members of the community. And to do that, he might as well not be a psychiatrist.

While the debate over social action continues, political developments at both state and national levels are having a pronounced effect on the future of the community mental health movement. For the last two years the Nixon Administration, which would very much like to see this and other Federal social programs terminate, has not been funding approved applications for new community mental health centers. It is hard to get precise information, but there appear to be fewer than four hundred Federally-funded centers in operation, as opposed to a goal of two thousand centers covering the entire United States.[31] The Administration argues that the Federal role was never meant to extend to the funding of all two thousand centers. The object was, rather, to test the feasibility of the concept. If it worked, it would then be up to local and state funding sources to implement the concept on a national scale. And it has worked, says the Administration; therefore it is time to end the Federal role and let others carry on. Congress argues, on the other hand, that alternate sources of funding are not available, at least not yet, that now, on the verge of success, is no time to abandon the program, and that in fact it ought to be extended.

Congress may be winning this debate. The original Act, which was to last only three years, has been extended several times, most recently in June, 1973, when it was extended for one more year. Right now Congress is considering a two-year extension of the Act (four years in the Senate version) which is in fact a complete rewriting of it, almost a new bill entirely. It mandates a whole range of new services for each center funded after it becomes law, including specialized services for children and the elderly and follow-up services for individuals discharged from state hospitals. In addition it requires centers to oversee community residences for state hospital dischargees and it also requires them to screen admissions to state hospitals from their catchment areas; it mandates that centers be run by a community board; it establishes a larger and better-funded monitoring system; it extends grants for poverty areas beyond the eight-year maximum; it allows for coverage of *all* operating costs at the same rate as the present staffing grants; and it mandates tighter administrative control over services generally.

The fact that Congress has to be so precise about these things is a sign, once again, that the centers are not doing them on their own. But Congressional commitment to the community mental health center concept runs very deep. Informed people in the mental health field anticipate that the bill will pass by a big majority, big enough to override a veto.[32] It appears that the community mental health center is here to stay. There has to come a time, however, when Federal funds are no longer available. No one believes that the Federal commitment is endless. What happens when it ends remains in doubt. Many of the early centers have already run their Federal grants out and have had to resort to other sources for funds. These other sources often turn out to be state departments of mental health, those massive bureaucracies that manage much of the present system of care. In Kentucky, the first state to enjoy complete coverage by mental health centers, 11 percent of center funding comes from the state, as opposed to 40 percent from NIMH.[37] As the NIMH share progressively shrinks, the state share has to grow. Already the Kentucky Department of Mental Health exercises considerable control over the centers in that state. The original Act was intended to create a local-Federal partnership bypassing these state bureaucracies. In Kansas local and state mental health agencies are separated by law and most of the local funding comes from a county tax. It is becoming increasingly difficult, however, to finance an adequate level of services, or what communities feel is adequate, on the county tax base. Kansas is now considering a revision of this separation of powers. If these are portents of the future, then we may wind up right back where we started in the 1800's: back with a mental health system which is a creature of the states. Back with bureaucracy and dehumanization.

But the picture is very complex and it would be wrong and simpleminded to pin all our troubles on state departments of mental health. The states themselves are making strenuous efforts in some cases to humanize their bureaucracies, or at least to make them more rationally responsive to people's needs. It happened briefly in Minnesota, as we saw, and it is happening in New York and in other states as well. We have already talked about the unified services system New York is trying to establish. In other states another type of service delivery model is emerging in which the state combines all its human services under one administrative umbrella. Thus public health, welfare, and mental health functions, among others, are joined in a Department of Human Services or Human Resources or whatever.[34] Massachusetts is moving in that direction and a new facility in Brockton, Massachusetts, combines a multitude of services, including community mental health, in a single building with one intake procedure for all services, one set of records, and so on. This approach is particularly appropriate for the multiproblem families of the inner-city who never have only financial or housing or mental health problems alone but may be at the same time poor, unemployed, alcoholic, and crazy, among other things. In Georgia, under its new Department of Human Resources, health, family and children's services, mental health services, vocational rehabilitation and other services have all been combined; a "human resources generalist," another name for a paraprofessional, provides continuity of care, making sure that people get to the right expert, whether it be a psychiatrist or a lawyer, for their particular problem or problems. The significance of this for community mental health has been

> a substantial clarification of the role of the mental health programs and a return to a more traditional model for the psychiatrist. He no longer needs to concern himself directly with the patient's broader social needs, but can rest assured that these are being taken care of within the larger system.[35]

The psychiatrist, that is, can get out of community politics.

Like all new ideas, of course, this one is facing intense opposition, and its success is in doubt.

> Continuing territoriality between different professional groups and between professionals and paraprofessionals has often frustrated the concept. Successful consolidation at the state level has often occurred only to be followed by rigid resistance at the local level, where control of local welfare and health boards is a political prize that is not willingly given up.[36]

It is an indication, however, of the ferment in the community mental health movement and the uncertainty of its future. For example, what happens to the mandate for community control, soon to be law, when a community mental health center comes under the bureaucratic aegis of a huge state agency, or even just turns to such an agency for funds? Should accountability be to the community or to the state bureaucracy? You can be sure that both are going to insist upon it, and they will probably make conflicting demands. That is only one of the impending problems which beset the community mental health movement. Even if Congress passes and the President signs the new law, we are not likely to see two thousand community mental health centers blanketing the United States, providing a permanent alternative to the present system, for decades, if at all. The future of the community mental health movement has not been assured, and meanwhile the search for alternatives continues.

The trouble with any alternative, however, is that new institutions of whatever kind, call them community mental health centers or human resource centers or whatever, do not in and of themselves necessarily constitute an improvement. In most of the community mental health centers in the country, as I have tried to make clear, it is business as usual. Morris S. Schwartz, a pioneer in social psychiatry, puts it this way:

> I don't care what form an institution or an organization may take, I predict that form will have the same dehumanizing qualities that I described in the mental hospital. The danger is that as we move from one form to another we keep repeating the same mistakes. We've decentralized the large state hospital and now we're going out into the community and we're finding people being dumped out there and neglected, and so we find another form. But there's some fundamental rot that we have not touched on, and I think it's in the area that I tried to describe.[37]

The "fundamental rot" Dr. Schwartz refers to is the tendency of any bureaucratic organization to dehumanize its clients, to treat them not as human beings but as objects. A real alternative to the mental health system, says Schwartz, must constitute a process of humanization:

> When humanization is present, one is accorded the status of a fellow human being with all the entitlements pertaining thereto. The individual is recognized and respected as a unique and worthwhile person; he is accorded the right to exist as a physical and psychosocial being; he is treated as an end in himself; he is included in a common humanity; he is responded to as a whole human being; and he is seen as one who has the potentiality of becoming other than what he is.[38]

This says it well. The question is whether the community mental health center is genuinely humanizing the treatment of the insane. So far it does not appear to be happening.

II

Even though the psychiatric establishment cannot agree on their value, community mental health centers are clearly the establishment's answer to the present mental health system. Groups outside the establishment and some opposed to it have also offered solutions, however, and it might be well to close this book by looking at some of them. But this will have to be a short section. For these nonpsychiatric or antipsychiatric alternatives are very rare.

Some would argue with this, and in fact the rarity of alternatives is partly a question of definition. If we define suicidal people, for example, as being crazy or "mentally ill" and count suicide centers and hotlines as alternatives, then we would have to admit that there are not few but many. Nearly every city and hundreds of smaller communities now have hotlines. The movement has its own publications, its own field—suicidology—and its own experts. According to one source, the number of hotlines in existence may be approaching one thousand.[39] Many of these are intended for drug users but the proportion devoted to suicide or other types of crisis is very large. The lines are almost always manned by lay volunteers trained to give counsel. What is unusual—nonpsychiatric, if you will— about hotline service is that intervention in another person's life is confined to the telephone. And it is definitely cheaper than going to a psychiatrist.

Even if you consider suicides "mentally ill," however, the hotline represents no real alternative to the mental health system, nor is it intended as such. Basically, it is a lifesaving service. Its therapeutic suggestions are brief and practical. Most volunteers are not equipped or trained to deal with delusional, hallucinating, or paranoid crazies and apparently they do not get many calls from them anyhow. Hotlines, in short, are simply not designed for dealing with truly crazy, unreasonable people.

Something of the same might be said of the crisis center, which has not developed as widely as the hotline but is becoming more and more popular in large cities. Some community mental health centers operate what they call crisis centers, but I am referring to non-establishment crisis centers like Number Nine in New Haven, Connecticut, which practice a "radical therapy" specifically differentiated from traditional psychiatric therapy by its elimination of the hierarchical status relationship between patient and therapist, its movement toward a self-help ideology, and its elimination of the fee. Number Nine grew out of a hotline service. It is a drop-in center where anyone can walk in and receive free counseling from people who, if they have professional degrees, suppress them. It is a prominent example of a counterculture institution, and that is what really distinguishes most crisis centers from the mental health system. They think of themselves as alternate services situated in and for the counterculture.[40]

Not unnaturally, therefore, they serve primarily a counterculture clientele: young people strung out on drugs. Matthew P. Dumont, a psychiatrist whose background is in community mental health, sees the growth of this type of crisis center and of other self-help organizations as the real answer to the mental health system:

> The self-help movement is the result of so many forces that its growth can be said to be overdetermined. It has obvious implications for the planning of mental health care, anticipated manpower needs, and the funding of human services. The more people rely on self-help programs for caregiving the less need there will be for professionals. Unless we can accommodate to and find some common ground with this movement, we will become increasingly cloistered, self-serving, and irrelevant.[41]

Dumont foresees an extension of the self-help idea to ever larger populations including alienated young married couples, criminals, spinsters, the elderly, the unemployed, and he cites the formation of the Massachusetts Association for Self-Help as evidence of the growth of the movement. But he does not, interestingly, mention the insane. Nowhere does he mention the insane. And it is not the insane that places like Number Nine welcome. Like the hotlines, these organizations are not for crazy people; they are for kids wired into the temporary insanity of speed or acid, or trying to get away from their parents. The people who staff these centers know as little about how to deal with truly crazy people as your typical dentist.

What I am insisting on is that to qualify as a genuine alternative to the mental health system an organization *must* open its doors to people like Noah who act up on airplanes or Sam who thought he was a superman who could take off to a womanless planet or to the thousands upon thousands of crazies in places like Queens Manor, the hardcore crazy people living from time to time in alien worlds with different value systems, different languages, different realities from ours. Such people exist in large numbers, they often know themselves that they are different, that they have stepped or been shoved over some ambiguous but definite line, and they have become all too familiar with the reaction their difference arouses in us. We reject them. Forcefully. There is no evidence that the counterculture crisis centers are any better in this respect than the rest of us.

I know of only one exception to this picture. A counterculture crisis center called Changes in Chicago takes all comers, and some of the people who walk through the door are crazy. The Changes workers call them "heavy" people: "A 'heavy' person is someone who gives you a gut feeling of 'oh, God, I don't think I can handle this!' Whether they would be labelled suicidal, hallucinating, needy, or just behaving in strange ways, you feel them as heavy." [42] It is a good term carrying a minimum load of value judgments, and Changes must be a good place, for it not only accepts these people, it has gone to a great deal of trouble to figure out how to relate to them freely and honestly. The staff works with heavy people in small teams and makes a maximum effort to understand their expressed and unexpressed needs and feelings; at the same time, staff members set well-defined limits to their own responsibility —"the team needs to feel very clearly that it doesn't have to control the heavy person or do anything about her/him 'getting better' "—and to what they will take from someone—"we don't want to be shit on, and violence is not acceptable." [43] It sounds like an intelligent, possibly helpful approach, a model for others crisis centers to follow. But Changes may be the only such crisis center in the country even *trying* to serve the insane.

One genuine alternative in the United States? No, there must be more. I do, in fact, know of one other. It is a sixteen-room house in San Jose, California, called Soteria House and it is the second (the first failed) institution in the United States modeled after R. D. Laing's Kingsley

Hall in London.⁴⁴ Kingsley Hall and its successors under
the Philadelphia Association and the Arbours House Association are justly famous. Organized as an alternative to
British mental hospitals, Kingsley Hall drew on Laing's
idea that madness has an enormous potential for healing
if the trip is not aborted. Accordingly people who came to
Kingsley Hall to live were allowed to be insane; the professionals who also lived there made no effort to control
them or their insanity, but only tried to *be with* them in
the same way an existential therapist tries to *be with* his
patients. In one well-known case, that of Mary Barnes,
healing did take place. Ms. Barnes descended to the absolute bottom of "schizophrenic" regression, not moving
from her bed for weeks at a time, smearing shit on herself
and on the walls just as an infant does; and she came out
of it a wholly reborn person.⁴⁵ She has since become successful as a painter. One swallow doesn't make a summer,
as Jack Benny used to say, but Kingsley Hall has given
meaning to the word asylum.

Now we have Soteria House, modeled after Kingsley
Hall. With this difference, however; Soteria is being spon-
sored by NIMH, and it is a scientific research project. One
of the two heads of the project is Dr. Loren Mosher, who
is chief of the Center for Studies of Schizophrenia at NIMH
and editor of the NIMH publication *Schizophrenia Bulletin.* Mosher is a rather unusual man to be in that position, however, as he does not believe schizophrenia exists,
at least as an identifiable disease entity, and he is that
rarity, an existential psychiatrist. Mosher's partner in the
project is Alma Menn, a social worker who works for the
prestigious Mental Research Institute in Palo Alto. The
two of them are using Soteria to "test what we have termed
the developmental-crisis orientation to an initial episode
of schizophrenia." ⁴⁶ This means that they regard a first-
break schizophrenic as going on one of Laing's healing
(developmental) trips into the mind. Mosher admits the

difficulty of constructing a research project around this idea; "it is mostly a nontheory with an associated non-technique," he writes, a laissez-faire approach to insanity which militates against the use of strict research methodologies.[47] Nevertheless research is the project's justification, and Mosher is diligently reporting the results at psychiatric conferences all over the country.

And what are the results? Matched against a set of eight controls from a community mental health center, six experimental subjects

> . . . demonstrated more "growth" from their experiences at Soteria, in that five or six of twelve Soteria and only one or two of seventeen control patients are functioning at higher levels than they had attained before admission. Also, nine of twelve Soteria residents, as compared with three of seventeen controls, lived apart from their parents after discharge, a reflection, we believe, of the Soteria residents' increased independence.[48]

The experimental subjects also scored higher on various psychiatric tests, and they were not on phenothiazines, whereas the controls were. The research results, then, which are necessarily thin to date, are positive.

Alma Menn says, furthermore, that many people who have lived in the house are leading successful lives: successful on their terms. She made it clear when I talked to her that the word "cure" was inappropriate. The relevant word is understanding; they try to understand what is happening to these people, not to stop it. She also told me something about what it's like to live there. The staff are not professionals, just people, she says. There are only two rules: no sex between staff and residents, and no illegal drugs. Staff members take turns living in the house. There is no set routine. They live as if in a relaxed commune; whoever wants to cooks or cleans, whoever doesn't, doesn't; but everybody takes responsibility for what they do and for the place itself. Most important of all, crazy behavior is not denied and not suppressed. Which has upset some of the neighbors. One girl liked to walk around nude, inside and outside the house, and the little old ladies who lived out back thought that was going too far.[49]

It all sounds slightly romantic, but I would not prejudge it on that account. There is an inherent attractiveness to Laing's theory which most of his psychiatric critics have missed. It is perhaps psychiatry's greatest failure—a failure built into its social role, however, as an enforcer of the accepted version of reality—that it has no vision. It cannot offer the insane a vision of the possible meaningfulness of their experience, an idea that their insanity fits a pattern and has a goal, however inscrutable. Psychiatry can only suppress the experience, drug it out of existence; that is its best, its most heartfelt answer to it. Laing holds out precisely the opposite: the possibility of meaning in an experience of the absurd. Laing sees insanity as a chance to be reborn. Psychiatrists say that insanity doesn't happen that way, that it destroys people, not saves them. Even if that is generally true, however, even if the possibility of rebirth seems remote, a chance in a thousand, something realized only in exceptional cases like Mary Barnes', the vision still glorifies. To put it another way, Laing has given us a vision of "mental health" which extends considerably beyond the adjustment to "reality" which is still the standard of psychiatry. Insanity is a chance to "grow," using Mosher's careful bracketing, and even if that chance is real only for a few, nevertheless it makes of insanity a possibly livable experience. It makes it human. That is why Laing has remained popular and his ideas have survived his critics. It is very exciting, then, to see his ideas actually being tested upon the insane in a place like Soteria House.

That makes *two* genuine alternatives to the mental health system in the United States, serving, at the outside, twenty or thirty of the country's insane. Loren Mosher could suggest no others when I wrote to him, although he did mention people in New York and Chicago who are trying to work out ideas similar in some respects to his. We are back to the great scarcity of nonpsychiatric institutions for crazy people in this country. They are as rare as Vermeers or Gutenberg Bibles.

Why should this be? I can only refer once again to the phenomenal success of the present mental health system, a success measured not by its ability to treat and rehabilitate the insane but by the strength of its power over them. As an enforcer of reality, a system that works to reassure *us* (not the insane) that everything is under control, the mental health system *works*. We, once again, are the system's patrons. It is we who cannot abide insanity and we who insist on having the insane out of our lives. We have seen no need for alternatives because the system has worked so well.

Even a large-scale community mental health system would not be an alternative to this public attitude. Again and again we have seen the community respond to its mad folk by casting them out. We withdraw from them in fear and terror, we turn our eyes from them. And this attitude only justifies those who would preserve the present mental health system intact.

The conception of the community giving a place to people who can then move creatively in it has to be tested against what it is like out there, not in the pages of a book or in one's hope of how people are. The ultimate elitism is to wish people to be better in some way that we want them to be. I think we're doing a disservice to them, to their fundamental right to lead their lives, and to the people we are supposed to look after. We need to be extremely careful about proposing alternatives in a world that doesn't yet exist, and may never exist. Utopianism is not the basis on which to throw people out

of settings that may be unesthetic, but that may indeed
be more humane than the alternatives that we in fact
have, not that we wish we had.[50]

The community, here says Dr. Vivian Rakoff, is no alternative for the insane if the community will not accept
them. Better to keep them in those "unesthetic" mental
hospitals. He is right in this sense, that as long as we reject
the insane, and there is no getting around the fact that
we do, the mental hospital will survive. Or else the community mental health center or some other "alternative"
will become another kind of mental hospital.

If I insist upon the fact of public rejection it is not
to lecture anyone. In a very large sense, community resistance to the insane is perfectly justifiable. The community defines its own reality and the community has a
right to enforce that definition, to set the limits of the
law. And even when the insane obey the law they can
present the community with unbearable problems. In *Relations in Public* Erving Goffman devotes an interesting
paper to what he calls "insanity of place," "place" being
roughly someone's situation in his immediate social order,
his niche in the setting which includes himself and his
significant others. When a person goes insane he steps out
of that niche, he violates everyone else's sense of place and
wreaks havoc with his "relevant bit of social organization." [51] The depth of the disruption Goffman talks about
cannot be ignored. Anyone who has had to live with a wife
who feels spiders crawling all over her and the spiders
are God, or a son who switches abruptly from grandiose
all-consuming identifications with a football hero to watching television eighteen hours a day, seven days a week,
knows how hard it is to live with people who have gone
crazy. While it may not destroy those afflicted with it, insanity can go a long way toward destroying those who must
live with the afflicted. You may withstand the aggravation

only to succumb to the guilt. Or vice versa. The insane can be relentless.

Yet the system we have established to deal with this problem cannot be justified. Nothing can justify the systematic dehumanization of the insane or excuse what happened to Sarah and Stan Hamilton and Noah and Sam and Melissa and is happening still to thousands of others. The search for alternatives must go on.

I do not myself have any to propose: more Soteria Houses, perhaps; more efforts on the part of mental patients' liberation groups to establish their own crisis centers. Perhaps the process of searching is more important than any particular institutional mode which might come out of it. Ultimately, I think, the only genuine alternative to the mental health system is greater public and personal tolerance for insane behavior. The impulse which automatically condemns the strange behavior we cannot understand builds a high wall between ourselves and the insane. While the wall may effectively confine them, simultaneously it limits our vision of the possibilities of life. Strangeness, as Laing perceived, may be a door to growth.

But I do not want to underestimate the challenge. I remember very clearly an incident at Hudson River State Hospital. The weather was warm for January while I was there and in the afternoons I used to walk out to the edge of the golf course which abutted the grounds and look north toward the Catskill Mountains, which I could see covered with snow in the distance. One day I noticed a woman sitting on one of the fairways about one hundred yards away. At the same time a man and a little boy walked over a short distance away from me to enjoy the view. They were obviously visitors; probably the man's wife was visiting a relative. At any rate the man also noticed the woman sitting there, and his initial impulse was to help.

"Is anything wrong?" he shouted out to her.

It took the woman a moment to realize that someone was offering to help her, but finally she turned around and shouted back to the man, "Would you get me a glass of water?"

A glass of water. We were hundreds of yards from the nearest building, half a mile from the coffee shop. It was difficult to believe she seriously expected this stranger to go and get her a glass of water. The man stood there for an instant, trying, perhaps, to decide whether he had heard her correctly, and then he asked her again.

"Can I do anything for you?"

Her answer, shouted over the fairway, was clear and unmistakable: "I want a glass of water."

At this the man took his little boy by the hand and turned away.

It is an easy thing to erect walls and build buildings and construct a system which takes care of such people. It is enormously hard to forego that system and accept them into our lives. Probably the woman was regressed back into her crib, asking her Daddy for a glass of water. She may well sit in her crib the rest of her life, persisting in that incredibly complex demand. Probably no glass of water would ever satisfy her, and in this context, far out on a golf course, from a stranger, it was a little like asking for blood. How can anyone possibly respond to such craziness?

I don't know. I really don't know. All I know is that people like her represent a supreme test of our humanity. Perhaps, however, a way to begin to respond, a first tentative step, would be to acknowledge our own insanity, to recognize that what divides us may be only a little thing. The possibility of going crazy is open to us all.

Notes

INTRODUCTION

1. The following account, including all quoted statements, is taken from an interview with Noah Levy (a pseudonym), June 6, 1973.

2. Many sociologists have noted this fact. The initial diagnosis of "mental illness," of being crazy, is usually made by nonprofessionals, by friends, family, employers, police, or what have you. See, for example, David Mechanic, "Some Factors in Identifying and Defining Mental Illness," *Mental Illness and Social Processes,* Thomas J. Scheff, ed. (New York: Harper & Row, 1967), pp. 23–32.

3. This one comes from an Ann Landers column, *Peekskill Evening Star,* Peekskill, N.Y., September 17, 1973.

I: REALITY POLICE

1. See, for example, Ian Stevenson and William M. Sheppe, Jr., "The Psychiatric Examination," *American Handbook of Psychiatry,* Silvano Arieti, ed. (New York: Basic Books, 1959), Vol. 1, pp. 215–234; or William L. Sands, "Psychiatric History and Mental Status," *Diagnosing Mental Illness,* Alfred M. Freedman and Harold I. Kaplan, eds. (New York: Atheneum, 1972), pp. 20–40.

2. Recent evidence of this may be found in D. L. Rosenhan's article "On Being Sane in Insane Places," *Science,* Vol. 179 (January 19, 1973), pp. 250–258. See also David Mechanic, "Some Factors in Identifying and Defining Mental Illness," *Mental Illness and Social Processes,* Thomas J. Scheff, ed. (New York: Harper and Row, 1967), p. 27; and Thomas J. Scheff, *Being Mentally Ill: A Sociological*

Theory (Chicago: Aldine, 1966), pp. 128–155. Scheff also notes the perfunctoriness of the examinations; he timed eight of them for an average of 9.2 minutes per examination.

3.   The following account of how reality is learned draws heavily on Peter L. Berger and Thomas Luckmann, *The Social Construction of Reality: A Treatise in the Sociology of Knowledge* (Garden City, New York: Doubleday Anchor, 1967).

4.   D. W. Winnicott, *Playing and Reality* (London: Tavistock, 1971), p. 12.

5.   On this point see the instructive book by Joseph Church, *Language and the Discovery of Reality: A Developmental Psychology of Cognition* (New York: Vintage Books, 1961).

6.   If further evidence is wanted, the reader might also look at a book by Joseph Chilton Pearce called *The Crack in the Cosmic Egg: Challenging Constructs of Mind and Reality* (New York: Pocket Books, 1973). Pearce's book summarizes a great deal of research and speculation along these lines.

7.   Marshall Edelson, *The Idea of a Mental Illness* (New Haven: Yale University Press, 1971), p. 32.

8.   Even psychoanalysis has begun to approach this point of view. Freud's work was based on the positivism of the nineteenth century; reality was one thing, it existed independently of our constructions of it, and it was the job of the scientist to delineate it. Now Hartmann goes so far as to suggest two kinds of reality, "objective" or "scientific" reality and "conventional" reality, the latter being the reality which the child absorbs from his family and his culture. See Heinz Hartmann, "Notes on the Reality Principle," *Essays on Ego Psychology* (London: Hogarth Press, 1964), pp. 241–267.

9.   Berger and Luckmann's discussion of spilling soup goes into this much more thoroughly (*op. cit.*, pp. 132–133).

10.   Whorf's brilliant work on the Hopi language may be found in several articles in his book *Language, Thought, and Reality*, John B. Carroll, ed. (Cambridge: The M.I.T. Press, 1964). For a fascinating account of the historical relativism of the concept of hallucination, see Theodore R. Sarbin and Joseph B. Juhasz, "The Historical Background of the Concept of Hallucination," *Journal of the History of the Behavioral Sciences*, Vol. 3, No. 4 [1967], pp. 339–358.

11.   Erik H. Erikson, *Childhood and Society* (New York: W. W. Norton, 1963), 2nd edition, pp. 133–165. Erikson's work with American Indian tribes is well known. Jules Henry talks about noncompetitiveness in tribes besides the Sioux in *Culture Against Man*,

quoted in R. D. Laing, *The Politics of Experience* (New York: Ballantine Books, 1968), pp. 70–71.

12. The classic instance is Chief Broom, the character in Kesey's novel *One Flew Over the Cuckoo's Nest*. From real life I refer you to Donald P. Jewell, "A Case of a 'Psychotic' Navaho Indian Male," *Deviance: The Interactionist Perspective*, Earl Rubington and Martin S. Weinberg, eds. (New York: The Macmillan Company, 1968), pp. 68–75. The literature on cultural relativism in general is vast. An excellent survey of it as it relates to the question of "mental illness" may be found in Roger Bastide, *The Sociology of Mental Disorder*, trans. by Jean McNeil (London: Routledge & Kegan Paul, 1972), pp. 53 ff.

13. Bert Kaplan and Dale Johnson, "The Social Meaning of Navaho Psychopathology and Psychotherapy, *Magic, Faith, and Healing: Studies in Primitive Psychiatry Today*, Ari Kiev, ed. (New York: The Free Press, 1964), pp. 203–229.

14. Scheff (*Being Mentally Ill*, pp. 47–50) summarizes some of the principal work on this score.

15. Berger and Luckmann, *op. cit.*, pp. 54–55.

16. This and the following paragraph are based on Gerald N. Grob, *Mental Institutions in America: Social Policy to 1875* (New York: The Free Press, 1973), the latest and best book on the subject, and Albert Deutsch, *The Mentally Ill in America* (New York: Columbia University Press, 1949), 2nd edition, which is more thorough than Grob on practices before the 1820's. My entire account has been heavily influenced by Michel Foucault, *Madness and Civilization: A History of Insanity in the Age of Reason* (New York: Pantheon, 1965).

17. We do have a microsociology of behavior in the work of Erving Goffman and his followers, but the only specifically historical work I know of is in a book by Lyn H. Lofland, *A World of Strangers* (New York: Basic Books, 1973).

18. This account of moral treatment is based on Foucault's chapter on "The Birth of the Asylum." Other accounts are available, for example Norman Dain, *Concepts of Insanity in the United States, 1789–1865* (New Brunswick: Rutgers University Press, 1964); J. Sanbourne Bockoven, *Moral Treatment in American Psychiatry* (New York: Springer Publishing Company, 1963); and David J. Rothman, *The Discovery of the Asylum* (Boston: Little, Brown and Company, 1971). None of these, however, penetrates as deeply into the ideas behind moral treatment as Foucault.

19. *Op. cit.*, p. 249.

20. Bockoven also makes this point.
21. Grob has written an interesting book about the history of this hospital: Gerald N. Grob, *The State and the Mentally Ill: A History of Worcester State Hospital in Massachusetts, 1830–1920* (Chapel Hill: University of North Carolina Press, 1966).
22. Grob, *Mental Institutions in America,* p. 132.
23. Grob, *The State and the Mentally Ill,* p. 49. Grob covers the process of bureaucratization thoroughly in both his books.
24. Clarissa C. Lathrop, *A Secret Institution* (New York: Bryant Publishing Co., 1890).
25. *Ibid.,* pp. 205–206.
26. Grob, *Mental Institutions in America,* p. 120.
27. Lathrop, *op. cit.,* p. 123. About the Welsh, see p. 138.
28. *Ibid.,* pp. 114–115.
29. *Ibid.,* p. 143.
30. The only work I have been able to find is a book by Anne E. Caldwell, *Origins of Psychopharmacology: From CPZ to LSD* (Springfield, Illinois: Charles C. Thomas, 1970), which concentrates almost exclusively on the phenothiazines. She does mention Chloral, however, on p. 10. Chloral (chloral hydrate) is still sometimes administered to alcoholics when they have the dt's.
31. *Op. cit.,* pp. 115–116.
32. *Op. cit.* p. 255.
33. Julius Chambers, *A Mad World and its Inhabitants* (New York: D. Appleton and Company, 1877).
34. "Inmate Ward 8" wrote *Behind the Door of Delusion* (New York: The Macmillan Company, 1932); he was an alcoholic. "Jane Doe" wrote *Crazy!* (New York: Hawthorn Books, 1966); she was a writer and went on spending sprees. A list of some of the books written by ex-mental patients of all descriptions may be found in the back of a book by Walter S. Alvarez, *Minds That Came Back* (Philadelphia: J. B. Lippincott, 1961), pp. 339–373. Alvarez's list is by no means complete.
35. Anne Barry, *Bellevue Is a State of Mind* (New York: Harcourt Brace Jovanovich, 1971).
36. Quoted in Grob, *Mental Institutions in America,* p. 204.

II: GETTING INTO THE SYSTEM

1. Barbara O'Brien, *Operators and Things: The Inner Life of a Schizophrenic* (Cambridge, Mass.: Arlington Books, 1959), p. 31.
2. Bert Kaplan, ed., *The Inner World of Mental Illness* (New York: Harper and Row, 1964), p. 188.

3.   *Ibid.*, p. 185.

4.   Emphasis mine. Quoted in Anthony Wilden, *System and Structure: Essays in Communications and Exchange* (London: Tavistock Publications, 1972), p. 60.

5.   The book was reprinted, with no author given, in New York in 1941, *The Maniac* (New York: Books for the Few), with illustrations by G. Christopher Hudson, and it is this edition which I have used. This passage appears on p. 97.

6.   This interpretation draws heavily on Gregory Bateson. Bateson applied Russell's Theory of Logical Types to schizophrenia, analyzing the difficulties of the schizophrenic as a learned inability to differentiate between levels of communication, between messages and messages about messages: the message you get, say, when your wife throws a snowball at you, and the metamessage of her grin, which tells you she is only playing. The schizophrenic, Bateson says, cannot tell which message is meant. I am generalizing these ideas here, suggesting that the insane are themselves engaged in games of communication and metacommunication, but that they play their games from a position outside the accepted social framework of communication.

7.   For another, much more thorough explication of this point of view, see Roger Bastide, *The Sociology of Mental Disorder,* trans. by Jean McNeil (London: Routledge and Kegan Paul, 1972); especially pp. 185–202. This chapter is deeply indebted to Bastide's book.

8.   See Bastide on this point (*Ibid.*, p. 196).

9.   *Ibid.*, p. 218.

10.   Jacques Lacan, *The Language of the Self: The Function of Language in Psychoanalysis,* trans. with notes and commentary by Anthony Wilden (Baltimore: The Johns Hopkins Press, 1968), p. 136.

11.   Isaiah Berlin, *Four Essays on Liberty* (London: Oxford University Press, 1969), p. 198.

12.   *The Social Construction of Reality* (Garden City, New York: Doubleday Anchor), pp. 112–115.

13.   In Samuel Wallace, ed., *Total Institutions* (Transaction, Inc. [n.p., n.d.]), pp. 115–130.

14.   Nicholas N. Kittrie, *The Right to be Different: Deviance and Enforced Therapy* (Baltimore: The Johns Hopkins Press, 1971).

15.   See *Behavior Today,* Vol. 3, No. 48 (December 24, 1973), p. 1.

16.   For the latest on this (as of this writing), see *Psychiatric News,* Vol. VII, No. 24 (December 19, 1973), p. 3.

17.   Only the schools appear to use psychological tests systematically. Most school systems segregate emotionally disturbed children, of course, in special schools.

18. Figures quoted in Leo Srole *et al., Mental Health in the Metropolis: The Midtown Manhattan Study* (New York: McGraw-Hill Book Company, 1962), pp. 143–144.

19. *Ibid.*, p. 135

20. *Ibid.*, p. 138.

21. *Ibid.*, pp. 148–149.

22. The authors tried to allow for interviewer bias, but only in terms of socioeconomic levels; they matched the socioeconomic and ethnic backgrounds of interviewers with that of subjects (*Ibid.*, pp. 411–412). This says nothing about their bias as professionals.

23. This was not the definition of being "Well" the Study started out with. But as the authors themselves admit, in practice the emphasis was not on the possible positive aspects of mental health but on morbidity. And the range of symptoms they were willing to admit (see pp. 395 ff.) is truly remarkable, everything from "I can't make up my mind" to someone's feeling he was "the worrying type."

24. For a convenient summary on this point see Daniel Offer and Melvin Sabshin, *Normality: Theoretical and Clinical Concepts of Mental Health* (New York: Basic Books, 1966).

25. New York: Basic Books, 1958. See pp. 22–64.

26. David Mechanic, *Mental Health and Social Policy* (Englewood Cliffs, N.J.: Prentice-Hall, 1969), p. 66.

27. Joseph Giordano, *Ethnicity and Mental Health: Research and Recommendations* (New York: Institute of Human Relations, 1973), p. 22.

28. Leo Srole *et al., op. cit.*, p. 5.

29. *Ibid.*, p. 147.

30. *Ibid.*, p. 149.

31. The classic discussion of the "sick role" is Talcott Parsons' *The Social System* (New York: The Free Press, 1964), Chapter X.

32. WNBC-TV, November 28, 1973.

33. Bastide, *op. cit.*, p. 188.

34. Richard W. Redick, Biometry Branch, NIMH, *Statistical Note 92: Patient Care Episodes in Psychiatric Services, United States, 1971* (Washington: Department of Health, Education, and Welfare, August, 1973).

35. Franklyn N. Arnhoff *et al.*, eds., *Manpower for Mental Health* (Chicago: Aldine Publishing Company, 1969), p. 10.

36. Marian Radke Yarrow et al., "The Psychological Meaning of Mental Illness in the Family," *Mental Illness and Social Processes*, Thomas J. Scheff, ed. (New York: Harper and Row, 1967), p. 44.

37. New York: Basic Books, 1964. Esterson has written another book, *The Leaves of Spring* (Harmondsworth: Penguin Books, 1972),

which takes one of the cases in the earlier book and treats it at much greater length. The most convenient source for the double bind hypothesis is Gregory Bateson, *Steps to an Ecology of Mind* (New York: Ballantine Books, 1972), pp. 201–227. The literature on family studies is rapidly becoming enormous.

38. Harold Sampson *et al.*, "Family Processes and Becoming a Mental Patient," *The Mental Patient: Studies in the Sociology of Deviance*, Stephen P. Spitzer and Norman K. Denzin, eds. (New York: McGraw-Hill Book Company, 1968), p. 204.

39. David Mechanic, "Some Factors in Identifying and Defining Mental Illness," in Spitzer and Denzin, *op. cit.*, pp. 195–203. Mechanic's most useful insight in my opinion remains his insistence on the importance of lay diagnosis for getting someone into the system.

40. *Ibid.*, pp. 200–201.

41. August B. Hollingshead and Frederick C. Redlich, *Social Class and Mental Illness: A Community Study* (New York: John Wiley & Sons, 1958), pp. 172-173.

42. *Ibid.*, p. 175. See also Jerome K. Myers and Bertram K. Roberts, *Family and Class Dynamics in Mental Illness* (New York: John Wiley & Sons, 1959), p. 214, who make the same observation.

43. Interview with Mrs. Diana Paul, Bronx, New York, May 16, 1973.

44. Joseph Giordano, *op. cit.*, p. 20.

45. Quoted in Giordano, *op. cit.*, p. 32.

46. Bateson, *op. cit.*, p. 357.

47. *Ibid.*, pp. 494 ff.

III: PATHS TO THE MENTAL HOSPITAL

1. This is increasingly becoming a port of entry into the mental health system.

2. "Stan Hamilton" is a pseudonym. Other details have been changed to protect his identity.

3. Interview with "Stan Hamilton." Subsequent quotes are from this interview.

4. This happened to Stan.

5. Common practice in many states, as we shall see.

6. Jules Henry, *Pathways to Madness* (New York: Random House, 1971), p. 5.

7. Talcott Parsons, *The Social System* (New York: The Free Press, 1964), Chapter X.

8. This phrase is from Jerome D. Frank, *Persuasion and Healing* (New York: Schocken Books, 1963), p. 2.

9. Rollo May, *Power and Innocence* (New York: W. W. Norton & Co., 1972), p. 100.

10. This is generally accepted. Parsons talks about it, and Frank devotes a chapter to it. Healing is partly a function of belief in the healer and his medicine.

11. This is a complicated matter and a subject of dispute in psychiatry. Parsons feels that psychiatrists are effective to the degree that they do *not* respond as people, but Parsons was writing in 1951, when virtually the only accepted mode of psychotherapy was psychoanalysis. As we shall see, psychoanalysis does not allow the therapist to respond as a person. Since Parsons published his book a good deal of work has been done on the personal qualities which make for an effective therapist, and the findings seem to indicate that these qualities include openness and what we are calling here genuine personal power. We will be talking about this again later on.

12. This rather arrogant phrase comes from Wendell Muncie, "The Psychobiological Approach," in *American Handbook of Psychiatry*, Silvano Arieti, ed. (New York: Basic Books, 1959), vol. 2, p. 1323. Muncie is a follower of Adolf Meyer, who might be said to be the founder of the eclectic approach in modern American psychiatry.

13. Leston L. Havens, "The Existential Use of the Self," *The American Journal of Psychiatry*, Vol. 131 (January, 1974), p. 4. Havens' italics. A good source for the existential psychiatric point of view is Rollo May *et al.*, eds., *Existence: A New Dimension in Psychiatry and Psychology* (New York: Basic Books, 1958).

14. The case will be found in Eugene Minkowski, *Lived Time*, trans. with an intro. by Nancy Metzel (Evanston: Northwestern University Press, 1970), pp. 179–193.

15. *Ibid.*, p. 182.

16. Rollo May, *Power and Innocence*, p. 23.

17. Louis S. Reed, Evelyn S. Myers and Patricia L. Scheidemandel, *Health Insurance and Psychiatric Care: Utilization and Cost* (Washington: American Psychiatric Association, 1972), p. 29.

18. *Ibid.*

19. *The Present and Future Importance of Patterns of Private Psychiatric Practice in the Delivery of Mental Health Services* (Washington: American Psychiatric Association, 1973), p. 19. This is a very crude estimate, and I am reluctant to assign much credence to this report, which reads like propaganda.

20. *Ibid.*, p. 19.

21.   William Ryan, ed., *Distress in the City: Essays on the Design and Administration of Urban Mental Health Services* (Cleveland: Press of Case Western Reserve University, 1969), p. 15.

22.   *Ibid.*, pp. 20–21.

23.   See *The Present and Future Importance* . . . , cited above, pp. 20–21.

24.   "Distress in the City—and in the Mental Health Field," in Ryan, *op. cit.*, pp. 90–91.

25.   Task Force on Children Out of School, *Suffer the Children: The Politics of Mental Health in Massachusetts* (Boston, 1972), pp. 17–18.

26.   Massachusetts Mental Health Center, *Annual Report, 1970–1971*, (mimeo), p. 39.

27.   *Ibid.*

28.   Interview with "Nancy O'Rourke." For another personal account of psychiatric abandonment see James A. Wechsler's book about his son, *In a Darkness* (New York: W. W. Norton & Co., 1972).

29.   "The Service Network as Heuristic and as Fact," in Ryan, *op. cit.*, p. 166.

30.   Psychiatric Emergency Committee, Northern Westchester Mental Health Council, *Study of Psychiatric Emergencies in Northern Westchester* (mimeo), July, 1972, p. 4.

31.   For further information on this and on the organization of mental health services in Boston, see Robert H. Marden, "Boston," in Robert H. Connery *et al.*, *The Politics of Mental Health: Organizing Community Mental Health in Metropolitan Areas* (New York: Columbia University Press, 1968), pp. 341–406. This volume contains useful accounts of the mental health situation in a number of other cities as well.

32.   Information about the status of psychoanalysts within the psychiatric profession may be found throughout Arnold A. Rogow's book, *The Psychiatrists* (New York: Dell Publishing Co., 1971).

33.   New York: Oxford University Press, 1971. Another excellent book on Freud's influence is David Shakow's and David Rapaport's *The Influence of Freud on American Psychology* (Cleveland: World Publishing Company, Meridian Books, 1968).

34.   An excellent source for an understanding of psychoanalytic practice is Ralph R. Greenson, *The Technique and Practice of Psychoanalysis* (New York: International Universities Press, 1967), Vol. I.

35.   Most of these alternate therapeutic systems, it should be noted, are oriented to group therapy.

36.   Rogow, *op. cit.*, p. 110.

37.   Allan E. Bergin, "The Evaluation of Therapeutic Outcomes," in *Handbook of Psychotherapy and Behavior Change: An Empirical Analysis,* Allan E. Bergin and Sol L. Garfield, eds. (New York: John Wiley & Sons, 1971), pp. 217–270. See also Charles B. Truax and Kevin M. Mitchell, "Research on Certain Therapist Interpersonal Skills in Relation to Process and Outcome," in the same volume, pp. 299–344; and Donald R. Stieper and Daniel N. Wiener, *Dimensions of Psychotherapy: An Experimental and Clinical Approach* (Chicago: Aldine Publishing Company, 1965).

38.   Sigmund Freud, "Analysis Terminable and Interminable," *Collected Papers,* James Strachey, ed. (London: Hogarth Press, 1950), Vol. V, pp. 316–357. Anna Freud has attempted to bring this paper up to date; see "Difficulties in the Path of Psychoanalysis," *The Writings of Anna Freud* (New York: International Universities Press, 1971), Vol. VII, pp. 124–156.

39.   Truax and Mitchell, *op. cit.,* p. 315.

40.   It is, in fact, very close to the position adopted by Carl Rogers, by the Gestalt therapy school, and others as well as the existential therapists.

41.   In face also of the fact that large numbers of people repudiate psychotherapy. The evidence on continuation in therapy indicates that most people do not know what to expect in psychotherapy before they go into it, do not understand what it is all about when they do become involved, and quickly discontinue it when they come to understand. Perhaps the majority of those who enter psychotherapy give it up after three or four interviews. See Sol L. Garfield, "Research on Client Variables in Psychotherapy," in Bergin and Garfield, *op. cit.,* pp. 271–298. See also Gerald Gurin, Joseph Veroff, and Sheila Feld, *Americans View Their Mental Health* (New York: Basic Books, 1960), pp. 302–344.

42.   Interview with Milton Greenblatt, November 14, 1972. I have seen one of the studies Greenblatt was referring to; it is by Lester Grinspoon, Jack R. Ewalt, and Richard I. Shader, *Schizophrenia: Pharmacotherapy and Psychotherapy* (Baltimore: Williams & Wilkins Company), 1972.

43.   *Ibid.*

44.   See, however, the Letters columns of publications like *Psychiatric News* or *The American Journal of Psychiatry* where old-line psychiatrists frequently publish their views.

45.   A good personal account of this training may be found in David S. Viscott, *The Making of a Psychiatrist* (New York: Arbor House, 1972).

46. This is from a document called "Relations of Medicine and Psychology" originally published by the American Psychiatric Association and reprinted in *Psychology, Psychiatry and the Public Interest*, Maurice H. Krout, ed. (Minneapolis: University of Minnesota Press, 1956), pp. 23–24. The same sentiments are operative today.

47. See Judd Marmor, "The Future of Psychoanalytic Therapy," *The American Journal of Psychiatry*, Vol. 130, No. 11 (November, 1973), pp. 1197–1202. On the question of lay analysis, see the powerful statement by Ernest Federn, "How Freudian Are the Freudians: Some Remarks to an Unpublished Letter," *Journal of the History of the Behavioral Sciences*, Vol. 3, No. 3 (1967), pp. 269–281. The author is the son of the well-known analyst Paul Federn.

48. These figures, conservative estimates, are taken from *The Present and Future Practice* . . . etc., p. 8 (for full reference, see n. 20 above). I have heard of charges by psychiatrists of up to $100 an hour.

49. Louis S. Reed *et al., op. cit.,* p. 35.

50. *Ibid.* for the 1966 figures. The AMA ranking comes from *The Present and Future Practice* . . . , p. 16.

51. An excellent account of precisely this procedure may be found in Viscott's book, *op cit.,* pp. 346 ff.

52. Biometry Branch, National Institute of Mental Health, *Statistical Note 99: Trends in Total Additions and Resident Patients at End of Year in Private Mental Hospitals 1968–1971* (Washington: Department of Health, Education, and Welfare, November, 1973), p. 6.

53. Biometry Branch, National Institute of Mental Health, *Statistical Note 92: Patient Care Episodes in Psychiatric Services, United States 1971* (Washington: Department of Health, Education, and Welfare, August, 1973), p. 22.

54. The attitude of insurers derives from their bad experience with the cost of psychoanalysis; see Louis S. Reed *et al., op cit.,* pp. 59–62.

55. *Ibid.,* p. 48.

56. Health Policy Advisory Center, *Health/PAC Bulletin,* No. 55 (November, 1973), p. 1.

57. *Psychiatric News,* Vol. IX, No. 1 (January 2, 1974), pp. 22–23.

58. Those HMOs already in existence have protested the inclusion of benefits for "mental illness," not because it would put the plans out of the reach of poor people but because they will not be able to compete with Blue Cross and Blue Shield. See *The New York Times,* February 14, 1974.

322   *REALITY POLICE*

IV: THE COMMITMENT EXPERIENCE

1. Whether it is based in behaviorism or Freudian psychodynamics, modern psychology generally denies any reality to what we call free will and the qualities associated with it, such as "will power," "determination," etc. Modern psychology sees a person's conscious mental states and his behavior as determined either by unconscious drives or by learned responses, so that a display of "courage" or "determination" becomes under psychological analysis some sort of learned counteraggressiveness or perhaps an unconscious search for parental approval. As Isaiah Berlin has pointed out, however, the psychologists, psychiatrists, and other behavioral scientists who adopt this deterministic stance rarely act as if they took it seriously. On the contrary, he says, "men evidently find it perfectly possible to subscribe to determinism in the study and disregard it in their lives." (Isaiah Berlin, *Four Essays on Liberty* [London: Oxford University Press, 1969], pp. xvi–xvii.)

2. Direct quotes from Sarah are taken either from her personal letters to me or from the affidavit she submitted to the Special Committee on Health of the Kansas legislature in 1973.

3. Interview with Dr. Herbert C. Modlin, Menninger Foundation, June 27, 1973.

4. Allan Smart, "Carriage House: A Setting of Compromise and Communication," *Menninger Perspective* I, August–September, 1970.

5. "At Menninger: Turning Psychiatry to Social Action," *Medical World News*, August 21, 1970.

6. See John Cumming and Elaine Cumming, *Ego & Milieu* (New York: Atherton Press, 1962), pp. 2–3.

7. See Anna Freud, "Acting Out," *The Writings of Anna Freud* (New York: International Universities Press, 1971), Vol. VII, pp. 94–109.

8. *The New York Times,* February 28, 1974.

9. J. Laplanche and J. B. Pontalis, *The Language of Psycho-Analysis,* trans. by Donald Nicholson-Smith (London: The Hogarth Press, 1973), p. 396.

10. *Insight and Responsibility* (New York: W. W. Norton & Company, 1964), p. 112.

11. Interview with Dr. Robert Haines, Topeka, Kansas, June 25, 1973.

12. Interview with psychiatric aide (anonymity requested), Topeka, Kansas, January 27, 1974.

13.   Interview with Dr. Roy Menninger, Topeka, Kansas, June 27, 1973.

14.   David L. Chambers, "Alternatives to Civil Commitment of the Mentally Ill: Practical Guides and Constitutional Imperatives," *Michigan Law Review*, Vol. 70 (1972), p. 1110.

15.   For example, *Wyatt v. Stickney*, now known as *Wyatt v. Aderholt*, seems destined for the Supreme Court; see pages 241 ff. *Lessard v. Schmidt* may also get there.

16.   For a compilation of sources on the legal issues involved in commitment, see Jay Katz, Joseph Goldstein and Alan M. Dershowitz, *Psychoanalysis Psychiatry and Law* (New York: The Free Press, 1967), Chapter II.

17.   Interview with lawyer (anonymity requested), January 26, 1974.

18.   See, for example, Jay Katz *et al.*, *op. cit.*, pp. 464, 467–468.

19.   The Kansas statute is K. S. A. 1973 Supp. 59-2901 to 59-2937. It is summarized in Samuel J. Brakel and Ronald S. Rock, eds., *The Mentally Disabled and the Law* (Chicago: University of Chicago Press, 1971) (revised edition), along with the laws of the rest of the states, and in Bruce Ennis and Loren Siegel, *The Rights of Mental Patients* (New York: Avon Books, 1973), pp. 154–157, which is a very useful handbook.

20.   Interview with Dr. Robert Haines, June 26, 1973.

21.   Thomas S. Szasz, *Law, Liberty, and Psychiatry* (New York: Collier Books, 1968), p. 40.

22.   This is standard operating procedure; I have seen it used a number of times. I particularly remember one occasion at the Massachusetts Mental Health Center, when a man in his early twenties, a college student, turned in his letter announcing his intention to leave. The young man had threatened to commit suicide, however, so the Chief Resident made out commitment papers and told him that he would sign them at once if he insisted on submitting the letter. The man withdrew his letter. Later he told me, "I feel like a caged animal here." The Chief Resident was rather embarrassed by the whole episode and assured me that it was rare to threaten a voluntary patient with commitment. Even in those places where it is a rare event, however, the very fact that a patient must submit a letter and wait a prescribed period of time before he can leave points up the actual nature of his situation. The hospital, not he, decides whether or not he will go. To call his status "voluntary" does violence to the language.

23. Interview with the "Warrens" (anonymity requested), January 27, 1974.

24. Louis Frydman, "Legal Rights and Psychiatric Confinement," paper presented to the Topeka Center, National Association of Social Workers, January 23, 1973 (mimeo), p. 4.

25. See n. 19 above.

26. Frydman, *op. cit.*, p. 2.

27. An interesting article on the "wild beast" metaphor is Anthony M. Platt's and Bernard L. Diamond's "The Origin and Development of the 'Wild Beast' Concept of Mental Illness and its Relation to Theories of Criminal Responsibility," *Journal of the History of the Behavioral Sciences,* Vol. 1 (October, 1965), pp. 355–367.

28. As reported in Jonas R. Rappeport and George Lassen, "Dangerousness—Arrest Rate Comparisons of Discharged Patients and the General Population," *American Journal of Psychiatry,* Vol. 121 (1965), pp. 776–783. See also the paper by J. Giovannoni and L. Gurel, "Socially Disruptive Behavior of Ex-Mental Patients," *Archives of General Psychiatry,* Vol. 17 (1967), pp. 146–153.

29. Rappeport and Lassen, *op. cit.*

30. Alan M. Dershowitz, "The Psychiatrist's Power in Civil Commitment: A Knife That Cuts Both Ways," *Psychology Today,* Vol. 2, No. 9 (February 1969), pp. 42 ff.

31. Scheff calls this a Type 2 error. It is very common with physicians, who overdiagnose the presence of illness in order to be on the safe side. Scheff comments cogently on its inappropriateness in psychiatry. See Thomas J. Scheff, *Being Mentally Ill* (Chicago: Aldine-Atherton, 1971), pp.105 ff.

32. J. M. Macdonald, "The Threat to Kill," *American Journal of Psychiatry,* Vol. 120 (1963), pp. 125–130.

33. Interview with Dr. Robert Haines, June 25, 1973.

34. Bernard Rubin, "Prediction of Dangerousness in Mentally Ill Criminals," *Archives of General Psychiatry,* Vol. 27 (1972), pp. 397–407. Rubin's article discusses the case of seventeen men who had originally been confined to the psychiatric division of an Illinois prison in the 1930's and early 1940's and had then been "forgotten." Although all of these men had been accused of crimes of various sorts, Rubin found that only one of them could be classified as still dangerous when he was released in 1968. "Of the rest who actually had committed a dangerous crime," he says, "there is little evidence in any of them to support continued dangerousness after two years of imprisonment." (p. 405.) Furthermore, although these men were all either brain-damaged or "mentally ill" to some degree, Rubin can find no clear causal connection between their "illnesses" and their crimes. Even where dangerousness exists, then, it may not be some sort of permanent "condition," like "mental illness" is supposed to be, but may instead arise from temporary social conditions and will disappear with them; and it need not have any connection with the person's "illness" in the first place.

35.   *Op. cit.*, p. 3.

36.   See Alan M. Dershowitz, "On 'Preventive Detention,'" *New York Review of Books*, Vol. XII, No. 5 (March 13, 1969), pp. 22–27.

37.   "Civil Commitment of the Mentally Ill: Theories and Procedures," *Harvard Law Review*, Vol. 79 (1966), p. 1290.

38.   See the paper by Laurence Tancredi and Diana Clark, "Psychiatry and the Legal Rights of Patients," *American Journal of Psychiatry*, Vol. 129 (1972), pp. 328–330, in which the authors report that only a small proportion of the admittedly small sample of psychiatric personnel they tested could answer questions about the legal rights of patients correctly.

39.   For a convenient summary of the ruling, see Robert Johnston and Margaret Fraser, "The Right to Treatment," *MH*, Vol. 56, No. 3 (Summer 1972), pp. 13–19.

40.   As of 1970, Alabama stood last among the states on three separate staffing scales (*Eleven Indices*, Washington: Joint Information Service, American Psychiatric Association and National Association for Mental Health). It stood almost equally low on other scales by which the psychiatric profession rates mental health services in a state.

41.   See *Lessard v. Schmidt* 349 F. Supp. 1078 (1972). Essential documents in the case have been reprinted in Bruce J. Ennis and Paul R. Friedman, eds., *Legal Rights of the Mentally Handicapped* (New York: Practicing Law Institute, 1974), Vol. I, pp. 131–240.

42.   *Psychiatric News*, Vol. IX, No. 2 (January 16, 1974).

43.   Ennis has written a book on his work: Bruce J. Ennis, *Prisoners of Psychiatry* (New York: Harcourt Brace Jovanovich, 1972).

44.   American Bar Association, News Release, December 8, 1973.

45.   A. Louis McGarry and Honora A. Kaplan, "Overview: Current Trends in Mental Health Law," *American Journal of Psychiatry*, Vol. 130 (1973), p. 625.

46.   Massachusetts General Laws, Chapter 123, Section 1.

47.   A. Louis McGarry, Division of Legal Medicine, Massachusetts Department of Mental Health, *Annual Report,* July 13, 1972 (mimeo), pp. 4–5.

48.   Yorihiko Kumasaka, "The Lawyer's Role in Involuntary Commitment—New York's Experience," *Mental Hygiene,* Vol. 56, No. 2 (Spring 1972), p. 22.

49.   *Ibid.*

50.   William B. Beach, Jr., and Anne Davis, "The Short-Doyle Program: Past, Present, and Future," *California Medicine,* Vol. 109 (November 1968), pp. 398–402.

51.   Note that the "need for treatment" standard has been dropped; a psychiatrist's or even a judge's opinion that you need treatment is not enough in California to get you committed.

52.   *Mental Health Laws* (Sacramento: Department of Mental Hygiene, 1970).

53.   "Replies to Questions Submitted to the Department of Health by the Senate Select Committee on the Proposed Phaseout of State Hospital Services," submitted by J. M. Stubblebine, Director, Department of Health, State of California, May 18, 1973 (Xerox). Approximately 2500 of the 7000 were committed under the criminal statutes.

54.   Three hospitals have been closed altogether, and the sections for the "mentally ill" in two other hospitals have been closed.

55.   Interview with Andrew Robertson, Deputy Director, State Department of Health, July 3, 1973.

56.   Marc F. Abramson, "The Criminalization of Mentally Disordered Behavior: Possible Side Effect of a New Mental Health Law," *Hospital and Community Psychiatry,* Vol. 23, No. 4 (April 1972), pp. 101–105. In some jurisdictions it appears to be true that police are picking up more "mentally ill" offenders on minor charges such as disturbing the peace.

57.   *Psychiatric News,* Vol. VIII, No. 8 (April 18, 1973). See also Janet Chase, "Where Have All the Patients Gone?" *Human Behavior,* Vol. 2, No. 10 (October 1973), pp. 14–21.

58.   *Ibid.,* pp. 14–16.

59.   Senate Select Committee on Proposed Phaseout of State Hospital Services, California Legislature, *Hearing,* June 15, 1973 (Sacramento: Senate Select Committee, etc.), pp. 48–64. (Hereafter referred to as *Hearing.*)

60.   *Ibid.,* Appendix.

61.   Janet Chase, *op. cit.,* p. 14.

62.   *Hearing,* June 15, 1973, p. 190.

63. *Ibid.*, pp. 121–123.
64. Telephone interview with Paul O'Rourke, February 6, 1974.
65. Draft of statement by Andrew Robertson before Senate Select Committee, October 9, 1973 (xerox).
66. *Hearing,* June 8, 1973, pp. 62, 93.
67. Telephone interview with Paul O'Rourke, February 6, 1974.

V: INSIDE THE FUNNY FARM

1. "The Arc," *American Review,* No. 20 (April, 1974), pp. 54–55. Reprinted with the permission of the author.
2. Biometry Branch, National Institute of Mental Health, *Statistical Note 98: State and Regional Distribution of Psychiatric Beds in 1972* (Washington: Department of Health, Education, and Welfare, November, 1973), p. 5.
3. The latest addition to the tradition, as I mentioned before, is D. L. Rosenhan, "On Being Sane in Insane Places," *Science,* Vol. 179 (January 19, 1973), pp. 250–258. For a discussion of the moral issues involved, see William Caudill, *The Psychiatric Hospital as a Small Society* (Cambridge, Mass.: Harvard University Press, 1958), pp. xiii–xvi. Caudill also pretended to be a patient. Both Caudill and Rosenhan justify their deceptions by appeal to the scientific nature of the work they were doing. For my own part, I am not going to try to justify what I did. It was undoubtedly wrong. But I saw no other way to find out what it means to be a mental patient.
4. Erving Goffman, "The Moral Career of the Mental Patient," *Asylums: Essays on the Social Situation of Mental Patients and Other Inmates* (Garden City, New York: Doubleday Anchor Books, 1961), pp. 125–169.
5. Except for this story, everything else I told the admitting psychiatrist was true. And I used my real name.
6. Cf. Erving Goffman, *Interaction Ritual* (Garden City, New York: Doubleday Anchor Books, 1967), p. 67.
7. The quote comes from an advertisement in the *American Journal of Psychiatry,* Vol. 130, No. 9 (September, 1973), pp. A50–52.
8. Erik H. Erikson, *Identity: Youth and Crisis* (New York: W. W. Norton & Co., 1968), p. 165.
9. Robert K. Merton, referring to the work of Karl Mannheim, describes the bureaucrat's life plan as follows: "The bureaucrat's official life is planned for him in terms of a graded career, through the organizational devices of promotion by seniority, pensions, incremental salaries, etc., all of which are designed to provide incentives

for disciplined action and conformity to the official regulations."
(Merton, *Social Theory and Social Structure,* New York: The Free
Press, 1968 [Enlarged Edition], p. 254.) Note that the bureaucrat's
life is also planned *for* him, not *by* him.
10.   Richard F. Salisbury, *Structures of Custodial Care: An An-
thropological Study of a State Mental Hospital* (Berkeley: University
of California Press, 1962), pp. 77–78 and elsewhere, talks about the
importance for some patients of their hospital jobs, and on p. 74 he
remarks in a footnote, "It may be noted in passing that although
very few chronic patients are released from hospital, the job to which
many of them gravitate is that of attendant in another State Mental
Hospital. Of the three cases of which I had knowledge, out of an
estimated ten leaving the hospital to work, all obtained attendant
jobs."
11.   There is nothing in his environment, of course, to gain his
interest in the first place.
12.   J. K. Wing and G. W. Brown, *Institutionalism and Schizo-
phenia: A Comparative Study of Three Mental Hospitals, 1960–1968*
(London: Cambridge University Press, 1970), p. 177.
13.   Alfred H. Stanton and Morris S. Schwartz, *The Mental Hospital* (New York: Basic Books, 1954). Stanton and Schwartz were
studying a small, elite institution, Chestnut Lodge Sanitarium, and
their findings, and those of their followers, cannot be said to apply
very well to large state hospitals. The best study of the latter, besides Goffman's, is probably Ivan Belknap's *Human Problems of a
State Mental Hospital* (New York: McGraw-Hill Publishing Co.,
1956). I know of no recent book-length studies of state mental hospitals since Wing and Brown, and their work was done in England.
A useful American study dating from 1967 is Leonard P. Ullman's
*Institution and Outcome: A Comparative Study of Psychiatric Hos-
pitals* (Oxford: Pergamon Press), which is a statistical investigation
of the effects of size and other factors on thirty Veterans Administration hospitals. Except to instigate change, however, more work
on the subject may be unnecessary. The early work such as Belknap's
is still valid. The situation has not changed.
       An interesting critical review of the entire literature on mental
hospitals from the point of view of organization theory is Charles
Perrow's article, "Hospitals: Technology, Structure, and Goals," in
Handbook of Organizations, James G. March, ed. (Chicago: Rand
McNally, 1965). Another, from a slightly different point of view, is
Amitai Etzioni, "Interpersonal and Structural Factors in the Study
of Mental Hospitals," *Psychiatry,* Vol. 23 (1960), pp. 13–22.
14.   Lee Gurel, "Dimensions of the Therapeutic Milieu: A Study

of Mental Hospital Atmosphere," *American Journal of Psychiatry*, Vol. 131, No. 4 (April, 1974), p. 413, agrees that the hospitals are here to stay, as do many others.

15.   Robert M. Edwalds, "Functions of the State Mental Hospital as a Social Institution," *Mental Hygiene*, Vol. 48, No. 4 (October, 1964), p. 666.

16.   *Ibid.*

17.   *Ibid.*, p. 667.

18.   See Dorothy E. Smith, "The Logic of Custodial Organization," *Psychiatry*, Vol. 28 (1965), pp. 311–323, especially p. 316.

19.   This description of mental hospital structure is necessarily rather broad and general. For more precision I refer the reader to some of the work mentioned above, such as Salisbury's book, Stanton and Schwartz, Belknap, or Caudill, or to two articles by Jules Henry, "The Formal Social Structure of a Psychiatric Hospital," *Psychiatry*, Vol. 17 (1954), pp. 139–151; and "Types of Institutional Structure," *Psychiatry*, Vol. 20 (1957), pp. 47–60. Another useful article is Merton J. Kahne, "Bureaucratic Structure and Impersonal Experience in Mental Hospitals," in *The Sociology of Mental Disorders: Analyses and Readings in Psychiatric Sociology*, S. Kirson Weinberg, ed. (Chicago: Aldine Publishing Company, 1967), pp. 201–211.

20.   Cf. Merton J. Kahne, "Some Implications of the Concept of Position for the Study of Mental Hospital Organization," *Psychiatry*, Vol. 25 (1962), p. 241: ". . . position in the hierarchy, hospital and community social status, and economic status all vary almost exactly inversely with the amount of clinical time spent with patients no matter what one's professional or nonprofessional affiliation."

21.   Amitai Etzioni, *Modern Organizations* (Englewood Cliffs, New Jersey: Prentice-Hall, Inc., 1964), pp. 75–93.

22.   We will discuss unitization in Chapter Six.

23.   Cf. Elaine Cumming and John Cumming, "The Locus of Power in a Large Mental Hospital," *Psychiatry*, Vol. 19 (1956), p. 364, noting the unwillingness of doctors to accept administrative responsibility.

24.   The nursing staff is normally more than content to have the doctors stay off the wards. Cumming and Cumming, in their book *Ego & Milieu* (New York: Atherton Press, 1962), p. 126, talk about this at length.

25.   Robert K. Merton, *op. cit.*, p. 253. (References omitted.)

26.   Dorothy E. Smith (*op. cit.*, pp. 314–315) insists on this point, as opposed to those who see anyone *in* an organization as a member *of* it.

27.   Shortly before I left, a nurse who did know some Russian

sat down and talked to the old man. According to her, he was rational. He told her he had known the last czar.

28.   Interview with "Sam," February 12, 1973. Subsequent quotes are taken from this interview.

29.   Benjamin M. Braginsky, Dorothea D. Braginsky and Kenneth Ring, *Methods of Madness: The Mental Hospital as a Last Resort* (New York: Holt, Rinehart and Winston, 1969), p. 72.

30.   *Ibid.*, p. 73.

31.   Erving Goffman, "The Underlife of a Public Institution," *Asylums,* pp. 171–320.

32.   Harold Garfinkel, "Conditions of Successful Degradation Ceremonies," *Deviance: The Interactionist Perspective,* Earl Rubington and Martin S. Weinberg, eds. (New York: The Macmillan Company, 1968), p. 189.

33.   This is a psychosomatic condition in which men mistake muscular aches and pains, shortness of breath, etc., for a heart attack. It may be thought of as a rather severe form of hypochondria. See Maxwell Jones, *The Therapeutic Community* (New York: Basic Books, 1953), pp. 2–3.

34.   *Ibid.,* p. 13.

35.   *Ibid.,* p. 14.

36.   *New York Times,* May 25, 1969, IV, p. 32.

37.   The origins of most doctors are middle or upper-middle class, while most patients in state mental hospitals, as we know, are lower-class in origin. It is not surprising, therefore, to find psychiatrists in those institutions unwilling to participate in its life as even pretended equals. The mental hospital, in other words, replicates the class structure of society at large, and only a significant shift in the larger social structure would be likely to effect this kind of restructuring in the mental hospital.

38.   Irving M. Berlin, "Resistance to Change in Mental Health Professionals," *American Journal of Orthopsychiatry,* Vol. 39, No. 1 (January, 1969), p. 111.

39.   *Ibid.,* pp. 111–112.

40.   Robert Rubenstein and Harold D. Lasswell, *The Sharing of Power in a Psychiatric Hospital* (New Haven: Yale University Press, 1966).

41.   Marvin I. Herz, "The Therapeutic Community: A Critique," *Hospital & Community Psychiatry,* Vol. 23, No. 3 (March, 1972), p. 70.

42.   John Bickford, "Democracy in the Multidisciplinary Team: Fact or Fiction?" *Hospital & Community Psychiatry,* Vol. 24, No. 10 (October, 1973), p. 701.

43.   *Op. cit.,* p. 257.

44.   *Ibid.*

45.   John Bickford (*op. cit.*) mentions this, and George J. Steinfeld devotes a whole article to it. See Steinfeld, "Parallels Between
the Pathological Family and the Mental Hospital: A Search for a
Process," *Psychiatry,* Vol. 33 (1970), pp. 36–55. Steinfeld draws heavily
on the work of Jay Haley in this connection, particularly Haley's
marvelous essay "The Art of Being Schizophrenic" (Jay Haley, *The
Power Tactics of Jesus Christ,* New York: Avon Books, 1971, pp.
145–176).

46.   Edwalds, *op. cit.,* p. 670.

VI: ADMINISTRATIVE DREAMS

1.   David J. Vail, *Dehumanization and the Institutional Career*
(Springfield, Illinois: Charles C. Thomas, 1966).

2.   Vail's actual title was Medical Director, Division of Medical
Services, Minnesota Department of Public Welfare.

3.   Much of this and the following information about Minnesota
is based on telephone interviews with William Hafling and Robert
Kuyper, April 26, 1974. Hafling is a doctoral candidate in forensic
psychology in Minnesota and Kuyper is a minister in the Minnesota
Church of Scientology. Kuyper is currently heading an investigation
for the Church's Citizens Commission on Human Rights into the
Minnesota mental health system. Hafling is a member of the Patrick
Henry Society, a Minnesota group of ex-mental patients, empathiz-
ing professionals, and others; see *Madness Network News,* Vol. 2,
No. 3 (June, 1974), p. 22, for information on this group.

4.   "Bronze Award: The Attack on Dehumanization," *Hospital &
Community Psychiatry,* Vol. 18 (1967), pp. 362–364.

5.   Telephone interview with William Hafling, April 26, 1974.

6.   *Ibid.*

7.   Leonard P. Ullmann, *Institution and Outcome: A Comparative Study of Psychiatric Hospitals* (Oxford: Pergamon Press, 1967),
is instructive on this point.

8.   Ray L. Birdwhistell, "Uncomfortable Room at the Top,"
Hospital & Community Psychiatry, Vol. 19 (1968), pp. 33–42.

9.   *Ibid.*

10.   New York State Department of Mental Hygiene, *Mental
Hygiene News,* Vol. 45, No. 7 (April 12, 1974), p. 1.

11.   State of New York, *Executive Budget for the Fiscal Year April
1, 1972 to March 31, 1973,* p. 432.

12.   State of New York, *Budget Summary 1973–74.*

13.   State of New York, *Executive Budget for the Fiscal Year April 1, 1972 to March 31, 1973*, p. 435.
14.   Interview with Dr. Alan D. Miller, March 28, 1973.
15.   *Ibid.*
16.   *Ibid.*
17.   New York State Planning Committee on Mental Disorders, *A Plan for a Comprehensive Mental Health and Mental Retardation Program for New York State* (July 1, 1965), Vol. I, p. 38.
18.   Robert H. Connery *et al.*, *The Politics of Mental Health* (New York: Columbia University Press, 1968), pp. 326–328, tells an interesting story about the decision to build the hospital in Syracuse.
19.   Interview with Dr. Alan D. Miller, March 28, 1973. I also interviewed Dr. Alvin M. Mesnikoff, Director of the new South Beach Psychiatric Center in Staten Island. When I asked him why the state had built South Beach, he pleaded ignorance.
20.   Interview with Dr. Alan D. Miller, March 28, 1973. For a further account of Miller's views on the future of the state system, see *Psychiatric News*, Vol. IX, No. 9 (May 1, 1974), pp. 3, 34.
21.   Interview with Dr. Alan D. Miller, March 28, 1973.
22.   Schools of social work in New York are now giving courses on unified services. The Department of Mental Hygiene spent three or four years preparing the legislation for unified services and did a great deal of educational work with legislators to explain it to them. Miller said that the legislative leadership was for it "on the basis of *some* understanding" of the ideas involved (Miller interview).
23.   New York State Department of Mental Hygiene, *Mental Hygiene News*, Vol. 45, No. 8 (April 26, 1974), pp. 6–7. This article is the clearest exposition I have seen of unified services.
24.   *Ibid.*
25.   Alvin M. Mesnikoff, "Unified Services: Promising Successor to the Mental Health Center," *The Bulletin* (New York State District Branches, American Psychiatric Association), Vol. 15, No. 8 (May, 1973), p. 1.
26.   See reference in footnote 23.
27.   Interview with Dr. Alan D. Miller, March 28, 1973.
28.   Several former staff members at Hudson River have painted this picture for me. According to them, Hudson River loses a good many younger staff members who become upset at the hospital's unwillingness to try new approaches.
29.   Alvin D. Mesnikoff, reference in footnote 25.
30.   Interview with Dr. Alan D. Miller, March 28, 1973.

NOTES 333

30a. Since finishing the manuscript for this book the situation in New York has changed. The people have elected a new Governor, Hugh Carey, and one of the first things Carey did upon taking office was to replace Alan Miller. Miller had been under attack for about a year in *The New York Times*. Carey adopted the *Times'* editorial position and made the Department of Mental Hygiene's track record a campaign issue. Miller's replacement is Dr. Lawrence C. Kolb, formerly Director of the New York State Psychiatric Institute, a psychoanalyst and a psychiatric conservative. His mandate from Carey (and *The New York Times*) will no doubt be to stop discharging mental patients from the hospitals.

You have to get through an enormous amount of rhetoric (a nice word for it) to see what is actually happening here. What is actually happening goes something like this. Alan Miller was a civil libertarian, a member of the ACLU, a man who, for all his polish and political savvy, really believed in liberating mental patients. *The New York Times*, on the other hand, for all its bland surface liberalism, really does not believe in civil liberties, did not like all those crazies in the streets messing up beautiful New York, and set out to destroy Miller. Hugh Carey bought the *Times'* position for emotional reasons of his own, was elected, and has appointed Kolb to undo Miller's work.

What will become of the unified services program under Kolb is an unknown at this writing. Unified services is in the statute books and it might be difficult to repeal it; on the other hand, everything depends on implementation, and Kolb could simply choose to ignore the law. The pity and the irony of it all is that unified services *could* be an instrument for constructive change and that Miller understood the interests of all the elements in the system and was trying—but too slowly—through unified services to find an accommodation. On the evidence of his record at New York State Psychiatric Institute, Kolb has little or no understanding of or sympathy for community interests or the rights or interests of mental patients. New York has probably taken, then, a giant step backward.

31. Interview with Dr. William C. Keating, Jr., July 3, 1973, Sacramento, California.

32. *Ibid.* For a more detailed explanation, see Richard R. Parlour, "The Reorganization of the California Department of Mental Hygiene," *American Journal of Psychiatry*, Vol. 128 (1972), pp. 1388–1394.

33. *Ibid.* Keating was for a time Director of the California

Medical Facility at Vacaville, which is under the Department of Corrections. Jessica Mitford *(Kind and Usual Punishment: The Prison Business,* New York: Alfred A. Knopf, 1973, pp. 157 ff.) writes unfavorably about Dr. Keating's lack of interest while Director in holding researchers at the prison accountable for their work. While the system Keating has instituted in the mental hospitals is an attempt to build greater accountability into the system, how well it works depends entirely on Keating's interest in applying it.

34.　　*Psychiatric News,* Vol. IX, No. 7 (April 3, 1974), pp. 1, 33.

35.　　*Community Mental Health and the Mental Hospital,* Final Report of the United Community Services of Metropolitan Boston–Massachusetts Department of Mental Health Mental Hospital Planning Project, November, 1973.

36.　　Edwin B. Newman in *Community Mental Health and the Mental Hospital,* p. 107.

37.　　For the situation in New Jersey see the excellent series of articles by Herb Jaffe in the Newark, New Jersey, *Star-Ledger,* starting with the issue of April 28, 1974.

38.　　Interview with Dr. Donald B. Rinsley, June 27, 1973, Topeka, Kansas.

39.　　See his review of *Treatment of the Borderline Adolescent: A Developmental Approach,* by James F. Masterson, in the *American Journal of Psychiatry,* Vol. 130 (1973), p. 228. Masterson is one of Rinsley's heroes and the review is adulatory. See also his strong response to a review by Paul M. Fine of another book in Rinsley's field, a review which called residential treatment a "court of last resort" in the treatment of children. Far from being a court of last resort, says Rinsley, residential treatment "is, rather, the treatment of choice for borderline and psychotic children and adolescents whose psychopathology . . . expresses profound failure of separation-individuation. . . ." (Letter to the Editor, *American Journal of Psychiatry,* Vol. 130 [1973], p. 721.) Dr. Fine apologized.

40.　　Letters column, *Psychiatric News,* Vol. VIII, No. 12 (June 20, 1973), p. 2.

41.　　Donald B. Rinsley, "A Contribution to the Nosology and Dynamics of Adolescent Schizophrenia," *Psychiatric Quarterly,* Vol. 46 (1972), pp. 159–186.

42.　　*Ibid.*

43.　　*Ibid.*

44.　　*Ibid.*

45.　　*Ibid.* The exclamation point is Rinsley's.

46.　　*Ibid.*

47. Rinsley sees it this way, too: "In the final analysis the operational definition, hence validity of any diagnostic nosology lie precisely in its therapeutic applicability." (*Ibid.*)

48. *Ibid.*

49. Donald B. Rinsley, "Intensive Residential Treatment of the Adolescent," *Psychiatric Quarterly,* Vol. 41 (1967), pp. 134–143.

50. *Ibid.*

51. *Ibid.*

52. *Ibid.*

53. Information about Rinsley's highly restrictive methods derives not only from Rinsley's own writings but from interviews with former patients and their families, as well as with the parents of Melissa whose story I am about to tell.

54. Interview with Melissa's parents, January 28, 1974.

55. *Ibid.*

56. *Ibid.*

57. *Ibid.*

58. *Ibid.*

59. *Ibid.*

60. They later abandoned the suit, not on its merits but because every lawyer they contacted advised them that the life of a crippled child has little monetary value.

61. This does not refer to Melissa. As far as I know, Rinsley had no part in taking legal custody of Melissa away from her parents. I am referring to another case.

62. Rinsley did do an unpublished follow-up study which indicates that at least 72 percent of those leaving his unit required further treatment, while a mere 6 percent were discharged as "Recovered." See Wilfrid T. Miller, Sherri Krentz, C. Lisa Lewis, and Donald B. Rinsley, *The Adolescent in Residential Treatment: A Twenty-Year Follow-Up Study,* mimeo, n.p., n.d.

63. *Mental Hygiene News,* Vol. 45, No. 9 (May 10, 1974), p. 6.

64. *The New York Times,* July 12, 1973, p. 43, states that 28 percent of New York's discharged mental patients return to mental hospitals within six months of discharge. This contrasts with the Department's official "Readmission Index," which shows the readmissions per one thousand discharges (but without indicating any time factor) to hover around two hundred. At the same time, readmissions as a percentage of all admissions reached nearly 60 percent by 1970 and was still climbing (State of New York, *The Department of Mental Hygiene Looks Ahead,* mimeo, January 1971, Charts 6a, 6b, 6c). There is, then, a "revolving door" phenomenon, with many patients reentering the hospitals soon after discharge, as critics have charged; at the same time it may be that many discharged patients do manage to stay out of the hospital.

65.   Interview with Dr. Anthony Primelo, May 22, 1973, Wingdale, New York.

66.   The following information about the operation of the Metro Unit comes from two site visits spaced a year apart, in May 1973 and May 1974, interviews with Martin Von Holden during these visits, interviews with his staff, attendance at meetings, various documents supplied me by Von Holden, and so on. On my second visit Von Holden gave me a set of keys and permission to roam the Unit at will. He obviously feels he has nothing to hide.

67.   On this issue see, for example, Shirley A. Freiff and Robert D. McDonald, "Role Relationships Between Nonphysician Treatment Team Leaders and Team Psychiatrists," *Community Mental Health Journal*, Vol. 9 (1973), pp. 378–387, Milton I. Roemer, "Training Health Administrators for New Responsibilities," *Hospital & Community Psychiatry*, Vol. 17 (1966), pp. 98–101, and Donald F. Moore, "The Inherent Limits of Nonmedical Administrators," *ibid.*, pp. 101–103. Psychiatrists tend to believe that no one but other psychiatrists should be in administrative positions, or in a position, that is, to direct their work; but very few of them are willing to take administrative responsibility. The typical result is an administrative vacuum; *no one* holds the psychiatrists accountable for their work.

68.   Von Holden's admniistrative structure, it should be noted, is not unique to him, nor did he originate it. It was first used at Creedmoor State Hospital on Long Island, where Anthony Primelo once worked, and variations of it have been used elsewhere as well. See "A State Hospital Changes, A Case Study of Staff Development, Creedmoor State Hospital, Queens Village, New York," *Innovations* [in] *Mental Health Services: National Institute of Mental Health Progress Report No. 2* (Rockville, Md: NIMH, 1971), pp. 31–39. See also William Polanka, "Using Ward Personnel as Case Managers," *Hospital & Community Psychiatry*, Vol. 20 (1969), pp. 93–95.

69.   Martin Von Holden, memo to staff, Metro Unit, April 4, 1973, p. 5 (mimeo).

70.   *Ibid.*

71.   See William Glasser, *Reality Therapy* (New York: Harper & Row, 1965).

72.   With one exception: a young psychiatrist who has since moved on to a better job.

73.   The use of foreign medical graduates is worth a book in itself and has, in fact, received one; see Harold Margulies and Lucille S. Bloch, *Foreign Medical Graduates in the United States* (Cambridge, Mass.: Harvard University Press, 1969). Most of them are unlicensed and many of those working in mental hospitals do not want to be psychiatrists; they are there because no general hospital would take them as residents. Needless to say, their dedication to their work is less than satisfactory.

74.   Zwerling is now on the staff of Hahnemann Medical College in Philadelphia. For an account of Zwerling's transformation of Bronx State from a custodial institution with not enough staff to a fully staffed treatment-oriented institution, see his deposition in the *Wyatt v. Stickney* case, printed in Bruce J. Ennis and Paul R. Friedman, eds., *Legal Rights of the Mentally Handicapped* (New York: Practising Law Institute, 1974), Vol. I, pp. 491–589, especially 508 ff. For an account of Boston State Hospital, see Milton Greenblatt, Myron R. Sharaf and Evelyn M. Stone, *Dynamics of Institutional Change: The Hospital in Transition* (Pittsburgh: University of Pittsburgh Press, 1971), pp. 49–50.

75.   Interview with Edward Hornick, May 15, 1973, Bronx, New York.

76.   Interview with Dr. Alan D. Miller, March 28, 1973.

77.   Juanita E. Bay and Christian Bay, "Professionalism and the Erosion of Rationality in the Health Care Field," *American Journal of Orthopsychiatry*, Vol. 43 (1973), pp. 55–64.

78.   Morton Birnbaum, "The Right to Treatment," *American Bar Association Journal*, Vol. 46 (1960), pp. 499–505.

79.   See Robert Johnston and Margaret Fraser, "Right to Treatment," *mh* (*Mental Hygiene*), Vol. 56, No. 3 (Summer 1972), pp. 13–19.

80.   Judge Johnson's order is reprinted in Bruce J. Ennis and Paul R. Friedman, *op. cit.*, pp. 295–331.

81.   A "Qualified Mental Health Professional" may be a psychiatrist who has completed three years of residency, a Ph.D. psychologist, a social worker with a master's degree and two years of clinical work or a nurse with a degree in psychiatric nursing and two years of clinical work.

82.   Ennis and Friedman, *op. cit.*, pp. 301.

83.   One of the lawyers in this case, Bruce Ennis, says that this was his actual goal, to force Alabama to turn its mental patients loose. See "Interview with Bruce Ennis," *Madness Network News*, Vol. 2, No. 2 (February 1974), p. 10.

84. *New York Times,* January 20, 1974, p. 64.
85. *Psychiatric News,* Vol. IX, No. 5 (March 6, 1974), p. 2.
86. See *Behavior Today,* Vol. 5, No. 13 (April 1, 1974), pp. 87–89.
87. *New York Times,* November 30, 1972.
88. *Psychiatric News,* Vol. IX, No. 6 (March 20, 1974), pp. 1, 24.
89. *Psychiatric News,* Vol. IX, No. 4 (February 20, 1974), p. 1.
90. *Psychiatric News,* Vol. IX, No. 8 (April 17, 1974), p. 12.
91. *Ibid.* The author of this remark is Alan A. Stone.
92. Bernard S. Arons, "Letter to the Editor," *Psychiatric News,* Vol. IX, No. 11 (June 5, 1974), p. 2.
93. Jonas Robitscher, "Courts, State Hospitals, and the Right to Treatment," *American Journal of Psychiatry,* Vol. 129 (1972), p. 303.
94. *Psychiatric News,* Vol. IX, No. 2 (January 16, 1974), p. 33. Judge Johnson's decision also takes note, however, of the right to refuse certain forms of treatment, including medication, so mental patients are not entirely alone in their perception of the dangers. Nevertheless the right to refuse treatment, especially medication, is the issue which frightens the professionals most, and I expect to see less and less mention of this right as the professionals take over the right to treatment movement.
95. See George E. Crane, "Clinical Psychopharmacology in its 20th Year," *Science,* Vol. 181 (July 13, 1973), pp. 124–128, which summarizes the evidence.
96. The writings of Peter Breggin are definitive on this issue. See his article, "The Return of Lobotomy and Psychosurgery," *Congressional Record,* February 24, 1972, pp. E1602–E1612.
97. For an extensive discussion of the legal and moral implications of behavior modification programs with respect to the right to treatment issue, see David B. Wexler, "Token and Taboo: Behavior Modification, Token Economies, and the Law," *California Law Review,* Vol. 60 (1973), pp. 81–109.

VII: GETTING OUT OF THE SYSTEM

1. The peak figure, reached in 1957, was 570,000 inpatients. The 1973 figure comes from Biometry Branch, National Institute of Mental Health, *Statistical Note 106: Provisional Patient Movement and Administrative Data—State and County Mental Hospital Inpatient Services, July 1, 1972–June 30, 1973* (Washington: Department of Health, Education, and Welfare, May, 1974).
2. *Ibid.* The admission rate now seems to be holding steady; in the last few years, in fact, it has been declining.

3.   Biometry Branch, National Institute of Mental Health, *Statistical Note 74: Length of Stay of Admissions to State and County Mental Hospitals, United States 1971* (Washington: Department of Health, Education, and Welfare, February, 1973).

4.   Reference in footnote 1 above, Table 3.

5.   A study made in Saskatchewan revealed that the cost of maintaining a patient in a foster home amounted to less than half the cost of maintaining him in a mental hospital. See Wilfrid A. Cassell, Colin M. Smith, Frederic Grunberg, J. A. Boan and Ronald F. Thomas, "Comparing Costs of Hospital and Community Care," *Hospital & Community Psychiatry*, Vol. 23 (1972), pp. 197–200.

6.   Thorazine and Stelazine, of course, are both phenothiazines whose major effect is to tranquilize (to be precise, their most dramatic effect is the elimination of thought disorders and manic excitement), while Artane combats their side effects, which mimic Parkinsonism: shaking hands, unsteady balance, and so on.

7.   It may be that no follow-up attempt was made because I had refused the "life plan" the psychiatrist wanted me to follow. Or because I was being discharged in the care of my wife. It seems more likely, however, that it was simply overlooked, which is usually the case.

8.   Cited in Clara D. Kimbro and Paul V. Lemkau, "Delays in Arranging Aftercare," *Hospital & Community Psychiatry*, Vol. 20 (1969), pp. 91–92.

9.   *Ibid.*

10.   Jack E. Sigler, *Comprehensive Planning for Mental Health: A Two-Year Follow-Up Study of Aftercare in Kansas* (Kansas City, Missouri: Community Studies, Inc., 1963), p. 50 (mimeo).

11.   See, for instance, Richard P. Fox and David N. Potter, "Using Inpatient Staff for Aftercare of Severely Disturbed Chronic Patients," *Hospital & Community Psychiatry*, Vol. 24 (1973), pp. 482–484.

12.   The best-known is the book by Howard E. Freeman and Ozzie G. Simmons, *The Mental Patient Comes Home* (New York: John Wiley and Sons, 1963). By and large the whole area of post-hospital experience has been seriously neglected. One reason for this may be that once a patient leaves the hospital he no longer constitutes a captive audience for research.

13.   Interview with Dennis McCarthy, White Plains, New York, June 22, 1974.

14.   See *The New York Times*, February 13, 1972.

15.   *The New York Times*, April 24, 1974.

16.   *The New York Times*, December 28, 1973.

17.   The source of this story is Dennis McCarthy (see footnote 14), who works for the Department of Social Services in New York City. The Department has fully documented the facts in this and many other cases, but it is relatively powerless to do anything about them. Proprietors discovered in a fraud are usually quick to pay the State back whatever the State says is due, and in only one case, a particularly horrendous one in the Bronx, has the matter been handed over to a district attorney.

18.   For a survey of family care, see James R. Morrissey, *The Case for Family Care of the Mentally Ill* (New York: Behavioral Publications [Community Mental Health Journal Monograph, No. 2] 1967).

19.   See "Illicit Foster Homes Here Victimize Mental Patients," *The New York Times,* June 10, 1973.

20.   *The New York Times,* February 7, 1974.

21.   For a psychiatric point of view on the large-scale release of mental patients from New York hospitals, see Henry Pinsker, Edwin Robbins and Gerald Kleinerman, "Psychiatric Hospitalization: Role of Administrative Policy," *New York State Journal of Medicine,* Vol. 72 (1972), pp. 1764–1768; and Edwin Robbins and Lillian Robbins, "Charge to the Community: Some Early Effects of a State Hospital System's Change of Policy," *American Journal of Psychiatry,* Vol. 131 (1974), pp. 641–645.

22.   "Are Foster Homes the New Back Wards? Canadian Study Says Yes," *Hospital & Community Psychiatry,* Vol. 23 (December, 1972), pp. 46–47.

23.   *Ibid.,* p. 46.

24.   Abbott S. Weinstein, Diane Dipasquale and Frederick Winsor, "Relationships Between Length of Stay in and out of the New York State Mental Hospitals," *American Journal of Psychiatry,* Vol. 130 (1973), pp. 904–909, found that the best predictor of length of stay out of the hospital was the number of previous hospitalizations, and a study by Aaron Rosenblatt and John E. Mayer, "Recidivism of Mental Patients: A Review of Research," *American Journal of Orthopsychiatry,* Vol. 44 (1974), p. 210, uncovered "one constant predictor of readmission: the numbers of patients' previous admissions. The more often patients are admitted to a mental hospital, the more likely they are to return again." The authors conclude:

> From our perspective the observed relationship is the outcome, at least in part, of certain patterned social processes. More specifically, some patients may seek readmission because living in a modern-day

mental hospital administered in accordance with humanitarian goals may prove more attractive to them than trying to exist in a deteriorating ghetto community on an insufficient welfare allotment. In their preoccupation with psychopathology as a determinant of rehospitalization, members of the psychiatric profession have tended to overlook the relevance of these and other sociological influences.

25.   Mrs. Helen Warnick, in Senate Select Committee on Proposed Phaseout of State Hospital Services, California Legislature, *Hearing*, June 15, 1973 (Sacramento: Senate Select Committee, etc.), pp. 169–170.

26.   Andrew G. Robertson, Deputy Director, Health Treatment Systems, in Senate Select Committee, *Hearings*, May 2, 1974, pp. 46–47.

27.   *The New York Times*, February 7, 1974.

28.   Bruce Ennis states:

> I think most people don't like "mental patients." They don't like anyone whom they cannot categorize neatly into an acceptable niche that is comfortable for them. I think if it were put to a popular referendum, the people in this country would favor massive custodial warehouses where people were swept off the streets and kept for the rest of their lives and drugged, tranquilized, shocked, whatever is necessary to keep them off the streets. I literally believe that is the way people feel about it.

"Interview with Bruce Ennis," *Madness Network News*, Vol. 2, No. 2 (February, 1974), p. 10.

29.   "Civil Liberties for What?" (editorial), *New York Times*, April 8, 1974.

30.   I want to acknowledge the great help the members of MPLP have been to me in my research. Some of them granted me interviews about their personal experience, others talked to me at length about the politics of the mental health system, and after my own experience at Hudson River State Hospital the group as a whole voted me an honorary member of the organization.

31.   A current list of these organizations is always available in the latest issue of *Rough Times*.

32.   *Rough Times*, Vol. 2, No. 6 (April, 1972), p. 1.

33.   For the rationale behind this publication see Joy Marcus, "I Did It and I'm Glad," *Issues in Radical Therapy*, Vol. 1, No. 1 (January 15, 1973), pp. 29–30.

34.   *Ibid.*

35.   See Terry Kupers, "Radical Therapy Needs Revolutionary Theory," in Jerome Agel, producer, *The Radical Therapist* (New York: Ballantine Books, 1971), pp. 35–46, and Kupers, "Synthesis of

Science?" in Phil Brown, ed., *Radical Psychology* (New York: Harper & Row, 1973), pp. 375–385.

36.   This is a point of view which these theorists have adopted wholesale from R. D. Laing. At the same time they reject the further development of Laing's thought.

37.   A superb summary of Laing's thought may be found in Edgar Z. Friedenberg, *R. D. Laing* (New York: Viking Press, 1973) (Modern Masters Series).

38.   The most familiar attempt in English is probably Erich Fromm's *Marx's Concept of Man* (New York: Frederick Ungary Publishing Company, 1962). For an analysis which sticks to Marx's writings see Bertell Ollman, *Alienation: Marx's Conception of Man in Capitalist Society* (London: Cambridge University Press, 1971).

39.   Michael Glenn, "Radical Therapy and Revolution," *Issues in Radical Therapy*, Vol. 1, No. 1 (January 15, 1973), p. 26.

40.   *Ibid.*, p. 28.

41.   For an illuminating discussion of serial groups and their opposite, pledged groups, see Friedenberg, *op. cit.*, pp. 73 ff.

42.   See *Free Expression: A Newsletter of the Mental "Patients'" Liberation Project*, New York: n.d. (1974).

43.   Held in Detroit, June 1–3, 1973. The conference title was "Human Rights and Psychiatric Oppression" and a Coordinating Committee came out of it. The second conference was scheduled for Labor Day weekend in Topeka, Kansas, in 1974.

44.   (Tony Colletti), MPLP, New York City, "The Jailers of the People," *Rough Times*, Vol. 3, No. 2 (November, 1972), p. 2.

VIII: ALTERNATIVES

1.   For a detailed history of the Act, see Robert H. Connery *et al*, *The Politics of Mental Health* (New York: Columbia University Press, 1968), pp. 1–64. Also useful is the report prepared for the Committee on Labor and Public Welfare, United States Senate, *Community Mental Health Centers Act: History of the Program and Current Problems and Issues*, Washington: April, 1973.

2.   New York: Basic Books, 1961.

3.   *Action for Mental Health*, p. xxi. Italics in original.

4.   Quoted in Committee on Labor and Public Welfare, *Community Mental Health Centers Act*, p. 1.

5.   Quoted in Connery *et al.*, *op. cit.*, p. 51.

6.   The Act actually called for ten services, but only five were "essential." The other five were diagnostic services, rehabilitative

services, precare and aftercare, training, and research and evaluation. A center incorporating all ten services qualified as a *comprehensive* community mental health center.

7.   Committee on Labor and Public Welfare, *Community Mental Health Centers Act*, p. 10.

8.   Franklin D. Chu and Sharland Trotter, *The Madness Establishment: Ralph Nader's Study Group Report on the National Institute of Mental Health* (New York: Grossman Publishers, 1974), p. 116.

9.   Barbara Ehrenreich and Maxine Kenny, "Up Against the Mental Bloc," *Health-PAC Bulletin,* December, 1969, p. 5.

10.   When I visited the Solomon Center in December, 1972, they were transferring about four patients a month to Worcester State Hospital.

11.   Dr. Harry C. Solomon Mental Health Center, *Sixth Annual Report, Fiscal Year 1972,* Part I, p. 13 (mimeo).

12.   *Ibid.,* p. 19.

13.   *Ibid.,* p. 18.

14.   Many psychiatrists have attributed much of the success in reducing state hospital populations to community mental health centers. Actually most of that reduction has come about, as we have seen, through the use of tranquilizers and through changes in administrative policy, particularly with regard to the discharge of long-term patients. In those areas where community mental health centers are operating there has been some reduction in the rate of admission to state hospitals (see, for example, the figures cited in George Dyck, "The Effect of a Community Mental Health Center Upon State Hospital Utilization," *American Journal of Psychiatry,* Vol. 131 [1974], pp. 453–456), although most centers still pass on some of their patients to the hospitals, primarily those patients whose behavior cannot be made manageable in less than ten-fourteen days. That figure is the maximum most mental health center inpatient wards, located for the most part in general hospitals, are willing to keep them. At any rate I regard these figures on the reduction of state hospital utilization rates as nothing but the very crudest measure of a center's success in creating an alternative. The figures tell us nothing about the quality of care.

15.   See Robert L. Leopold, "The West Philadelphia Mental Health Consortium: Administrative Planning in a Multihospital Catchment Area," *Administration in Mental Health,* Fall, 1973, pp. 83–91.

16.   Leopold, "The Consortium Revisited," in *ibid.,* p. 94.

17. Interview with Robert Blake, Topeka, Kansas, June 26, 1973.
18. Betty Cochran, reporting on a recent speech by Paul R. Dingman, writes:

> Dr. Dingman listed commonly accepted functions of state hospitals —providing temporary respite, treatment, protection for the patient from others, protection of others, research, training, and long-term care for the chronically disabled—and argued that although those tasks have been poorly carried out by state hospitals, there will be no improvement if they are transferred to other organizations.
> The comprehensive community mental health center is the most popular nominee to take over those tasks, he said, but many of the defects of the hospitals are already evident in the centers. He cited, among other problems, centers' lack of flexibility, and their control by monolithic and authoritarian units such as medical schools and general hospitals. The centers share with state hospitals the crippling defect of low political popularity, with resultant loss of funds. Moreover, the mode of treatment is dictated by socioeconomic rather than mental status; emergency services are of poor quality if they exist at all; there is no continuity of care between services; and a patron can't select the professional who will treat him.

("Where Is My Home? The Closing of State Mental Hospitals," *Hospital & Community Psychiatry*, Vol. 25 [1974], p. 395.) The psychiatric literature is full of similar criticisms.

19. The Nader report was first issued in mimeograph form in 1972 and published as a book in 1974 (see Chu and Trotter, *op. cit.*). Bertram Brown, Director of NIMH, has criticized the report in various forums, and a recent set of psychiatric replies may be found in the July, 1974, issue of the *American Journal of Psychiatry*. Privately, however, many psychiatrists have told me that the report is generally accurate.

20. U.S. Congress, *Community Mental Health Centers—Oversight*, Hearings before the Subcommittee on Public Health and Environment, Committee on Interstate and Foreign Commerce, House of Representatives, May 9 and June 15, 1973 (Washington: Government Printing Office, 1973), p. 80. Hereafter referred to as *Oversight Hearings*.

21. Franklin D. Chu, "The Nader Report: One Author's Perspective," *American Journal of Psychiatry*, Vol. 131 (1974), p. 778.

22. Ehrenreich and Kenny, *op. cit.*, pp. 5–6. The story as presented here is based on this source and on the testimony of William Hatcher in *Oversight Hearings*, pp. 169–171.

23. Ehrenreich and Kenny, *op. cit.*, p. 10.

24. *Oversight Hearings*, p. 170.

25.   *Ibid.*

26.   For the workers' point of view see Barbara and John Ehrenreich, *The American Health Empire: Power, Profits, and Politics* (New York: Vintage Books, 1971), pp. 253–267. For the psychiatric point of view see Seymour R. Kaplan and Melvin Roman, *The Organization and Delivery of Mental Health Services in the Ghetto: The Lincoln Hospital Experience* (New York: Praeger, 1973).

27.   Robert L. Leopold, reference in footnote 16.

28.   Jules Kluger, "The Uninsulated Caseload in a Neighborhood Mental Health Clinic," in H. G. Whittington, ed., *Development of an Urban Mental Health Center* (Springfield, Illinois: Charles C. Thomas, 1971), pp. 87–99.

29.   New York: Basic Books, 1964, p. 26.

30.   A notable exception is Matthew P. Dumont. See Dumont, *The Absurd Healer: Perspectives of a Community Psychiatrist* (New York: Viking Press, 1971).

31.   Jonas V. Morris, Director of the National Council of Community Mental Health Centers, cites a figure of 389 operating centers (*Oversight Hearings*, p. 38), but others in the same hearings talk about five hundred centers, although they do not state whether or not they are all in operation. Probably Morris is closer to the truth.

32.   Telephone interview with Jonas V. Morris, Director, National Council of Community Mental Health Centers, August 1, 1974, and with an official of the National Association of Mental Health, same date.

33.   *Oversight Hearings,* p. 108.

34.   See Peter G. Bourne, "Human Resources: A New Approach to the Dilemmas of Community Psychiatry," *American Journal of Psychiatry,* Vol. 131 (1974), pp. 666–669.

35.   *Ibid.,* p. 668.

36.   *Ibid.*

37.   Quoted in Teddye Clayton, "The Changing Mental Hospital: Emerging Alternatives," *Hospital & Community Psychiatry,* Vol. 25 (1974), p. 389.

38.   *Ibid.*

39.   Jim Burns and Michael C. Dixon, "Telephone Crisis Intervention and Crisis Volunteers," *Crisis Intervention,* Vol. 5, No. 2 (1974), pp. 2–7.

40.   For an account of Number Nine, see Ted Clark and Dennis T. Jaffe, *Toward a Radical Therapy: Alternate Services for Personal and Social Change* (New York: Gordon and Breach, 1973).

41.   Dumont, "Self-Help Treatment Programs," *American Journal of Psychiatry*, Vol. 131 (1974), p. 634.

42.   Kristin Glaser, "Suggestions for Working with Heavy Strangers," *Rough Times*, Vol. 2, No. 8 (July, 1972), p. 12.

43.   *Ibid.*, p. 13.

44.   The first was the so-called "blow-out" ward at Agnews State Hospital in California. Agnews is now closed.

45.   See Mary Barnes and Joseph Berke, *Mary Barnes: Two Accounts of a Journey Through Madness* (London: MacGibbon and Kee, 1971).

46.   Loren R. Mosher, "A Research Design for Evaluating a Psychosocial Treatment of Schizophrenia," *Hospital & Community Psychiatry*, Vol. 23 (1972), p. 231.

47.   *Ibid.*

48.   Loren R. Mosher, Susan Matthews, and Alma Menn, "Soteria: A New Treatment for Schizophrenia—One Year Follow-up Data," *American Journal of Orthopsychiatry*, Vol. 44 (1974), p. 208.

49.   Interview with Alma Menn, Palo Alto, California, July 17, 1973. Visitors are discouraged at Soteria so I have not seen the place.

50.   Quoted in Teddye Clayton, *op. cit.*, p. 388.

51.   Erving Goffman, *Relations in Public: Microstudies of the Public Order* (New York: Basic Books, 1971), pp. 356–357.

Index